CONTENTS

SUPER GIANT BOOK OF
SEEK-A-WORD

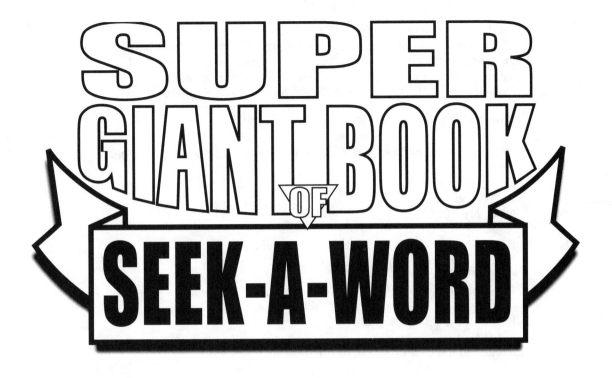

SUPER GIANT BOOK OF SEEK-A-WORD

Richard Manchester

BRISTOL
PARK
BOOKS

First Bristol Park Books edition published in 2002

Originally published as *The 3rd New Mammoth Book of Seek-A-Word*

Bristol Park Books, Inc.
252 W. 38th Street
NYC, NY 10018

Bristol Park Books is a registered trademark of
Bristol Park Books, Inc.

Published by arrangement with Crosstown Publications

ISBN: 978-0-88486-429-5

Printed in the United States of America

PUZZLES

Here is a group of words for "small fry," or the children who will grow up to be "big fry" and run the world. When you have circled all the terms, the uncircled letters will spell out a comment about child-rearing.

BABE
BABY
BAIRN
BAMBINO
BOY
CHERUB
CHICK
CHILD
CHIT (child)
GIRL
INFANT
JUNIOR
JUVENILE
KID
LAD
LASS
LITTLE ONE
MINOR
MISSY
MOPPET
NEONATE
   (newborn)
NESTLING
NEWBORN
OFFSPRING
PAPOOSE
SHAVER

TAD
TODDLER
TOT
TYKE

YOUNGLING
YOUNGSTER
YOUNKER (youth)
YOUTH

```
G N I L G N U O Y S P S O I
I E N O E L T T I L S L C E
R T D D T C H H Y A I H L M
L A D D Y J T O L B E K I D
T N R E K N U O Y R A S G R
O O E E E N O V U N S B N A
F E R W G E Y B E Y E R I D
F N E S B B B R O N I M L S
S L T S I O A A T A I I T H
P E T Y O B R M B I H L S A
R E L D D O T N B C H T E V
I N F A N T P K C I H C N E
N L E S O T I A J U N I O R
G N K T E M O P P E T O R S
```

Solution is on page 362.

1

PARTY SHOP

A well-equipped party shop has everything we need to celebrate special occasions, including some entertainment items like joke **BOOKS**, jigsaw **PUZZLES**, and an assortment of party **TOYS**. When you have circled all these party shop items, the uncircled letters, when read from left to right down the page, will spell out a comment about parties. FORKS has been circled to start you off.

ALBUMS	INVITATIONS
AWARDS	KNIVES
BALLOONS	LEIS
BANNERS	MUGS
BASKETS	NAPKINS
BOOKS	NOTES
BOWS	PENNANTS
BOXES	PIÑATAS
CAKE TRIMS	PLATES
CANDLES	POSTERS
CANDY	PRIZES
CARDS	PUZZLES
COASTERS	RIBBONS
COSTUMES	SIGNS
CREPE PAPER	SPOONS
CUPS	STENCILS
DOILIES	STREAMERS
FAVORS	STRING
FLAGS	TABLECLOTHS
FORKS	TAGS
GIFT BAGS	TAPE
GIFTS	TISSUE PAPER
GIFT WRAP	TOYS
HATS	TRANSFERS
HELIUM (for balloons)	T-SHIRTS
HOOKS	

```
N S E Z I R P O S T E N C I L S T
H I N P B O O K S R E N N A B Y P
S R O V A F G P R E E G M A D U K
N E S G S T S I E U T M S N Z M O
O S N I K P A N F S R A A Z R E T
I D O F E O L A S T R C L E E R C
T R O T T A H T N N B E P P R U T
A A L S S S E A A O S A T F P T A
T C L T W H L S R S P P G S N O S
I A A O S M I R T E K A C S A B I
V H B Y S S U R P Y S R E T S O P
N S O L P T M E T D E W O A R X C
I T S T E S R S O S M T Y F T E K
H N K N P C M I A N U F L A G S N
B A O O G U L E N S T I I W G N I
S N O B B I R O G G S G N A G O V
I N H L E I S U T N O V T R I T E
S E A S T E M D T H C A N D L E S
O P R E P A P E U S S I T S I S T
```

Solution is on page 362.

JACKPOT BINGO

The words in the Jackpot Bingo card are your word list. Find as many words as you can in the diagram, crossing them off the Jackpot card as you go. When you have found all the words you can, use the uncircled letters to form the single 5-letter word, which, when crossed off the Bingo card, will give you Jackpot Bingo, which is seven words in a row, across, down or diagonally. Hint: There will be 17 uncircled letters from which to form the Jackpot word. EPOCH has been looped to start you off.

J	A	C	K	P	O	T
CAROL	ALOHA	SAVER	EGRET	PARCH	HASTE	REARM
CHOCK	AMUSE	SHARE	ELOPE	PETAL	HAUNT	REBEL
CHORE	APART	SLAKE	EMOTE	PHOTO	HEART	REFER
COBRA	ASCOT	SPECK	~~EPOCH~~	PITCH	HINGE	RESIN
COLIC	ASSET	SPELL	EVOKE	PLACE	HORSE	RIGOR
CREPE	ATOLL	STAIR	EXILE	PROSE	HOVEL	ROACH
CRUST	AVAST	STEER	EXIST	PRUDE	HUMAN	ROGUE

Solution is on page 362.

```
A M U S E R U P A R C H
E S M T G I T S A V A C
R D S E H G C A P A R T
C A E E V O K E H E O I
H E A R T R V P P O L P
O U N E S K P E T A L L
C R O G U E P O L E V A
K I N N R O L E R O H C
C O L I C M L E E C A E
E R A H S I F N A M U H
P T S I X E S O R P N U
S A V E R C R E M O T E
```

Jackpot word: __ __ __ __ __

For the beginning home gardener, assembling the right equipment to grow plants and herbs is an important necessity for a successful project. In addition, the right amount of sunlight and careful watering and cultivating habits insure beautiful, healthy, indoor greenery. This list of plant care accessories and necessities can help to get you started.

E	J	N	Q	Z	S	S	H	E	A	R	S	N
V	S	E	G	N	O	P	S	A	M	A	W	O
B	E	C	O	I	Y	U	R	I	O	K	I	I
O	L	R	L	X	E	A	Y	S	X	P	N	H
Y	B	O	M	U	N	G	A	H	P	S	D	T
A	B	U	C	I	T	U	R	Q	E	L	O	A
S	E	S	E	U	C	S	T	C	A	M	W	L
D	P	E	D	E	L	U	T	E	T	U	B	A
H	N	K	R	E	T	I	L	R	E	P	O	M
U	X	A	I	W	C	V	I	I	E	O	X	N
R	E	T	S	I	M	E	G	J	T	T	Y	E
Z	I	S	D	G	I	F	H	U	O	E	A	O
E	R	E	Z	I	L	I	T	R	E	F	A	W

Solution is on page 362.

FERTILIZER
INSECTICIDE
LIGHT
MALATHION
   (all-purpose
   insecticide)
MISTER
   (to moisten leaves)
PEAT (good
   seedling soil)
PEBBLES (to provide
   drainage)
PERLITE (sterile
   mineral; provides
   soil aeration)
POT (to hold plant)
SAND
SAUCER
SHEARS
SOIL
SPHAGNUM (dried
   moss; adds
   acidity and
   retains water)
SPONGE (to clean
   leaves)
STAKES (to prop
   large plants)
TRAY (to cultivate
   seeds)
VERMICULITE
   (sterile mineral;
   retains water)
WATER
WINDOW BOX

What family lives at the address "698 Sycamore Road?" The "Partridge Family" lives at this address in the television series of the same name. This fictional address is in San Pueblo, California.

8	9	7	1	6	7	1	4	1	6	4	1	5	5
4	0	0	6	4	9	6	4	1	4	9	3	1	4
1	4	7	4	5	9	2	1	5	7	6	1	9	6
4	1	6	9	1	8	9	2	4	7	1	7	3	2
6	9	6	7	4	9	7	6	8	6	4	1	3	7
3	7	6	7	1	0	9	8	1	0	7	6	9	7
4	5	9	4	1	6	9	4	6	9	1	6	4	9
9	1	6	7	2	7	4	1	8	7	4	4	9	4
1	9	7	6	3	4	7	0	1	9	2	2	1	8
7	6	4	7	4	1	2	9	9	3	5	7	1	8
6	8	9	4	6	9	0	1	1	9	4	4	6	1
7	5	6	6	1	9	2	9	3	7	7	7	6	4
5	7	9	4	3	6	1	6	0	7	6	4	1	6
8	0	6	4	1	3	7	0	1	9	7	9	2	8

Solution is on page 362.

0064	5514
0074	5597
0141	5746
0176	5767
0217	5941
0291	5967
2291	8064
2296	8079
2346	8241
2361	8297
3124	8414
3171	8499
3369	8676
3391	8691
3566	8849
3571	8876

TRIVIA TOURNEY

Who says that trivia is trivial? We happen to think it's educational and fun. Use the trivia clues listed below to determine the 34 words that are hidden in the diagram on the facing page. The clues are listed so that each answer is in alphabetical order down the page.

_____ 1. Typing cockroach

_____ 2. Acetylsalicylic acid

_____ 3. Baby elephant

_____ 4. Kasparov's game

_____ 5. First honorary US citizen

_____ 6. Patron saint of France

_____ 7. Pink Panther gem

_____ 8. First US satellite

_____ 9. Most photographed mountain

_____ 10. Group of geese

_____ 11. Silk produced by spiders

_____ 12. Moscow's largest department store

_____ 13. Home of NASA's mission control

_____ 14. Gem State

_____ 15. The Simpson baby

_____ 16. Baja California's country

_____ 17. Eleanor Roosevelt's column

_____ 18. First nuclear-powered submarine

_____ 19. October birthstone

_____ 20. Deepest ocean

_____ 21. Banks family nanny

_____ 22. Family name of the Lone Ranger and the Green Hornet

_____ 23. Largest desert

_____ 24. Rotary Club motto

_____ 25. Brightest star

_____ 26. Female US Coast Guard member

_____ 27. The Waltz King

_____ 28. Heaviest US President

_____ 29. London's river

_____ 30. _The Hobbit_ author

_____ 31. Model Leslie Hornby

_____ 32. Bridge of Sighs city

_____ 33. "Small Wonder" robot

_____ 34. Rabbit's home

```
P M U G O S S A M E R G H F
E I S F G S O A R A H A S L
J C U G U E H T W I G G Y A
T J I A O H C O R N T G D C
I R R N D C T R U E F L I Y
C T I N E R R A W S A E A E
S H S O N V A P A L T D M T
N A U T I L U S Y C Y O O S
A M N R S A P T H M E V N E
R E I D C I F I C A P I D R
C S T E R H L L R E P C O V
M E X I C O I L A P O K L I
E C N N E I K L O T I Y K C
O H A D I E X P L O R E R E
```

Solution is on page 362; list, page 395.

The city of Damascus is situated on the Barada and Awaj rivers, lies southeast of Beirut, Lebanon, and has a population of over one million people. An aspect of its historical significance is noted below. When you have circled all the terms, the uncircled letters will spell out the handicrafts that have made Damascus famous.

The oldest
city
in the
world is
Damascus,
the chief
city
of Syria.
It was
founded
by Uz,
the great-
grandson
of Noah,
and
it is
mentioned
in the
Bible
with
Abraham
at least
two
thousand
years
before
Christ.
Its site
has been
continuously
occupied
by a
city
longer

than   other   on the
any   spot   earth.

```
G A I R Y S F O A A M D S T
O R O E S D A E T N I E I H
C W A G S A R L Y S Y I T E
E H T N I M E B I T T P I G
T L K O D A H I B W I U W R
Z H I L S S T B A M C C I E
U R E T O C O S E C A C T A
Y T I C S U D N A S U O H T
B D H D H S T M A H A R B A
S R A E Y I I E H Y O E N C
I O S D O P E T B I F P A E
D A B N R L R F E O N T H E
L N E U A A D N R D O T T B
R D E O E L O E W P A N H G
O L N F C H R I S T H A S E
W Y L S U O U N I T N O C S
```

Solution is on page 362.

TANGLEWORDS

This is a Word Search in reverse. Circled letters are the initial letters of one or more words, and any letter may be part of more than one word. Fill in each word in a straight line without crossing any black squares; when you're done, every square will be filled. OZONE has been entered for you.

ADULT	BRAG	ELEVATOR	GEOLOGIST
AGENDA	CHORE	ERROR	HIDE
APHID	COGNIZANT	FLAGRANT	HOEING
AUTHOR	CONVERT	FUNNEL	INTEGER
BAGGAGE	EASTERNER	GARCON	LARIAT

LEARNING
MERGED
MOTTO
OBLIGATION
OCHRE
OZONE
PROTEGE
REINFORCED
REMEMBER
REPUGNANT
SCROLL
TREND
TYMPANIC
UNTIE
VILLAGE
VOTE
VOWING
WILE
ZEALOUS

Solution is on page 362.

ON THE SEASIDE

Listed here are the names of 49 seaside resorts located in Great Britain. Many of them are part of the Isle of Wight, which is in southern England. The Isle of Wight, aside from being a famous vacationing spot, is known for sheep raising and dairy farming.

ABERDEEN (Scotland)

ABERYSTWYTH (Wales)

BATH (England)

BEAULIEU (England)

BEXHILL (England)

BLACKPOOL (England)

BOGNOR REGIS (England— Regis denotes that a reigning monarch stayed there)

BOURNEMOUTH (England)

BRIGHTON (England)

BRISTOL (England)

CARDIFF (Wales)

CORK (Ireland)

COWES (Isle of Wight, England)

DOUGLAS (Isle of Man, England, home of the tailless Manx cat)

DOVER (England)

DUNDEE (Scotland)

ELGIN (Scotland)

ENNIS (Ireland)

FELPHAM (England)

FOLKESTONE (England)

FRESHWATER (Isle of Wight)

GRETNA GREEN (Scotland— famous for eloping couples who wed here)

GURNARD (Isle of Wight)

HASTINGS (England—scene of the Battle of Hastings, 1066)

HERNE BAY (England)

HYTHE (England)

ILFRACOMBE (England)

LAND'S END (England)

LIMERICK (Ireland)

MARGATE (England)

MILFORD HAVEN (Wales)

NAIRN (Scotland)

PAISLEY (Scotland)

PENZANCE (England)

PLYMOUTH (England)

POOLE (England)

RYDE (Isle of Wight)

SANDOWN (Isle of Wight)

SCARBOROUGH (England)

SLIGO BAY (Ireland)

SOUTHEND-ON-SEA (England)

SOUTHPORT (England)

ST. IVES (England)

VENTNOR (Isle of Wight)

WESTON-SUPER-MARE (England)

WEYMOUTH (England)

WHITBY SPA (England)

WORTHING (England)

YARMOUTH (Isle of Wight)

```
A N O S H A S T I N G S L I G O B A Y S
X B L I M E R I C K B I L N A I R N C O
E M E O J N I N L O T S I R B A K A P U
H C L R A N R E T A W H S E R F R L E T
T O N L Y I Z A B S T F A D L B Y O D H
Y N P A I S L E Y R E H T U O M R A Y E
H H R S Z H T O O S B W S R O U O V R N
M T J L I N X W L O R D O U I V G A E D
I A U E E G E E Y U I U T C E Q M L G O
L B E O B Y E P B T G H L N N R D O A N
F E I X M S I R A H H V T N E L O O P S
O N L O O E E L R P T N I P E M V P S E
R O U Y C F N V T O O S U Q R C E K Y A
D T A A A E F R I R N S N S G U R C B B
H S E B R L D I U T N G C M A R G A T E
A E B E F P U H D O S N O P N N F L I R
V K O N L H N T T R B E Z B T O D B H D
E L J R I A D S E L A N D S E N D O W E
N O A E K M E Q K R O C O J R C R E W E
A F Y H R W E S D R A N R U G E L G I N
```

Solution is on page 362.

MATH FUN

Here's a puzzle of a different sort. First complete each of the simple arithmetic problems in order, from left to right. Then write the answer in the space provided and search for that word in the diagram. We've done number 16 to show you what we mean. Warning: If you're looking for six, be careful not to circle part of sixty or sixteen! Answers may be repeated.

1. $15 + 31 - 43 = $ _____

2. $4 \times 44 \div 8 = $ _____

3. $14 + 19 + 17 = $ _____

4. $16 \times 6 \div 12 = $ _____

5. $12 \times 4 + 19 = $ _____

6. $98 \div 7 \div 7 = $ _____

7. $6 \times 3 \times 5 = $ _____

8. $52 \div 4 - 10 = $ _____

9. $31 + 48 - 23 = $ _____

10. $4 \times 49 \div 28 = $ _____

11. $176 \div 2 \div 4 = $ _____

12. $26 + 39 - 48 = $ _____

13. $108 \div 36 \times 2 = $ _____

14. $4 \times 8 - 30 = $ _____

15. $27 + 43 - 19 = $ _____

16. $6 \times 44 \div 3 = $ EIGHTY-EIGHT

17. $270 \div 9 \times 3 = $ _____

18. $320 \div 2 \div 4 = $ _____

19. $79 - 12 - 45 = $ _____

20. $4 \times 41 \div 82 = $ _____

21. $9 \times 12 - 97 = $ _____

22. $14 + 24 + 12 = $ _____

23. $54 \times 2 \div 6 = $ _____

24. $42 + 33 - 58 = $ _____

25. $100 \div 4 \div 5 = $ _____

26. $152 - 36 - 40 = $ _____

27. $12 \times 33 \div 6 = $ _____

28. $105 \div 5 \div 7 = $ _____

29. $180 \div 2 \div 5 = $ _____

30. $19 + 26 - 34 = $ _____

31. $3 \times 11 \times 3 = $ _____

32. $16 \times 3 \div 24 = $ _____

```
N F F N I N E T Y N I N E T
O I I I E L E V O O O E E O
R W F F N V L E W W W E R Y
O W T Y T N E W T M R T H T
X W Y Y O Y R S Y H R H T E
O O S R T L O X T Y G G Y N
F R I T Y N I N N O V I E I
S I X T Y S E V E N T E E N
M F F N Y N L W W E T Y L N
I I O T I E E O T N R T R E
F N X R Y N T V E R Y H I V
X I S Y T N E V E S Y G T E
S I V W I Y E T E L H I R L
X N O E E S E T Y T E E N E
```

Solution is on page 363; list, page 395.

This is a two-part puzzle. The first part involves finding the 26 letter-and-symbol combinations hidden below. (Each combination has one letter among the symbols.) After you have circled all 26 combinations, write down the first five uncircled letters that occur when reading from left to right down the page. Then turn to page 39 for the second part to this special puzzle.

A * @ / !
B # ? : &
C – % & +
D $ = ! :
E @ – # /
F ? + & *
G % $ = @
H & / ? $
I : * % –
J / ! + &
K ! # @ ?
L $ % + :
M – & * =
N @ ? / #
O $ + – :
P * ! % =
Q & # ? /
R ! @ : –
S % * = +
T – $ @ %
U # / ! ?
V : = * &
W + % $ @
X / – + !
Y ? : # $
Z = – & *

```
K  #  /   ?  @ N !  +  =  *  % S  #
$  !  ?   &  M $ A  F  @  %  *  :  %
T  ?  #   –  /  = %  ?  C  –  !  +  &
:  +  &   @  J  E !  +  –  /  X  *  R
!  *  Q   *  ?  /  $  &  W Z  =  ?  P
=  S  %   N  @ !  !  *  :  :  U  !  O
$  I  :   *  % – W +  V  B  #  /  $
D  #  A   @  V  : H  *  &  :  ?  #  B
X  /  D   $  –  @ &  &  C  H  :  U  %
J  /  #   +  K  ! G  –  /  ?  +  I  :
% @  $   –  T  R %  =  Y  ?  %  M  –
–  O  F   ?  @ &  ?  Z  G  %  $  =  @
=  /  P   *  +  E L  $  Q  &  L  ?  Y
```

Solution is on page 363.

FULL HOUSE ——————————————— 12

There are 56 terms in this puzzle, and they all have four or more letters.
Words entirely within other words are not included. When you finish the
puzzle, every letter will have been circled at least once.

ASCENT	DECREE	GRADUATE	LIST	NOTICE
BOSSES	EERIE	HERO	LUSH	NUMERAL
BRINE	ENRICHED	HINT	MEASURE	OATS
CHART	ENTIRETY	HORIZON	MEWL	PATHWAY
CHORES	EWER	JESTERS	MICE	PIQUE
CLUMP	FAMOUS	LEES	MOLAR	QUAINT
COURTS	FOURTH	LIQUID	NOTE	RASHER

REQUEST
RESIST
ROSES
RUER
SCANTY
SEALS
SEETHE
SORTS
STACKS
STRETCH
STREW
SUED
TALKS
TAPE
TEMERITY
TONER
WILL
WORK
YACHT
ZIPPY
ZITHER

```
M E S C A N T Y T S I S E R
O N H B O S S E S R K W H A
L R H T R U O F E C I M C S
A I I B E K R H A L H E T C
R C N D R E T T L M I A E E
E H T O C I S T S R O S R N
M E W L Z E N R E S R U T T
U D U I U I J E S T E R S I
N M P Q A S R N O R H E K R
P P E U I C H O R E S C L E
Y R Q I E P A T H W A Y A T
G R A D U A T E M E R I T Y
```

Solution is on page 363.

17

TAIL TAG

Solve this puzzle by forming a chain of circled words in which the last letter of one word is the first letter of the next. The number in parentheses tells you the length of the word you're looking for. We have provided FOCUS to start you off.

FOCUS _____(5)	_____(3)	_____(4)
S_____(5)	_____(7)	_____(3)
_____(5)	_____(6)	_____(5)
_____(6)	_____(6)	_____(3)
_____(4)	_____(5)	_____(3)
_____(4)	_____(3)	_____(5)
_____(5)	_____(6)	_____(6)
_____(5)	_____(7)	_____(4)
_____(5)	_____(4)	_____(6)
_____(4)	_____(3)	_____(4)
_____(9)	_____(9)	_____(6)
_____(5)	_____(5)	

```
W O B B L E J T H R I L L U U T F
O Z T T Y A R E S G S T L O I O O
R H K H J C O J V U T H I A C N R
H F E A U H E L P E R E P U Y A R
T E Y I E R S W E N W F S L O U L
C Q Z E F R O A Z R Y T W A R H E
T E N T Q C B V S A H E Y T H U G
R N O V F Q N J Z E S T N S E R E
E Y E S T E R D A Y O I U M U I N
S T Q N S Y C I F F A R T F W A D
S F I N Q H L K T R R Y F I R T O
E O G O C O E B T N A I L L I R B
D I C A L P N U H A J O U E T H M
R G E R Z W C T T S E S I B E S U
E R O B R A H I J U Y O D A R E D
```

Solution is on page 363; list, page 395.

Here's another puzzle like the one on page 11. We INVITE you to PLUNGE right in and begin the search for all 39 words hidden below.

ACETATE	LEXICON	RECITAL	THROB
ARCHITECT	MOCHA	RIFT	THROUGHOUT
BEHIND	OBDURATE	RUDIMENT	TOPICAL
CHUTE	PANACHE	SENSITIVE	UPRIGHT
COMPLACENT	PLUNGE	SIBLING	URBANE
DANK	PRECINCT	THIEF	XENON
DECIPHER			
DEMERIT			
ELECTION			
EPIC			
FACT			
FEDERAL			
FIERY			
FISCAL			
GAZE			
GLUCOSE			
HUMAN			
HYENA			
INCUMBENT			
INVITE			
LAIR			

Solution is on page 363.

TANGLEWORDS ———————— 15

Surprise! Here's another Tanglewords puzzle. Have a MERRY time solving this puzzle and all the others featured throughout this issue. See page 11 for solving directions.

ATRIUM
BENIGN
BREATH
CAPON

CAUSE
CLARINET
DEMURE
DRAMATIC

DUCAT
ESTOPPEL
EXIT
FAILURE

FALSIFY
FAWN
FEINT
GAINFUL
GHOUL
GREATEST
HEATHEN
HORNET
LIMBO
LITER
MERRY
MISCHIEF
MISLED
MONSTROUS
NEBULOUS
OPINION
PACHYDERM
PROBLEMATIC
RETURN
RIPEN
RUSE
SILT
SLANTED
STREET
SUBLIMINAL
TELEVISION
TENET
TUSSLE

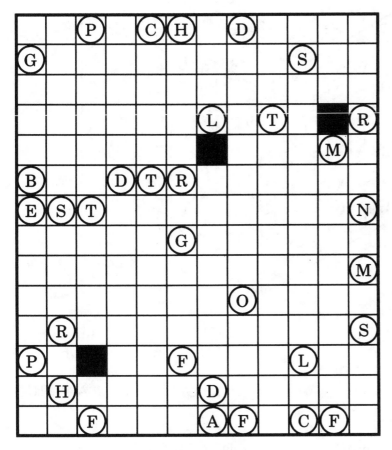

Solution is on page 363.

All the terms in the puzzle below are parts of an automobile. You'll find them hidden diagonally, horizontally or vertically on all three sides of the cube-shaped diagram. One term may be entirely hidden on one face of the cube or it may bend onto a second, or a third. IGNITION has been circled as a starter.

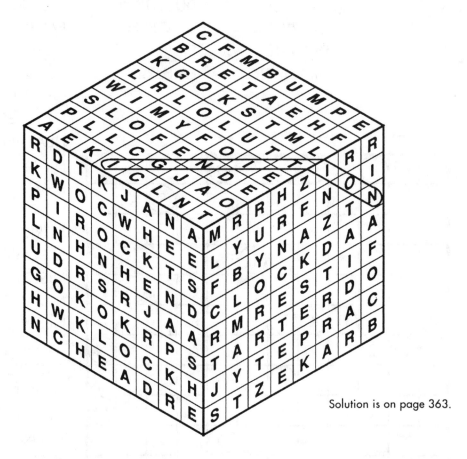

Solution is on page 363.

ANTENNA	CONSOLE	HOOD	RADIO
ARMREST	DASH	HORN	ROOF
BATTERY	DOOR	HUBCAP	SEAT
BRAKE	FAN	IGNITION	SPARK PLUG
BUMPER	FENDER	LOCK	STARTER
CARPET	GRILLE	MUFFLER	TRUNK
CLOCK	HEADREST	ODOMETER	WHEEL
COIL	HEATER	RADIATOR	WINDOW

Solve this puzzle like the one on the opposite page. This time we've hidden 33 "people movers." You can solve this puzzle on an AIRPLANE or on a FERRY, but we don't advise you to solve it while riding a MOTORCYCLE.

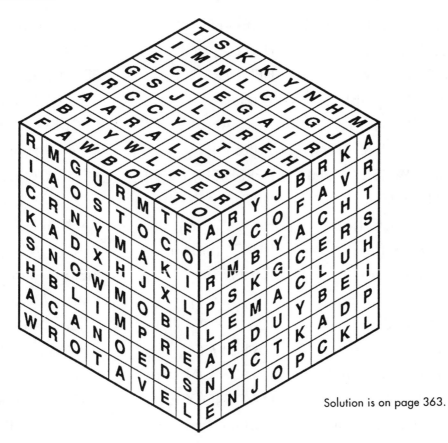

Solution is on page 363.

AIRPLANE	CATAMARAN	RAFT
AUTO	ELEVATOR	RICKSHAW
BARGE	ESCALATOR	SHIP
BLIMP	FERRY	SLEIGH
BOAT	GONDOLA	SNOWMOBILE
BOBSLED	HORSE	SUBWAY
BUS	HYDROFOIL	TAXI
CABLE CAR	JUNK	TRAIN
CAMEL	KAYAK	TRAM
CANOE	MOTORCYCLE	TROLLEY
CARRIAGE	MULE	YACHT

BIG BUCKS BALLPLAYERS

After they retire from their careers on the diamond, the ballplayers below will be rich enough to be able to buy diamonds! The baseball stars in this puzzle all earn at least $1,000,000 a year, making them "Big Bucks" ballplayers! Step up to the plate and find each one!

BEDROSIAN (Steve)

BELL (George)

BOGGS (Wade)

BOONE (Bob)

BRETT (George)

BROWNING (Tom)

BRUNANSKY (Tom)

BURKE (Tim)

CANSECO (Jose)

CARTER (Joe)

CLARK (Jack)

CLEMENS (Roger)

DARLING (Ron)

DAVIS (Alvin)

DAWSON (Andre)

DELEON (Jose)

EVANS (Dwight)

FERNANDEZ (Sid)

FISK (Carlton)

FRANCO (John)

GALARRAGA
   (Andres)

GOODEN (Dwight)

GUBICZA (Mark)

GUERRERO (Pedro)

HAYES (Von)

HENDERSON
   (Rickey)

HERNANDEZ
   (Keith)

HERSHISER (Orel)

HIGUERA (Ted)

HRBEK (Kent)

HURST (Bruce)

JOHNSON
   (Howard)

JOYNER (Wally)

KEY (Jimmy)

LANGSTON (Mark)

MATTINGLY (Don)

MCGEE (Willie)

MCGRIFF (Fred)

MCGWIRE (Mark)

MITCHELL (Kevin)

MOLITOR (Paul)

MORRIS (Jack)

MURPHY (Dale)

MURRAY (Eddie)

PARRISH (Lance)

PEÑA (Tony)

PENDLETON (Terry)

PLESAC (Dan)

PUCKETT (Kirby)

RAINES (Tim)

REARDON (Jeff)

RIGHETTI (Dave)

SANDBERG (Ryne)

SCOTT (Mike)

SIERRA (Ruben)

SMITH (Bryn)

STIEB (Dave)

STRAWBERRY
   (Darryl)

SUTCLIFFE (Rick)

TARTABULL (Danny)

TRAMMELL (Alan)

VALENZUELA
   (Fernando)

VIOLA (Frank)

WHITAKER (Lou)

WINFIELD (Dave)

YOUNT (Robin)

```
J T T E K C U P Y L G N I T T A M A V Q
O E A H R B E K R B L Y Y H P R U M I N
H E R S H I S E R O O E F T R O Q H O M
N G T I W N O Y E U R G M I T C H E L L
S C A P A Z C I B U G B G M S V L R A K
O M B N A I R E W V A H U S A E Z O V G
N U U T S R U H A Y E S E R D R N T N J
K R L R A H R L R T M N R E K A T I H W
B R L L E B E I T S O E R M Z E L L A Y
D A W S O N A I S O R D E B C R U O J R
F Y O C Z O Y T B H R O R K A G Z M W K
E Z C U A T A O T N I O O D Y N R A I N
R P E N A S Y G J O S G B R O W N I N G
N L S D I G E R A S C S U T C L I F F E
A H N V N N E L K R I S E E Y K K S I F
N I A S N A V E P E R L C A R T E R E J
D D C U R L N O R D D A K A J A T E L F
E H M D E R F R A N C O L Q M O X E D W
Z Y O U N T A W E E B C S A N D B E R G
S N E M E L C P C H E R I W G C M J I B
```

Solution is on page 363.

RECIPE: STUFFED TOMATOES ————————————————

At the bottom of the page you will find a recipe for tasty stuffed tomatoes, perfect for a light lunch on steamy days. The list below consists of 34 terms from the recipe, all of which are hidden in the diagram on the opposite page.

ADD	FIRM	SCOOP OUT
BACON BITS	GARNISH	SEASON
BOWL	LARGE	SERVE
CELERY SALT	LETTUCE LEAVES	SLICED
CHILL	MINCED	SMALL
CORE	MOISTEN	STUFF
CUCUMBER	ONION	TABLESPOONS
CUP	OPTIONAL	TOMATOES
DASH	PEPPER	TO TASTE
DICED	PLACE	WASH
DRESSING	PULP	
EGGS	REMOVE	

STUFFED TOMATOES

4 large tomatoes
1 small cucumber, diced
2 tablespoons onions, minced
⅛ cup bacon bits
Thousand Island dressing
   (to moisten)

dash celery salt
salt (to taste)
pepper (to taste)
4 lettuce leaves
2 hard-boiled eggs, sliced
   (optional)

Wash tomatoes, core, scoop out interior leaving enough pulp so that tomato remains firm. Place pulp in a bowl. Add cucumber, onion, and bacon bits. Moisten with dressing, then season. Stuff tomatoes, then chill in refrigerator for ½ hour. Remove chilled tomatoes from refrigerator and serve on individual lettuce leaves. Garnish with hard-boiled eggs. Serves four.

```
Q L Q C K H J Q S E O T A M O T
C E L E R Y S A L T C H C K L J
K N E T S I O M C P K C L E C S
C S T I B N O C A B L A D V G E
H T C K I C U P D F O A E O N V
L U Q O J N O D I M S W C M I A
R F N L E O A R C H I L L E S E
I F J A V S M E E Q J N M R S L
H S I N R A G G D L Q R C Q E E
P C K O E E G R L E L J A E R C
E U H I S S W A S H C R Q Y D U
P J L T J K M L Q X J I J Q J T
P Q L P C S N O O P S E L B A T
E S C O O P O U T T O T A S T E
R E B M U C U C X Y A E O I Q L
```

Solution is on page 364.

TELEPHONE PRACTICE

Using the telephone is so much a part of modern life that few of us ever stop to think that it might require practice. The inventor knew that it did, and he even advertised his new product with the following message. When you have circled all the terms, the uncircled letters will spell out a comment about ringing telephones.

When the
telephone
was
first
introduced
in eighteen
seventy-
seven,
many
people
suffered
from
stage
fright
and
were
reluctant
to speak
into it.
To encourage
use
of the
telephone,
Alexander
Graham
Bell

and
his
business
partners
began to
advertise
their
new
gadget
with
this
promise:
"Conversations
can be
easily
carried on
after
slight
practice
and
with
occasional
repetitions
of a word
or sentence."

```
W R E P E T I T I O N S S S O B G
E A R E N M O I N D W N D L F U A
E H T N E H W S L E O I B I A S D
S U F F E R E D P I V E T G W I G
E I A F T E R A T E L E P H O N E
G N H E H D W A S L A W S T R E T
E H O T G E S S E N D K T H D S T
G E F D I R R R S E V E N T Y S E
A O R S E N T E N C E P M E H U L
R I O V N I N N W E R L A A S A E
U E N R I I R T N P T S P E N G P
O O L T S F A R R N I F T O D Y H
C W R U R D N A A L S E I P E I O
N M H I C O C P Y C E S O R S P N
E A G T E T D B E G A N T O S H E
O H O D I H A U P C N E N M I T N
T A T C N W T N C I D S I I O E N
O R E B N A C O T E G A T S W R T
F G O R A L E X A N D E R E U S F
```

Solution is on page 364.

This puzzle is solved in two parts. The first part requires that you guess 30 words needed to complete the chart below. Beginning with each letter in the chart, there is an appropriate dance, fish, fabric, unit of measure and US President. Using the same words you used to complete the chart, you may begin the second part of this puzzle by finding them all in the diagram. If you can't find the word that you're looking for, you may have to guess another word that fits the chart. We've entered POPLIN in the chart and circled it in the diagram for you. The completed chart is on page 395.

	C	F	M	T	W	P
Dances						
Presidents						
Fish						
Measuring units						
Fabrics						POPLIN

```
M  A  T  O  R  T  X  O  F  L  O  T  U  N
R  I  N  E  O  P  M  W  L  M  E  R  D  D
W  O  L  T  N  I  P  T  A  U  S  O  E  N
A  Y  E  E  L  E  H  T  N  L  I  U  O  A
T  H  C  M  A  R  L  I  N  I  L  T  R  L
T  P  A  N  Z  C  M  U  E  N  G  E  R  E
O  E  N  D  E  E  W  T  L  N  C  C  Y  V
E  R  C  I  T  C  U  P  I  O  O  A  T  E
O  C  A  A  L  A  T  H  Z  T  T  R  O  L
R  H  N  O  O  P  S  A  E  T  F  P  N  C
N  G  T  Z  O  A  O  T  P  O  L  K  A  D
O  T  Y  L  W  O  O  P  O  C  S  A  R  A
M  U  S  L  I  N  N  T  R  Q  U  O  W  R
Y  L  E  R  E  D  N  U  O  L  F  O  O  N
```

Solution is on page 364; chart, page 395.

Scan the grid in all directions for 50 familiar five-letter words, arranged in pairs. Each word in a pair crosses its partner through the center letter, forming either a "+" or an "x" shape. One pair has been circled to start you off.

YOUR WORD LIST

```
B D L U Q T S V B O C H N Ü
H K E B N J I L R R L G W E
D I M I T I R E D A I S Y E
H L A R G E E T N E C S H L
B F C T S N N T R P K T K S
T O O H S A H I S S A D O U
R I R S T E E R A B E N A R
O E N N I C H L N L A R E N
D K A R E O F C B R S T C L
D L S C W S L R V L T E O B
S R L H T H O S E O A V U N
T N I A P O A L I T E R E B
W L C N M I T W C T R E U G
E K E H K S U Y B O I N A M
```

Solution is on page 364; list, page 395.

This list may seem to be a potpourri of famous names with nothing in common, but there is definitely a connection among all of them. The people in this puzzle became well-known during their lives, and each one is or was left-handed.

ALEXANDER (the Great)
BAILEY (F. Lee)
CARROLL (Lewis)
CHAPLIN (Charlie)
CHARLEMAGNE
DARROW (Clarence)
DA VINCI (Leonardo)
FORD (Gerald)
FRANKLIN (Benjamin)
GARLAND (Judy)
GOBEL (George)
GRABLE (Betty)
HOLBEIN (Hans)
HOOVER (Herbert)
HUDSON (Rock)
KLEE (Paul)
MARX (Harpo)
MONROE (Marilyn)
MUSIAL (Stan)
PICASSO (Pablo)
PORTER (Cole)
RAPHAEL
REDFORD (Robert)
RUTH (Babe)
SPITZ (Mark)
STARR (Ringo)
STENGEL (Casey)
VALLEE (Rudy)
VICTORIA (Queen of England)

```
G J X N O K N I L K N A R F
R R A T S I O D C A N Z F Q
P R A M E Y B A H R I J Z S
A E C B F O R D A O U S P H
K V L A L R X I P S Q I U O
C O F I O E W C L F T D N M
H O H L I T Z N I Z S F S O
A H L E B O G I N O W G R N
R L I Y G L R V N I K E S R
L V E J D X R A M S D L T O
E E N X N P N D P F T H E E
M P I C A S S O O H Z T N E
A D O X L N A R R I A H G L
G W O R R A D O T M T E E L
N R Q V A L R E E U E F L A
E O D G G L A I R O T C I V
```

Solution is on page 364.

Many of our solvers have sent us MEMOs telling us how much they enjoy these puzzles. So, we've put lots of Tanglewords puzzles in this book. Solving directions are given on page 11.

ATTRACTED	DAFFODIL	FERN	HECTIC
AWHILE	DELICATE	FETCHING	INTUITION
BONNET	EMOTE	GAMINE	ITSELF
CHIN	EPISODE	GRANDIOSE	LIBERATED
CONTENTED	EXTOL	HALO	MAGNETO
			MEDIOCRE
			MEMO
			MODIFY
			NAIL
			NEAREST
			NOMAD
			ORIGINATE
			OVERT
			PETAL
			PIONEER
			PROVEN
			REALISTIC
			RECEIPT
			SHEEPISH
			SNARE
			TUMBLED
			VEILED
			WARMER

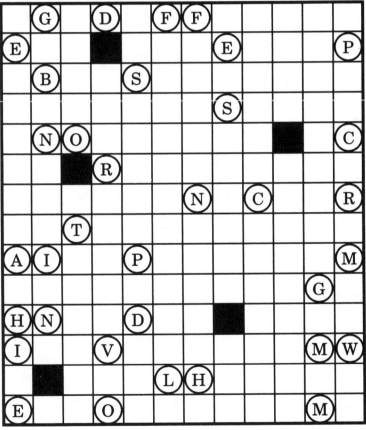

Solution is on page 364.

D. J. DAYS

A disc jockey is a person employed by a radio broadcasting company to play music, report news items, weather, traffic, and perform a variety of other duties. In addition to the considerable vocal training involved in learning to be a disc jockey, one must also learn the use of technical broadcasting equipment and become familiar with the specialized vocabulary involved with the job. A sampling of terms and items from the disc jockey's world appears in this puzzle.

BACKTIMING	OUTCUE
BOARD	PATTERN CHANGE
BRIDGE	PROGRAM LOG
BROADCAST	RECORD
CARTRIDGE	SCORES
COMMERCIAL	SIGNAL
CROSSFADE	SPORTS
CUE	TAPE
CUT	"TESTING"
EARPHONES	TIME
HIT CHART	TRANSMITTER
MICROPHONE	TROLLEY CHAIR
MUSIC	VU METER
NEWS	WATTS
"ON AIR" SIGN	WEATHER
ON CUE	

```
E R M Z F O T P Y B O T A D N P
C O M M E R C I A L U V A E R Y
O T L P G A R Q U A T U N G X O
N U A E N O H P O R C I M D M T
V T L Y G X S A R H U F L I M R
T E S T I N G T I M E B R R E O
M U G L S A R T T R U P E T I L
A C Y D R O C E R A R S T R E L
P R S Y I H R R A B W I I A M E
R O B O A R D N A R M L O C A Y
O S V R N O B C R S P O R T S C
G S T U O M K H N A L H T C A H
R F W O M T E A S A R T O M F A
A A N E I E R N N O Z R Y N L I
M D O M N T T G A W E A T H E R
L E I S T E I E R S V M U T S S
O N C U E S U B R O A D C A S T
G R O N K T V A D L K M D O U A
```

Solution is on page 364.

"N" DEFINITIONS

Here's a Word Search that takes some extra brain power. You form the word list by placing the answers to each of the 37 definitions on the blanks provided. All the answers are hidden in the diagram and each one begins with the letter "N." Additional hints: The answers will be in alphabetical order, and the numbers in parentheses indicate the number of letters in each word. Words are listed on page 395.

1. Hammer target (4) _____
2. Title (4) _____
3. Nursemaid (5) _____
4. Dinner "hanky" (6) _____
5. Tell a story (7) _____
6. Wide's opposite (6) _____
7. Country (6) _____
8. Military branch (4) _____
9. Close by (4) _____
10. Tidy (4) _____
11. Giraffe feature (4) _____
12. Require (4) _____
13. Sewing item (6) _____
14. Jittery (7) _____
15. Bird's home (4) _____
16. Butterfly snare (3) _____
17. At no time (5) _____
18. Rather's field (4) _____
19. The one after (4) _____
20. Pleasant (4) _____

21. 5¢ piece (6) _____
22. Evening hours (5) _____
23. 6 and 3 (4) _____
24. Shake one's head "yes" (3) _____
25. Sound (5) _____
26. Not any (4) _____
27. Midday (4) _____
28. Everyday (6) _____
29. Compass point (5) _____
30. Face feature (4) _____
31. Musical sign (4) _____
32. Famous (5) _____
33. Become aware of (6) _____
34. Work of fiction (5) _____
35. Poke (5) _____
36. 1, 2, or 7 (6) _____
37. Doctor's aide (5) _____

```
N E W S N N I N E N E Y
I O N L A O K E D C E V
K Q I K I E R X I B I A
P J C T L E N T H G I N
A E K D A I O U H C T O
N P E M A N O R M A L T
A E L N A O Q T E B K E
N A R R A T E N N N E S
N N R V X E U O O F O R
Y O O N O D Q I N V A U
W S Z O G U W S D E E N
R E V E N T S E N K M L
```

Solution is on page 364; answers, page 395.

This puzzle is filled with the names of 24 islands that line the Canadian coasts. Instead of a straight line, you will find that each word in this special puzzle twists around other letters, making several turns. Each letter in the diagram is used only once, and no two entries cross. We've looped the island of PRINCE EDWARD to show you how it's done.

AKIMISKI

AKPATOK

ANTICOSTI

BAFFIN

BANKS

BATHURST

BELCHER

BORDEN

BYLOT

COATS

CORNWALL

DEVON

ELLESMERE

KING WILLIAM

MANSEL

MELVILLE

NOTTINGHAM

PRINCE CHARLES

~~PRINCE EDWARD~~

PRINCE OF WALES

RESOLUTION

SALISBURY

SOMERSET

VICTORIA

```
T S O E B C N I R S T S R U
I C C L O C A P E O R D E H
I E H R E W K L I K B P N T
T R N E F S I M N A R E A L
N A W A D O I C I I L B V E
S K D L L W E K N G L I O M
O V N R A T A O E W I R M T
N L E A B S S E C L I A A C
O T Y D Y L E R E L I L I I
B E L B R R E S C N N R L V
A S A M U A M E M O S O P U
F N N T B H C E R S A I T L
F I H T O S I K O E T K R O
M A G N I N L A S T A P E S
```

Solution is on page 364.

This is the second part to Word Search 11 on page 16. Unscramble the first five uncircled letters from the puzzle on page 16 to form the only word that will be found just once in the diagram below. None of the other possible words are in the diagram. (The word you're looking for can be found under the solution to puzzle 11 on page 363.)

```
K W F N Z D D Y I S M N
A I R A I Y T L B H I F
O H X T R E H U R F D V
W L A G L N J I P O Y O
O D P T Y R O C L E U S
S C Z A V B R E S M L G
J V R H D T K Q U S T I
B N P U G M D L U R W P
N I C B X F O W A E H T
E U Q W K E S C Z Q U C
R S H E Z P E O J T X S
B O S A R I N G U A T K
```

Solution is on page 365.

SQUARE PAIRS ————————————————

The two diagrams on the facing page each contain the first and last words of a common three-word phrase, all with "of" as the middle word. To solve, find the first word in Square 1, then search for the last word in Square 2. Write each word that you find on a line in the corresponding column below. There are 25 phrases, each containing words of three letters or more, to find. We've completed the first phrase to show you how it's done. The beginning phrase word, MANNER, was found in the first square and listed in the Square 1 column. SPEAKING, the last phrase word, was found in the second square and listed under the Square 2 column.

SQUARE 1		SQUARE 2
MANNER	of	SPEAKING
	of	THUMB
GAME	of	
	of	
	of	
	of	
	of	
	of	
	of	
	of	
	of	
	of	
	of	
	of	
	of	
	of	
	of	
	of	
	of	
	of	
	of	
	of	
	of	
	of	
	of	

1

```
R  I  N  G  J  G  A  T  E  S
U  E  Q  C  E  C  E  I  P  E
L  I  N  E  T  S  F  E  G  T
E  D  Z  N  D  F  E  Q  S  R
N  H  I  N  A  D  I  J  H  F
A  O  I  T  E  M  A  G  C  O
P  W  S  B  T  S  O  D  U  U
M  Y  I  I  S  I  V  N  O  R
U  L  M  X  A  D  P  A  T  T
L  E  E  H  W  E  A  L  T  H
```

2

```
E  C  N  A  H  C  L  A  S  S
N  W  A  R  O  S  E  S  P  U
U  P  L  E  N  T  Y  E  T  N
T  S  I  N  E  V  A  E  H  D
R  T  S  E  F  K  D  O  G  A
O  R  B  A  I  Y  N  F  I  Y
F  U  A  N  L  O  T  E  L  S
I  T  G  U  R  G  I  E  A  A
R  H  J  T  H  U  M  B  O  L
E  X  P  E  R  I  E  N  C  E
```

Solution is on page 365; lists, page 395.

"WHEEL OF FORTUNE" ———————————————

One of the most POPULAR of all GAME SHOWs, "WHEEL of Fortune" made its DEBUT on the NBC television NETWORK on January 6, 1975. Chuck WOOLERY was the original host, and Susan STAFFORD was the first turner of LETTERS. (Vanna WHITE replaced her in 1982.) In the fall of 1983, Pat SAJAK began presiding over the SYNDICATED version. Find 54 terms related to this LONG-running series.

AUDIENCE
BANKRUPT
BEFORE AND AFTER
BENIRSCHKE (Rolf, former host)
BOARD
BONUS ROUND
BOOK
BUY A VOWEL
CASH
CLUE
CONTESTANTS
CREATED (by Merv Griffin)
DEBUT (January 6, 1975)
EVENT
FICTIONAL CHARACTER
FREE SPIN
GAME SHOW
GOEN (Bob,
   daytime host)
GUESS (letters)
HANGMAN (game's basis)
HOME VERSION
I WON!
LETTERS
LONG
LOSE A TURN
NETWORK
NEWSPAPER FEATURE
PEOPLE
PERSON

PHRASE
PLACE
POPULAR
PRIZES
PUZZLES
QUOTATION
SAJAK (Pat,
   nighttime host)
SAME NAME
SEEN (by millions)
SOLVE (the puzzle)
SONG (& Artist)
SPIN (the wheel)
STAFFORD (Susan, original
   hostess)
STUDIO
SYNDICATED
TAPING
THING
THREE DAYS (tenure for a
   champion)
TITLE
TOURNAMENTS (such as
   Teen Week)
TRY OUT (for the show)
USED (letter board)
WHEEL
WHITE (Vanna, hostess)
WOOLERY (Chuck, original
   host)

```
W O H S E M A G P B L K V A N T U K B J
Z T Z K R Y M O N P R E C N E I D U A G
J U O Y S E T R M O R S W C O N E E N B
S O L V E N T E W W S Q D O G G R I K N
B Y O D E B U T X O T B W E V U P Z R Z
O R S V N Q E C E O A N O I T A T O U Q
Q T E C O N H A U L F F S A T A Y S P U
M S A J A K A R Z E F I E E R E E U T I
R E T F A D N A E R O F E B L D W R B N
B Z U D N A G H E Y R J T T E Z M E C C
E I R Y M E M C G E D T I Z M O Z O L N
N R N E E C A L P T O T H S A C N U H O
I P N I W O N A K H F H W R N T E W P S
R T L Z P V P N O I S R E V E M O H T R
S B O N U S R O U N D O E S M E R I A E
C T L A W M G I L G E F T E A A D L R P
H Q U E N U V T T O J A C I S P U A V T
K M N D E T A C I D N Y S E M P Q Z Y A
E O P S I H Y I C T O G N Q O L I P J S
J X S A Z O W F S E P E O P L E S N A W
```

Solution is on page 365.

HELLO there solvers! You are ABOUT to embark on the solving of another Tanglewords puzzle. See page 11 for solving directions. See pages 55, 61 and 70 for more Tanglewords.

ABOUT	MUSTACHE	POET	STATION
AMIABLE	NEIGHBOR	RESCIND	STREUSEL
AMINO	NEON	RETREAD	THERMOS
BARBECUE	NICKEL	ROUGE	TRUMPET
BEATEN	PATENT	SAPPHIRE	VERGE
BOOR	PIGMENT	STAGE	WHEEL
CASTE			
DISRUPT			
ERRATIC			
EVER			
FAULTING			
FURL			
GONG			
GRUNION			
HELLO			
HEMISPHERE			
HERITAGE			
KNIFE			
LATHE			
LILTING			
MILITANT			
MINUET			

Solution is on page 365.

Don't THROW in the towel over this puzzle, which is made up of the 60 words listed below. Solve it as you did the one on page 17.

ACTRESS
AGENTS
ALTO
BALLOT
BOWL
BUTTE
CALL
CARD
CHEERS
CHEF
CHEST
CHOSE
EDIT
ENLIST
ERASER
ESSENCE
FATS
GOVERN
HALIBUT
HIES
HOSED
ITCHING
JOSTLE
JUNKET
JUSTIFY
LAKES
LATER
LENS
LIVEN

LUNGE
MOTION
NESTLED
NINES
ODES
PERFECT
READY
RENTS

SANITY
SEAR
SERF
SKIP
SPREAD
STEAL
SUCCESS
TACKLED

TALL
TARS
THEE
THREAT
THROW
TIARA
TICKET
TIMIDITY

TRAIL
UNDER-
   NEATH
VERITY
VITALLY
YEARS
YIELDING
YOLKS

```
Y T I D I M I T C E F R E P
O D E S O H C T H R E A T I
L L A T E R A S E R H A T K
K B I E C N E S S E C C U S
S O A A R A I T T K H Y B S
N W L L R P E N L I S T I E
E L D E L T S E N E V I L R
L U N G E O D G K R S R A T
T T E K C I T A S R E E H C
S A N I T Y L L A T I V A A
O U N D E R N E A T H R O W
J U S T I F Y I E L D I N G
```

Solution is on page 365.

Here's another puzzle like the ones on pages 22 and 23. The terms used to fill the cube-shaped diagram below include a BASKET, an AIR CON-DITIONER, a COFFEEPOT and other household items that begin with the letter "A," "B," or "C."

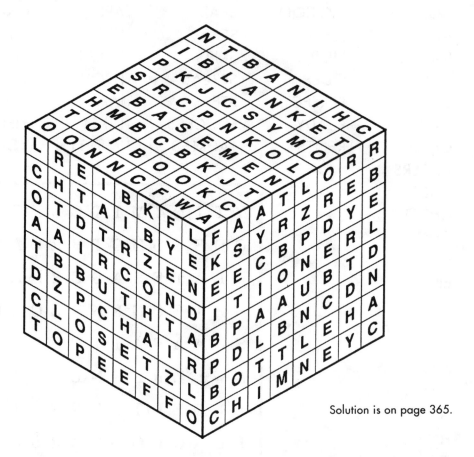

Solution is on page 365.

AIR CONDITIONER	BOTTLE	CLOSET
ATTIC	BOWL	CLOTHESPIN
BASEMENT	BROOM	COAT
BASKET	CABINET	COFFEEPOT
BATHROOM	CALENDAR	COFFEE TABLE
BATHTUB	CANDLE	COLANDER
BED	CARPET	COUCH
BEDROOM	CHAIR	CRIB
BLANKET	CHIMNEY	CUP
BOOKCASE	CHINA	CURTAIN

Solve this puzzle like you did the one on the opposite page. But as you search for the terms listed below, you may want to SIP on a CUP of STRONG LEMON tea, as this puzzle contains terms associated with tasty tea.

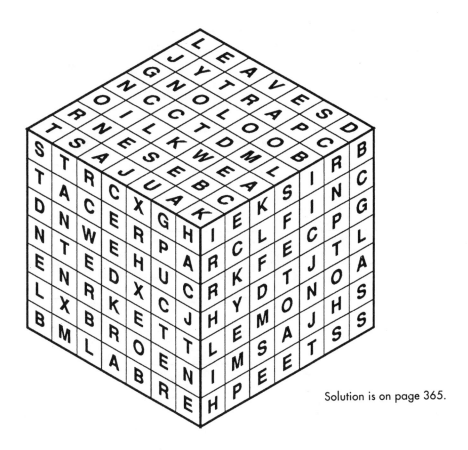

Solution is on page 365.

AROMA	CUP	INSTANT	POT
BAG	DARJEELING	JASMINE	SIP
BLACK	DRIED	KETTLE	STEEP
BLEND	GLASS	LEAVES	STRONG
BREW	GREEN	LEMON	SUGAR
BRISK	HERBAL	OOLONG	WEAK
CLEAR	HOT	PARTY	
CREAM	ICED	PITCHER	

TAIL TAG CHALLENGER

Here's another Tail Tag puzzle like the one on pages 18 and 19. This time we give you no help in finding the 36 words of 3 letters or more used to complete this puzzle. The directions are on page 18, but here's a hint: You will complete this puzzle wherever you begin it.

_____   _____   _____

_____   _____   _____

_____   _____   _____

_____   _____   _____

_____   _____   _____

_____   _____   _____

_____   _____   _____

_____   _____   _____

_____   _____   _____

_____   _____   _____

_____   _____   _____

_____   _____   _____

```
H G I H T T D N E I R F I T W L L
E A Q N N W E N R E L O E D E A O
L S E A I H S O H E O O T V O S V
L P I T H C T E R J V R O M U H I
O T R I A T I W N P E N O S R L T
S I E O B O N N R O T H E H D O N
W S A N U M Y O U N G A A M N W E
A M A A E A O W Q M T I R I O I T
L E L L N T T F R E E V C H E W X
L G I Z O M L H I M E T R I P L E
O O E J E A A T B G W E E C T H T
W I T C H A Z R E Y R N O L H U S
E S P O S T A L O H T A E R B W O
Q I U J N C Z B R R O L P R P E R
R E G A E D U G T U M P M H U F F
```

Solution is on page 365; list, page 396.

TRIVIA TOURNEY

Can you name the smallest continent? And what city is known as the "Diamond of the Desert"? If you came up with Australia and Las Vegas, this puzzle won't leave you stranded! Solve it like the one on page 8.

_____ 1. Seward's Folly

_____ 2. Shakespeare's river

_____ 3. Subject of _Funny Girl_

_____ 4. Australia's Great Barrier Reef substance

_____ 5. Newsman with the tag line: "And that's the way it is"

_____ 6. Location of ancient Greek oracle

_____ 7. City with treasury mint mark of "D"

_____ 8. Winnie the Pooh's donkey friend

_____ 9. Country whose flag is St. George's cross

_____ 10. Sport held on 6-foot by 40-foot strip

_____ 11. Location of US gold bullion

_____ 12. What a topi is

_____ 13. Modern name for Sandwich Islands

_____ 14. Author of the _Iliad_

_____ 15. Country led by Mahatma Gandhi

_____ 16. One of the four Gospel writers

_____ 17. First gorilla to learn sign language

_____ 18. Composer of _The Pink Panther_ theme

_____ 19. Author of famous series of school readers

_____ 20. Whale with a tusk

_____ 21. State once represented in the senate by Bobby Kennedy

_____ 22. RCA Victor dog

_____ 23. Center of an atom

_____ 24. Mickey Mouse's dog

_____ 25. Number of continents

_____ 26. Mountain where Moses received the Ten Commandments

_____ 27. Sport where one can "hang ten"

_____ 28. Nickname of the Model T

_____ 29. What Gunga Din carried in Rudyard Kipling's poem

_____ 30. She sewed Peter Pan's shadow back on

```
H T I E I Z Z I L N I T N I
C O R A L S F W A T E R N I
A L M O R E C L P N N D D A
D A D E N V E R L O I N K W
N S L C R E U S U A P S O A
A K I A U N W H T E P U K H
L N W D S E E Y O R E R O E
G I E E U K D K O X R F T C
N P N L E E A N B R I I C H
E H D I L B F O R T K N O X
H I Y P C R I J V N A G O N
C A H H U N C H O E C I R B
K I T T N N A R W H A L P H
Y E F F U G C M E R N O V A
```

Solution is on page 365; answers, page 396.

This puzzle contains 21 eight-letter terms, each with a number following it in parentheses, which refers to the numbered dashes below. Each word will form a box, reading either clockwise or counterclockwise. (LORDSHIP has already been boxed to start you off.) As you find each term in the diagram, enter the letter in the middle of each box on the corresponding dash below the diagram ("O" has already been entered.) When you have finished, the letters on the dashes will spell out a popular line from a famous movie.

AARDVARK (7)

AMBROSIA (11)

DECIPHER (1)

DOMINION (20)

EPIDEMIC (13)

FOUNTAIN (2)

GADABOUT (5)

GOATSKIN (21)

HEADACHE (6)

IMBECILE (10)

LOATHING (14)

LOLLYGAG (9)

LORDSHIP (19)

LOVESICK (16)

NONRIGID (12)

POTBELLY (17)

PROVIDED (3)

RAVENOUS (18)

REGIMENT (8)

REHEARSE (15)

TACITURN (4)

```
A H C Z I C K T I C E F G
I S O R S K L U R A I N H
J I A B E V O R N T H F K
K A A M M I E P L N U O N
R N R O L D E D R E S H E
A V D O P E C T E I R A V
N O S H I E I P H E A B O
V U O E D E M T E S D E U
K I N O R W X Y H C A G T
S E G E D I L E C B E N T
T A O F G C L I H I M O R
H L L O L E B M O D I G E
I N G P L E T I M N C I J
M L A G Y P O N I O N R K
```

Solution is on page 366.

``
— — — — — — — — — — — — —
1 2 3 4 5 6 7 8 9 10 11 12 13

      — — — —   — — — —
      14 15 16 17 18 19 20 21 ''
```
```

Many jobs require a worker to wear special apparel like a hat, which may be a health or safety aid or merely an official part of a uniform. The names of 18 types of employment which may require the worker to wear headgear have been hidden in the diagram. Can you find them all without the aid of a list?

YOUR WORD LIST

```
B R S T R P C R C B P R N I M
R E C I F F O Y R A T I L I M
Z Y K Q A Z R L U S I T L O F
N A M E R I F R I E E K Z O Z
J L F C M O L J N B M S O K T
O P B L E A I A G A M J R Q U
T L D E R R M H N L K I S U A
B L C Z E E H I D L O T N G N
A A J O C K E Y N P S M A E O
O B L I W A E Y F L F T M Q R
P T L T K B C E C A U C R C T
L O U Y R A O D P Y H T O J S
P O S T M A N Y O E S T O C A
H F K A C E L C F R R P D O M
```

Solution is on page 366; list, page 396.

Solve this puzzle like the one on page 30. This time the categories are sewing items, movies directed by Alfred Hitchcock, words that contain two sets of double letters, universities and birds. The completed chart is on page 396.

	P	V	F	N	R	M
Sew what?						
Hitchcock						
Double letters						
Universities						
Birds						

```
N  R  A  V  E  A  R  L  L  E  P  S  S  I  M
O  O  D  O  O  V  L  U  O  V  I  R  E  O  P
L  N  A  G  F  A  N  I  T  R  A  M  E  S  I
Y  A  F  I  B  N  E  P  A  G  M  O  Y  A  G
N  H  C  T  A  H  T  U  N  M  E  C  M  I  E
N  F  O  R  F  T  I  N  F  I  H  R  U  R  O
A  O  E  E  N  L  E  V  R  O  F  E  S  W  N
F  I  T  V  I  E  M  A  D  E  R  T  O  N  P
E  N  A  E  D  F  I  E  P  A  E  D  R  I  O
P  I  M  L  C  H  C  N  I  F  N  O  H  M  R
O  L  E  V  A  N  H  V  E  I  Z  P  U  A  O
S  S  O  E  N  O  I  R  W  U  Y  R  Y  R  M
S  U  R  T  M  E  G  R  A  C  C  O  O  N  V
E  M  V  A  S  S  A  R  P  A  N  B  L  I  O
S  F  U  N  U  E  N  P  O  P  L  I  N  E  O
S  U  O  I  R  O  T  O  N  V  I  N  U  E  V
```

Solution is on page 366; chart, page 396.

Here we pay HOMAGE to all of our Tanglewords puzzle lovers. The directions for this puzzle are given on page 11.

ADMONISH   CUPFUL   FOREIGN   LIGHTEN

AEROBIC   DELICIOUS   FRIVOLOUS   LISP

AURAL   DISMANTLE   GAUCHERIE   LOCATE

BICUSPID   EARLY   HARMONICA   MARACA

CALCIUM   ENDORSED   HOMAGE   NEWSMAN

CLIMATE   FLEE   ISLAND   NURTURED

OCEAN

PITON

PRESUME

PRIMITIVE

ROMP

ROUGHAGE

SAUTE

SILICA

SILO

STIPPLE

TAILOR

TOFU

TREASURE

WAGER

ZENITH

Solution is on page 366.

PHRASE PLAY

Welcome to "PHRASE PLAY." Each column below represents a portion of an old cliche or a familiar phrase. Column A is the beginning, Column B is the middle, and Column C is the end. See if you can pick an entry from each column to complete a common phrase. After you have connected all the phrases, you can then find each column entry in the diagram. Completed phrases are on page 396.

A	B	C
A CHIP	A DAY'S	BARREL
A FLASH	BEHIND	DOGS
ALL IN	CATS AND	DONE
A METHOD	CAUTION TO	FLOOR
AT A LOSS	FOR	HAND
BARK	FROM THE	LIFE
EASIER	HELPING	MADNESS
GET IN ON	IN THE	OLD BLOCK
HOOK	LINE, AND	PAN
LEND A	MEETS	PRINT
LOCK	OFF THE	RED
MORE THAN	OF ONE'S	SHOULDER
NOT YET DRY	SAID THAN	SINKER
PAINT	STOCK, AND	THE EARS
RAIN	THE FINE	THE EYE
READ	THE GROUND	THE WIND
STRAIGHT	THE TOWN	WORDS
THE TIME	TO ONE'S	WORK
THROW	UP THE	WRONG TREE

```
B S H O U L D E R S F I S N D S R
E H T F F O W S L L S T T O F E O
H A A C H I P S O D O E G H A N D
I O F T E K G O C C N S N D R O N
N M E L F E R L K C O L B D L O I
D M E R A S R A E E H T E A A T W
A T O E P S N T C L I F E R R M E
Y F N R T D H A G S Y A D A R K H
R U B I E S U N O N I T E G E A T
D E P L R T H E G R O U N D I S B
T T D T I P H S N N C R E J S E D
E G H O H T N A D R I B W N A T D
Y H N E M E O U N L T P A N E N D
T T T O F M F W T E S H L R A I N
O S R N S I O Y H N T I E E L A A
N F E D I T N L M D D O N E H P S
W O R K E E E E I A N I W K Y M T
K O O H L H S A L A L L I N E E A
W L T B D T S T R A I G H T G R C
```

Solution is on page 366; phrases, page 396.

To solve this puzzle, insert a letter from below into each of the circles in the diagram. This letter should be one that will let you form as many 5- and 6-letter words as possible. If you have entered the correct letters into the circles, you should be able to find 38 words in total. We've inserted the letter "G" to start you off.

C	G̸	H	M	N	P	R	S

YOUR WORD LIST

```
C H P L N R E S S Y J B D E
R U R K E R A ◯ S I D A R T
B E O T W U O R C H A ◯ G E
W E ◯ I A R V I L I A K A C
F I E O E L N M R N N E L H
M K I Y L E H P D W Y R L N
O E Z A ◯ A N N E R A M O S
G L E A O E C K A C C E ◯ T
C Y F B R H N E C J M A I H
E E D J A E K E M H R D E K
D U E N L S ◯ A R E J V C G
R E G E N T A A W F H I E N
C E A R R V L H J R E ◯ A L
Q U R Y A N B I K W T E S W
```

Solution is on page 366; list, page 396.

HIDDEN NUMBERS ——————————— 43

Can you guess the Queens, New York address of the Bunkers from the television series "All In The Family"? It's 704 Hauser Street. Before this, the family lived on Union Street.

0767	2049
0784	2098
0845	2245
0848	2259
0954	2467
0969	2476
1188	2645
1196	2693
1354	2848
1443	2894
1569	3369
1587	3385
1786	3676
1794	3685
1976	3969
1985	3987

```
2 4 5 7 6 7 0 7 8 3 9 6 2 9
5 4 9 9 4 5 1 6 9 9 5 6 4 9
7 8 6 4 5 3 1 7 4 8 9 0 7 5
9 5 8 7 5 1 5 7 8 7 2 6 5 2
1 6 9 6 8 2 8 6 8 6 4 5 9 2
7 8 9 8 9 8 9 9 7 1 1 9 6 0
4 5 8 3 5 4 1 9 5 6 1 7 8 2
2 6 7 1 9 8 1 3 4 4 1 5 8 9
8 2 7 0 8 4 8 7 6 6 5 9 8 4
8 9 4 8 9 0 2 4 5 8 4 0 5 7
4 6 9 5 9 5 3 6 7 2 5 8 6 5
5 5 4 6 4 8 6 8 4 9 4 4 7 8
9 7 8 6 3 5 7 7 8 9 4 5 5 3
0 9 2 4 5 3 6 7 0 7 8 4 6 3
```

Solution is on page 366.

You'll be a real cut-up when you finish solving this puzzle. Listed below are the names of different kinds of scissors or shears. A pair of scissors is really two knife blades joined to form a double-lever scissors. In the hardware trade, shears refers to scissors with blades more than six inches long.

ANVIL

AUTO BODY

BANDAGE

BARBER'S

BELT

BLUEPRINT

CABLE (cutters)

CARPET

CUTICLE

DRESSMAKING

EMBROIDERY

FLORIST

HEDGE

KITCHEN

LEATHER

METAL SNIPS

PAPERHANGER'S

PINKING

POCKET

PRUNING

RUG

SAILMAKER'S

SEWING

SHEEP

THREAD CLIPS

TIN SNIPS

UPHOLSTERER

WIRE (cutters)

```
U K H R E R E T S L O H P U Y G
B A N D A G E V Q C A G F D P N
F L O P G L T O U R N N O A P I
S O U E H N E T R I B B P F S W
P T N E L O I A K O O E L E S E
I D U H P C L N T T R L L J S S
N C R S L R I S U H T G I T P R
S Z P E O P I A A R E U M V I E
N R J K S L S N T E P R A C N K
I J E P T S G I T A M F I E S A
T M T B O E M E G D E H H W L M
S Y E R R C K A S C R C E K A L
S N L S M A R C K L T T M D T I
R I A M E M B R O I D E R Y E A
C A B L E B J C K P N O T M M S
E K C S F L O R I S T G K A C K
```

Solution is on page 366.

A lot of these puzzles can be used to EDUCATE our solvers. This one in particular may do just that. As you search for SELENIUM, BEDLAM and FRIEZE, you can consult a dictionary to find out exactly how these words should be used in speech.

ABBOT

ADMITTED

AMETHYST

BAILIFF

BEDLAM

BIBLE

CONCEDE

CONSTABLE

CURT

DISCIPLINE

EDUCATE

ESKIMO

FENCE

FRIEZE

GRAIN

HISTAMINE

INSIST

INSURED

LEISURE

MISFIT

MUSEUM

NICEST

OBSOLETE

OMEN

OPINION

PLAZA

PRECEDENT

PRIME

RESET

RESIDENTIAL

SAUTERNE

SELENIUM

TISSUE

TREAT

TRIBUTE

UNUSED

UNZIP

VENTURESOME

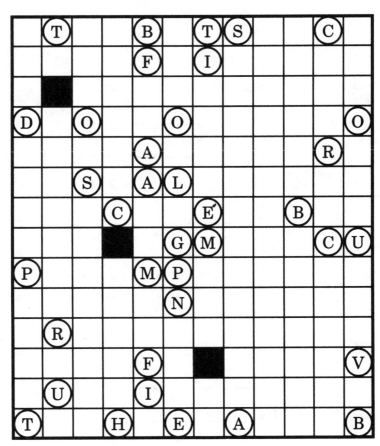

Solution is on page 366.

MATH FUN

Here's another puzzle that tests your math skills. To solve, first determine the answer to the first math problem, then take that answer to solve the second problem, and so on, until you have solved all 34. Then look for the answers in the puzzle diagram on the facing page. Your final answer should be FIVE. A similar puzzle is on page 14.

1. $14 \times 2 = $ _____
2. $+ 16 = $ _____
3. $- 28 = $ _____
4. $\div 2 = $ _____
5. $\times 7 = $ _____
6. $- 14 = $ _____
7. $\div 3 = $ _____
8. $+ 36 = $ _____
9. $- 15 = $ _____
10. $- 11 = $ _____
11. $\times 2 = $ _____
12. $\div 4 = $ _____
13. $\div 6 = $ _____
14. $\times 2 = $ _____
15. $+ 36 = $ _____
16. $+ 21 = $ _____
17. $- 58 = $ _____

18. $\times 10 = $ _____
19. $\times 3 = $ _____
20. $\div 5 = $ _____
21. $\div 6 = $ _____
22. $\times 13 = $ _____
23. $- 33 = $ _____
24. $+ 3 = $ _____
25. $+ 61 = $ _____
26. $- 20 = $ _____
27. $- 28 = $ _____
28. $- 2 = $ _____
29. $\times 3 = $ _____
30. $\div 12 = $ _____
31. $\times 6 = $ _____
32. $- 9 = $ _____
33. $\div 3 = $ _____
34. $- 2 = $ _____

```
F F S R S F I F T Y S F T T
W O S I X T Y O N E I S W N
N R X S X O N R T F X E E T
R T X F E T E T T W L V S H
Y Y R E I E E Y W V E E E G
O F O U R V S E E S W N Y I
W O O H O I E I N T I T T E
T U T Y X F O G T N H Y I Y
Y R O T Y Y Y H Y W I G G T
T T U E H T O T O T H N I N
R E R N F R R R N T R N E E
O E V I F I E O E E T I N W
F N F N H H E E F X W R H T
O O W T Y T N E W T O T O T
```

Solution is on page 367; list, page 396.

BIOGRAPHY: CHUBBY CHECKER —————————————————

The puzzle below is a story of how one man went from a singing chicken plucker to a famous pop-star. Solve the puzzle, then put on a record and do "The Twist."

Ernest Evans, while in high school, worked in a poultry shop. He entertained customers with songs and jokes as he plucked chickens. His boss put him in touch with a record company. His first single was only a minor hit, but a year later, in nineteen-sixty, "The Twist" gave him stardom under a new name. Ernest Evans became Chubby Checker.

```
H N E W C H U B B Y R T L U O P A D
T I N I R E T A L W O E H I W T E H
E N S H O L V N S D S K C T L N R S
V E C F M E O L R H R J U O I K N E
A T L H I S B O S S E B O A X R E K
N E G G A R C I H N K H T I B W S O
S E A W N E S P G T C R A E Y A T J
B N V I R I X T I S E V D S T M U D
E Y E A U C S F H T H E T W I S T N
C Y H S N L K I N A C D N O K X R A
A O I H D S O E I R Y O E R I F T P
M W M O E D W T S D B J W K P L U Y
E I F P R N J H P O U L T E C T O S
S T L S A R O N I M A V R D H U Y H
G H K M T N I A G L E N G I E B L O
N A E Y H M Y X T N E L M N C T N P
O C U S T O M E R S W I T H K I O H
S N E K C I H C T G N L N I S H C E
```

Solution is on page 367.

RECIPE: BRUNCH PIE

Here's a delicious recipe for a brunch pie. Instead of having an early breakfast, sleep late and have a brunch, and use this recipe as your guide.

BACON	EGGS	POUR
BOWL	FORK	SALT
BROILER	FRY	SET ASIDE
BUTTER	HALF-AND-HALF	SKILLET
CHIVES	LINK SAUSAGES	SLICE
COMBINE	LOW HEAT	TABLESPOONS
COOK	MELT	TOP WITH CHEESE
CRUMBLED	PARSLEY	TO TASTE
CUP	PIE SHELL	WHIP
DASH	PLACE	WIRE WHISK

BRUNCH PIE

3 tablespoons butter
1 small package link sausages
  (8 ozs.)
6 eggs
½ cup half-and-half
salt, to taste

pepper, to taste
dash chives
⅛ teaspoon parsley
¼ cup cooked bacon, crumbled
1 cup jack cheese
9-in. pie shell (baked)

Fry link sausages, slice, and set aside. Melt the butter in a large skillet. Meanwhile, combine all remaining ingredients (except the cheese) in a bowl and whip with a wire whisk. Pour into the skillet and cook on low heat, stirring with a fork until the eggs are cooked, but still soft. Pour the mixture into a 9-inch pie shell. Place sausages on top of the egg mixture, top with cheese, and place under the broiler until the cheese is melted (approximately 3-4 min.). Serves four.

```
E S E E H C T I W P O T R
Q J L S N O O P S E L B A T
I F P P O U R E T S A T O T
H O A L C J H S A D Q J A S
A R R D A J H R G P I E E E
L K S S B C S M I G H T N T
F S L E A O E H Q W E I I A
A I E V P L W S O L B F R S
N H Y I T U T L L M R R E I
D W Q H Q C C I O Y O Q T D
H E J C O O K C Y J I J T E
A R P I E S H E L L L L U J
L I N K S A U S A G E S B Q
F W J D D E L B M U R C R J
```

Solution is on page 367.

LETTER-CLUE WORDS

To get the list for this puzzle, take each given letter and put it in front of the three-letter word defined by the clue. All 36 four-letter answer words are hidden in the grid.

1.	B	+	Finale	=	_____
2.	B	+	Less than two	=	_____
3.	B	+	Unwrought metal	=	_____
4.	C	+	Large monkey	=	_____
5.	D	+	Hearing organ	=	_____
6.	D	+	Possess	=	_____
7.	D	+	Not cooked	=	_____
8.	D	+	Tear	=	_____
9.	G	+	Consumed	=	_____
10.	G	+	Young boy	=	_____
11.	G	+	Beam of light	=	_____
12.	H	+	Large shade tree	=	_____
13.	H	+	Night bird	=	_____
14.	L	+	In addition	=	_____
15.	M	+	Noah's boat	=	_____
16.	M	+	Fire residue	=	_____
17.	M	+	Inquire	=	_____
18.	M	+	Lyric poem	=	_____
19.	N	+	Be in poor health	=	_____
20.	N	+	Have a meal	=	_____
21.	N	+	Frozen water	=	_____
22.	O	+	Ballpoint	=	_____
23.	P	+	Expert	=	_____
24.	P	+	Colony-living insect	=	_____
25.	P	+	Museum display	=	_____
26.	R	+	Assist	=	_____
27.	R	+	Pen's contents	=	_____
28.	S	+	Little jump	=	_____
29.	S	+	Short sleep	=	_____
30.	S	+	Many times, to poets	=	_____
31.	S	+	Ancient	=	_____
32.	S	+	Belonging to us	=	_____
33.	S	+	Cooking utensil	=	_____
34.	S	+	Expert golf score	=	_____
35.	T	+	Everything	=	_____
36.	T	+	Earthen vase	=	_____

```
D E R P L L W N S O U R
K N W H S A M A D R I P
R S E O M K O P E N D D
A L F B G S D S K C R E
M T G M R A E D B A A R
G R A Y A M O N W X I P
D W O E W W T A Z E D A
A C T R N A I L T M O N
L A A I P E L L W S P T
G P C A R S L Z R O O R
S E N O B I A S N L H A
T S B N R U T V O D S P
```

Solution is on page 367; list, page 397.

If you've solved the other Tanglewords puzzles in this book, you should have no trouble entering the 37 words below into the diagram. Complete solving directions are on page 11.

ALLEGED

APPELLATE

BANISTER

BOWLING

CHARISMA

CRADLE

DIESEL

DOCENT

ENDURING

ENEMY

ETHIC

FIFE

FORENSIC

GULPED

INSTRUMENTAL

JOURNAL

JUDGMENT

KNOWN

LARCENY

LENIENCE

MANEUVER

MOLECULAR

NICHE

OBSTACLE

OMEGA

OVERUSE

PAYOLA

PRATTLE

PUFFED

RUST

SHORN

SOLOIST

STEW

TAUNT

TRENCHED

UPHELD

VARIED

Solution is on page 367.

One of the tallest office buildings in the world is the Sears Tower in Chicago, Illinois, with 110 stories. It houses a population of 10,700 people, and it was completed in 1974, and was made with most of these building materials. When you have circled all the terms, the uncircled letters will spell out the name of one of the largest ground-area office buildings, which employs 29,000 people a day.

ADOBE
ALUMINUM
BOLT

BRICK
CAULK
CEMENT

CLAY
CONCRETE
COPPER
FIBERGLASS
GLASS
GLUE
GRANITE
GROUT
IRON
LUMBER
MARBLE
MORTAR
NAIL
PITCH
PLASTER
PLASTIC
RIVET
SCREW
SHINGLE
SIDING
SLATE
SPACKLE
STEEL
STONE
TARPAPER
TILE
WALLBOARD
WOOD

```
G T N T A R P A P E R B H E
R G Y A L C M S T D L R E F
A S R E I D A E L G N I H S
N L T O N L R S B A E C T D
I R U O U C B A M O T K E S
T I P M N T L W O O D E S I
E V B O I E E T R B A A R D
T E C M U N L N T G L P P I
R T L L E O U E A G L L C N
E N G K B S T M R S A A A G
P P E N C L E E T S U S S W
P N O R I A B C T L T T A S
O G E O N I P E K B U I I L
C W D I F N R S P I T C H G
```

Solution is on page 367.

Everywhere we go, we see signs that tell us to do or not do something. Below are just a few of the signs we run into everyday. The uncircled letters spell out something we all must do once in a while.

BEWARE
BRIDGE
BUS
CAUTION
CLOSED
COMBUSTIBLE
CROSS
CURVE
DANGER
DEEP
DIM LIGHT
DOWN
ELEVATOR
END
ENTRANCE
EXIT
EXPRESS
FLAMMABLE
HELP
LEFT
LOAD
LOW GEAR
MEN
MERGE
M.P.H.
NEXT
NO SMOKING
ONE WAY
PASS
PULL
PUSH
SLOW
STEEP
STOP
TAXI

TOLL
TOW
TOXIC
TRAIL

TURN
WAIT
WALK
WANTED

WET PAINT
WOMEN
YIELD
ZONE

```
C Y O E C N A R T N E U B E
L O W G E A R C R O S S E L
O N M P H N C U R V E E W B
S E P B E A T X E N D E A A
E W L L U P T R O S T N R M
D A A T E S S A P F E E M
P Y I L T H T Y A I E M S A
L O A D K O P I F H L O S L
N O T A X I N E B U S W E F
W O L S R T O L L A U R N
T H G I L M I D S T E E P W
O T R R E G N A D E E P X O
X I B R I D G E W A N T E D
I X G G N I K O M S O N E S
C E L E V A T O R T Z O N E
```

Solution is on page 367.

TOASTING GOBLET —— 53

Here is a New Year's Eve toasting goblet that is full of goblets. See if you can find the word "GOBLET" 22 times. When you have circled all the entries, the leftover letters will spell out an appropriate toast for New Year's Eve.

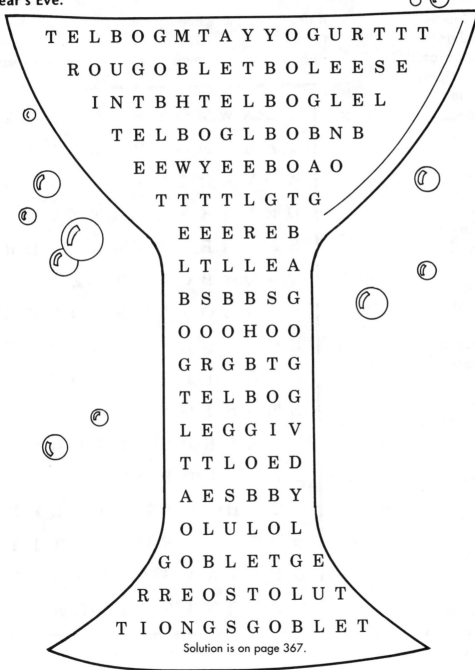

T E L B O G M T A Y Y O G U R T T T
R O U G O B L E T B O L E E S E
I N T B H T E L B O G L E L
T E L B O G L B O B N B
E E W Y E E B O A O
T T T T L G T G
E E E R E B
L T L L E A
B S B B S G
O O O H O O
G R G B T G
T E L B O G
L E G G I V
T T L O E D
A E S B B Y
O L U L O L
G O B L E T G E
R R E O S T O L U T
T I O N G S G O B L E T

Solution is on page 367.

Our modern custom of observing New Year's Eve with a noisy celebration was popularized by the seventeenth-century Dutch settlers of New Amsterdam. How and why they adopted this practice is noted below.

Iroquois Indians celebrated the ripening of their corn crop with a noisy New Year's. They wildly smashed their furnishings and tossed them into a bonfire to signify the start of a new life. Dutch settlers saw them and copied the custom of a

noisy New Year's

Eve to chase away the

spirits of the old year.

```
I S N W M O T S U C E H T L
T E R E N G I R O Q U O I S
W O V A O T N I A B D M W N
D E R A E Y D L O T E E O S
E S T H E Y I Y W H S I D R
T A Q Y B O A E T C S E E S
A H N E O F N W R Y O D H E
R C E A N A S O A D T U S T
B O W R F P P O E Y Q T A T
E T O S I G N I F Y T C M L
L C A R R P P C L T C H S E
E W I A E O E D M E H T E R
C T N H C Q L N L I F E F S
S D T H E I R W I T H A I T
O F A T W Y S I O N W H N R
O F U R N I S H I N G S A D
```

Solution is on page 367.

"Ho-Ho-Ho" is the jolly sound of someone many of you know and remember well. He wears a bright red suit and he has filled this puzzle with 53 words that contain the letters "HO." Solve this puzzle and have a good time. "Ho-Ho-Ho!"

ABHOR	CHOCK	CHOSE	HOBNOB	HONEST
AHOY	CHOKER	COHO	HOCKEY	HOODOO
ANCHOR	CHOMP	ECHO	HOLIDAY	HOOF
ANCHOVY	CHORE	GAUCHO	HOLLOW	HOOKAH
AUTHOR	CHORUS	HOAX	HOMAGE	HOOP

HOPS
HORIZON
HORNET
HOTBED
HOTEL
HOUR
KEYHOLE
MACHO
PATHOS
PHONIC
PHONOGRAPH
POTHOLE
SCHOOL
SHOAL
SHODDY
SHOO
SHOOT
SHOT
SHOULD
SHOUT
SHOW
SIPHON
TELEPHONE
THORN
THOSE
UPHOLD
WHOLLY
WHOOP

```
C I N O H P A R G O N O H P
L H R O A O B N X A O H O T
A P O T H O L E C T U O H S
O U H R N P Y L R H H C U E
H O T B E D I E O W O R H N
S P O H D L K S N W O V T O
H H E O O O O C H O E Y H
O O H S H R Z H C N H R P
U S W C O I H T Y R O O S E
R P E H R H X O O E H M G L
Y S H O O T C H O C K A P E
O S H O U L D S N D M C X T
H B P L L Z L A F O O H O O
A H O L I D A Y H A K O O H
```

Solution is on page 368.

RECIPE: PASTA SALAD

This recipe for PASTA salad is perfect for summer days when it's too hot to cook and almost too hot to eat! The list below contains 39 terms from the recipe, all of which are hidden in the diagram on the opposite page.

ADD	HAM	PLUS
BLENDED	HOURS	PREP
CHEDDAR	LIGHTLY	PREPARED
CHEESE	MAKES	RELISH
CHILL	MEAT	SERVINGS
CHOPPED	MIX	SEVERAL
COMBINED	MUSTARD	SHREDDED
COOKED	NATURAL	SOUR CREAM
CORKSCREW	ONION	SUBSTITUTE
CUP	OPTIONAL	SWEET
DICED	PASTA	TABLESPOON
DRAINED	PICKLE	TIME
GREEN	PIMENTO	UNTIL

PASTA SALAD

1 cup sour cream or sour cream substitute

1 cup (4 oz.) shredded natural cheddar cheese

1½ cups (5 oz.) corkscrew pasta cooked and drained

1 cup diced ham

¼ cup sweet pickle relish, drained (optional)

¼ cup chopped pimento

2 tablespoons chopped green onion

1 tablespoon prepared mustard

Mix pasta, meat, cheese, relish, pimento and onion until blended. Add combined sour cream and mustard; mix lightly. Chill several hours. Makes 6 to 8 servings. Prep time: 20 minutes plus chilling.

```
Y N O O P S E L B A T S A P
L I T N U L A R U T A N R S
T A N H C O R K S C R E W W
H D E S H L C H O P P E D E
G R M I E T A E M A I R E E
I A I L E M R R R I C G N T
L T P E S A A E E D K A I U
B S H R E D D E D V L M B T
L U S N E E D O R L E E M I
E M E O N P E A I C A S O T
N I K I O O H H O U R S C S
D X A N D E C I D P L U S B
E R M O E L A N O I T P O U
D E K O O C S G N I V R E S
```

Solution is on page 368.

Instead of words or letters, this puzzle is filled with number and symbol combinations. Each combination has one digit among the symbols, and there are 27 such combinations to find.

1 = * ¢ @	# ¢ @ / 5
– : 1 ? /	6 $ – + %
+ % ¢ # 1	: ? 6 = *
¢ 2 – : ?	@ ¢ % 6 $
@ # / 2 +	7 + @ % /
% ? ¢ $ 2	* 7 # – :
3 * : @ –	? $ 7 ¢ =
/ 3 = + $	/ # 8 * +
# – % * 3	$: = 8 ?
= 4 + ? ¢	% – ¢ @ 8
: / 4 % #	9 = ? : %
$ @ * 4 =	¢ 9 + # –
? 5 # – /	+ @ / 9 *
* + 5 = :	

```
*  9  +  6  %  *  2  /  3  =  +  $  –
4  =  4  +  ?  ¢  #  3  *  5  / . :  –
3  ?  6  =  2  8  #  ¢  :  %  *  9  :
/  :  $  ?  *  /  /  8  @  ¢  *  =  1
8  %  7  +  :  –  #  +  –  /  5  9  ?
+  @  /  9  *  #  7  @  #  +  5  2  /
¢  ?  ¢  7  4  5  –  %  *  #  ¢  @  7
2  $  #  –  –  ?  4  %  2  $  ¢  ?  %
–  –  6  #  %  /  2  +  *  3  %  6  $
:  6  +  %  :  =  /  –  %  3  8  :  4
?  9  :  1  ¢  *  ?  $  7  ¢  =  @  +
¢  $  9  =  5  @  5  6  –  8  #  8  7
¢  1  =  4  *  @  $  2  ?  ?  =  1  +
```

Solution is on page 368.

Christmas tree ornaments have great variety, and when you trim your Christmas tree, you will probably be using some of these shapely ornaments. When you have circled all the entries, the leftover letters will spell out what the German people, the originators of the Christmas tree idea, hung on their trees many years ago.

APPLE
BALL
BEAR

BELL
BIRD
BLOCK

BOW
CHIMNEY
CLOCK
COOKIE
COW
DOLL
ELF
HORSE
HOUSE
LAMB
MANGER
MOUSE
NUTCRACKER
PRESENT
REINDEER
SANTA CLAUS
SHEPHERD
SKATER
SKIER
SLEIGH
SNOWMAN
SOLDIER
STABLE
STAR
STOCKING
STORYBOOK
TRAIN
WISEMAN

```
D L A P K O O B Y R O T S N
P R L D L C E E E E L P P A
S E E E O L O K E S U O H M
U T L H B L C L S S U P A W
A A F A P A L P B L E O R O
L K T R R E I N D E E R M N
C S S C O B H S R H C I S S
A E T N A M E S I W O T G S
T U A W A A A O B S O R F H
N E R N T L C L O C K R S S
A G G B R I L D K C I I T E
S E A R A E B I A O E N E D
R L C H I M N E Y W O B S R
L U G A N G P R E S E N T R
```

Solution is on page 368.

Country music fans are sure to be familiar with Minnie Pearl's trademark hat with its dangling price tag. But did you know that the price tag reads $1.98?

0034	5934
0076	5967
0234	8232
0242	8267
0427	8424
0434	8432
1123	8626
1134	8634
1363	8864
1367	8876
1523	9706
1567	9767
5023	9847
5076	9867
5626	9923
5676	9963

```
4 2 4 8 2 3 8 4 4 3 6 8 6 9
3 7 7 0 6 4 0 2 3 2 4 7 8 6
6 9 2 3 4 0 4 3 3 7 6 6 3 7
9 7 2 7 3 3 2 1 3 2 7 4 6 2
9 0 6 4 6 7 4 1 6 2 3 9 4 4
5 6 6 4 7 3 6 2 7 2 5 6 4 2
3 8 8 7 6 6 1 3 7 7 6 5 1 0
1 1 3 6 3 5 7 6 0 3 2 5 7 6
3 5 2 6 9 7 8 6 3 0 8 6 2 6
4 4 2 3 3 2 4 9 8 4 7 4 6 2
6 2 4 3 7 3 3 9 6 3 7 6 7 0
8 7 2 3 1 2 2 4 7 6 7 6 4 2
8 2 6 1 7 9 3 4 2 6 7 2 6 3
6 7 0 5 6 9 4 8 3 2 7 3 7 4
```

Solution is on page 368.

ANGELs are beautiful creations of white. Children make them in the snow by lying down and fanning their arms and legs in a continuous manner. An ANGEL is easy to recognize because of its halo and wings. Can you find the 40 ANGELs hidden in this puzzle?

```
E G A L E G N A N G E L E L
L E G N A A N G E L E G N A
E L L N G L L L E G N A L N
A N G E L E E E N N A N E G
G E N A G G L A G L E G N A
L E G N A N L E G N A E L L
E L A A L A A E G N A L E G
G E N L E G N A L A E G A N
N G G N G A G L E G N A N A
A A E L N L E G N A L G G L
N G N G A G L A N G E L E A
G L E G N A N G E L G G L L
E L E A E N A L E G N A E L
L E G N A L E G N A A G N A
```

Solution is on page 368.

TRIVIAVISION

This puzzle is for you dial-flippers, or, nowadays, remote "zappers." Fill in each answer below, then find the answers in the diagram on the facing page. As a help, questions are listed in the alphabetical order of the answers.

1. **Moonlighting** Receptionist Ms. Dipesto's first name was _____
2. **Happy Days** Fonzie's real first name was _____
3. **Head of the Class** The class nerd was _____
4. **The Jetsons** The family dog was named _____
5. **Hill Street Blues** The scruffy, maniacal cop was _____
6. **The Phil Silvers Show** The sergeant Silvers played was named _____
7. **Thriller** The host's first name was _____
8. **Kung Fu** The main character was _____
9. **The Patty Duke Show** Patty's look-alike cousin was _____
10. **Topper** Topper's first name was _____
11. **The Price Is Right** The first emcee was _____
12. **Taxi** Dispatcher De Palma was played by _____
13. **The Jeffersons** The maid's name was _____
14. **Perry Mason** D.A. Berger's first name was _____
15. **Shaft** The theme music was written by _____
16. **Knight Rider** The car was called _____
17. **The Slap Maxwell Story** Maxwell's newspaper was The _____
18. **The Munsters** Herman's wife was _____
19. **BJ and the Bear** The sheriff who got his own spinoff was _____
20. **Gilligan's Island** Mrs. Howell's first name was _____
21. **Hollywood Squares** The best-known center square was _____
22. **Mork and Mindy** The pair named their son _____
23. **The Monkees** The drummer's first name was _____
24. **Hardcastle & McCormick** Hardcastle's first name was _____
25. **My Two Dads** The daughter's name was _____
26. **Julia** Julia worked as a _____
27. **The Andy Griffith Show** Ron Howard played _____
28. **The Odd Couple** Felix's housemate was _____
29. **Have Gun, Will Travel** The gunfighter was called _____
30. **Baa Baa Black Sheep** Boyington's nickname was _____
31. **The Smothers Brothers** The "presidential candidate" was _____
32. **Empire** The ranch manager was _____
33. **Miami Vice** Tubbs' first name was _____
34. **My Living Doll** Julie Newmar played a _____

35. **Kojak** Telly's real-life brother played a cop named _____
36. **Bewitched** The baby daughter's name was _____
37. **I Spy** Agent Kelly's cover sport was _____
38. **The Honeymooners** Ed Norton's wife was _____
39. **Mickey Spillane's Mike Hammer** Mike's secretary was _____
40. **The Flintstones** Fred was married to _____
41. **Rawhide** The cattle-drive cook was _____
42. **The Snoop Sisters** The sisters made a living as _____

```
N E S L U A P W I S H B O N E
O E E D N Y L O G T N A F A R
T P L B N H O S C A R R S R E
L T I L Y T B V C V J T I E K
I K I E U A Q O I R R H N G L
M I C K Y C H D M O O U N D E
A U N W R I T E R S B R E E B
H M I L T O N T M P O F T L E
A W C X B B R H J A T C O S C
H M O O T I V E D P O V R E N
T Y L G X L E Q U P E U B Y E
I X E I L K L I L Y N P O A R
B M E D W O D R A C I R R H O
A G N E S V A P A L A D I N L
T H T R A E M N B V C O S T F
```

Solution is on page 368; list, page 397.

The puzzle below contains 39 plants that are considered good luck and have been used in Christmas or New Year's celebrations around the world.

ALMOND
APPLE
ARBORVITAE
CEDAR

CHERRY
COWSLIP
FERN
FIGS

FIR
FLAX
HAREBELL
HAZEL
HOLLY
IRIS
LADY'S-TRESSES
LAUREL
LENTIL
LILIUM
LILY
MALLOW
MARIGOLD
MISTLETOE
MOSS
NETTLE
OAK
OLIVE
ORCHID
ORNITHOGALUM
PANSY
PEACH
PEAR
PINE
PRIMULA
PULMONARIA
ROSEMARY
SAINFOIN
THYME
VIGNA
VIOLET

```
M R L P E M Y H T H H N R E
Q Z E D K I S N A A E A V N
O A R N A S B Z R T D I I A
R R U O O T E E T E L O I V
C B A M S L B L C O F R T M
H O L L Y E E P C N A P U A
I R V A L T M P I N E I X L
D V I L Y O L A O P L L B L
F I G S H E S M R I I S X O
G T N C N I L I L Y F W A W
H A A T R U M A R I G O L D
P E I I P U Y R R E H C F N
P L M U L A G O H T I N R O
Z H L A D Y S T R E S S E S
```

Solution is on page 368.

84

The poinsettia was first brought to the U.S. from Mexico in 1828 by Dr. Joel Roberts Poinsett, the first U.S. ambassador to Mexico. The plant was renamed poinsettia in honor of the doctor, and its flaming red color helped establish it as a Christmas flower. When you have circled all the entries, the leftover letters will spell out a comment about Yuletide decorations.

The first association of the poinsettia plant with Christmas began in the eighteenth century when the Mexican people referred to their native plant as the "flower of the blessed night," because of the bloom's resemblance to the Star of Bethlehem.

```
D E S S E L B P E R E W E M
H E A P Y S T S H E H P V E
E F R B E R S A T E T L I H
C Y L R U B U M N L F A T E
N O L O E E O T T P O N A L
A I F G W F H S N O E T N H
L S A T T E E I D E E D E T
B N S H H M R R T P C C O E
M R E O A E T H G I N T I B
E O E N C X G C S T A R O F
S T H E F I R S T M I S P B
E E T B E C A U S E O L I N
R G O H W A H T I W A O R E
I N T H E N A T I N H E L D
I S N S R I E H T O T M I B
A L E S A I T T E S N I O P
```

Solution is on page 368.

The list for this puzzle consists of verses 11, 12 and part of 13 in Chapter 14 of Romans just as it appears in the King James Version of the Bible.

For

it is

written,

As I

live,

saith

the Lord,

every

knee

shall bow

to me,

and every

tongue

shall

confess

to God.

So then

every

one of

us shall

give

account of

himself

to God.

Let us

not

therefore

judge

one

another

any

more.

```
W O B L L A H S O T H E N E
E N A T N Y N Q E A W Y M S
V S E R O E U D I N R O T S
I L D S T G L M E Y T N U E
G E L T I D O A O V H T S F
H T I A S T N D Y R E V E N
O R V N H O I R O L L R L O
W E E R T S O F I V O N Y C
T V U H I M S E L F R E H L
O J E G R K T U E G D U J S
G R V I N I H R R V T L E H
O O N E D O E Y O N E O F A
D M E L Y H T S M I D R W L
O T F O T N U O C C A E Y L
```

Solution is on page 369.

Probably the most common New Year's resolution is to lose weight. If you are planning to go on a diet, be prepared to live without the foods and beverages listed below, since they are all high in calories!

BACON
BEER
BLINTZ
BUTTER
CAKE

CHEESEBURGER
CHILI
COBBLER
COOKIE
CREPES

CRESCENT
DANISH
ECLAIR
EGGNOG
FRENCH FRIES
FUDGE
GRAVY
HAM
HOT DOG
JELLY
LASAGNE
MALT
NUTS
PIZZA
POTATO CHIPS
POT PIE
PRETZELS
RAVIOLI
RIBS
ROLL
SAUCE
SAUSAGE
SCONE
SODA
STRUDEL
SUGAR
TAMALE
TOAST
TORTE
WAFFLE
WINE
YAMS

```
G W R E G R U B E S E E H C
O N C K I E M T L I N B E S
N T O A S T W E Y G K N L P
G S L C A T D R A V I O L I
G C B M A U U S M W A M O H
E C A I R B A N S C A R R C
E L R T R L H J E H T P G O
E L S E P E R C D I Y R B T
G C F Z S T L A M L P E E A
A O U F R C N B L I N T Z T
S O D A A I E E B O R Z O O
U M G T S W J N C O I E T P
A U E H O L P S T P C L E J
S E I R F H C N E R F S R B
```

Solution is on page 369.

The Tournament of Roses has been held in Pasadena, California, nearly every year since 1890. The tournament includes a parade of colorful floats competing for prizes, a beauty contest, and kicks off the annual ROSE BOWL football game between the two college teams selected to play. Find 34 ROSEs and 29 BOWLs hidden in this puzzle.

```
R O S E L L W O B E B O W L
B E S B E S O R R O S E R W
L O O W S B B O W L W O B O
R W E S O R E L B E S L R B
L E O W R B R O S E S W S R
B S L B B O W L L L W O B O
O O W R S W S W L W O B R E
W R O E O L O E S O R L L S
L S B S W B W S S B W O W O
E L W O B E S O R O S E O R
S R B R W R S R B R R S B O
O B O W L L O O O E S O R S
R S E S O R W S R O W R S E
E S O R E L E E E L W O B E
```

Solution is on page 369.

The Grand Marshals selected to lead every Tournament of Roses Parade are usually well-known public figures. Listed below are the names of some Grand Marshals selected in the past.

AARON (Henry L.)
BARTLETT (E.L.)
BEAN (Alan L.)
BRADLEY (General Omar)
BROWN (Perry)
CONRAD (Charles Jr.)
DEAN (General William F.)
DIRKSON (Everett)
DISNEY (Walt)
EISENHOWER (Dwight)
EVANS (Dale)
FORD (Gerald)
GORDON (Richard F., Jr.)
GRAHAM (Reverend Billy)
HALSEY (Admiral William)
HOFFMAN (Paul G.)
HOOVER (Herbert)
HOPE (Bob)
KHOMAN (Thanat)
LEISHMAN (Lathrop K.)
NIXON (Richard)
PALMER (Arnold)
PICKERING (William, Dr.)

QUINN (William)
RICKENBACKER (Eddie)
ROSELLINI (Albert)
SINATRA (Frank)
SMITH (Kate)

SPROUL (Robert)
STAGG (Alonzo)
WARREN (Earl)
WAYNE (John)
WELK (Lawrence)
WILSON (Charles)

```
Y D A F C S R E V O O H D A C
B E O R P O F S E R H A N H D
L R N R A Y C A I V R T N R I
D C O S R E W O H N E S I E R
C U X W I L S T O N A C U M K
L G I F N D N C T L K T Q G S
W C N G R A H A M E I U R W O
A I I I E R A W N I L A D A N
Y T L D R B F B G S S T A G G
N P L S B E A N K H N W R P W
E A E T O C K H O M A N V A H
L A S H K N E C R A V L R L B
C R O E A P R S I N E R S M C
G O R D O N K A C P E K L E W
H N M H O F F M A N B J C R Y
```

Solution is on page 369.

To solve this puzzle, you must first fill in the circles with letters from the words below. The number in parentheses indicates how many circles to fill in in order to find that word in the diagram. When you have solved the puzzle correctly, the circled letters will reveal the last line of this joke:

Mary: I had a terrible time at the party last night.
Jane: But you said your date was "out of sight!"
Mary:

BANJO (2)	PECAN (2)	SOLVE (1)	TONE (2)
BATON (2)	PLAIT (2)	TIMER (2)	TORSO (2)
BEAU (2)	PUNISH (2)	TITHE (2)	VINYL (1)
BRASS (3)			
BUOYANT (2)			
BYPASS (3)			
BYPATH (2)			
COOL (1)			
DEVOTE (2)			
EASILY (3)			
EDIBLE (2)			
EMBARK (3)			
EXACT (2)			
EXCEL (2)			
EXHALE (3)			
FILMY (2)			
GIVEN (2)			
GOVERN (2)			
GYPSUM (2)			
HAVING (2)			
IMPASSE (3)			
INSTILL (3)			
ISSUE (2)			
LAVA (2)			
MELON (3)			
NATIVE (3)			
NICHE (2)			
OBLATE (2)			
OPERA (2)			

```
O  J  O  A  B  B  G  B  S  O  O  V  E  I
P  T  A  T  N  A  O  O  U  O  A  O  M  V
O  X  O  E  L  P  P  P  E  Q  V  P  O  E
R  I  E  A  A  M  S  A  A  J  O  Z  U  C
A  Q  P  T  X  P  O  N  I  O  H  S  N  E
O  X  O  A  L  O  M  V  S  O  O  R  O  O
O  L  G  E  T  H  R  O  M  O  T  A  O  A
C  A  O  O  D  T  G  A  V  F  T  O  R  L
I  Z  O  L  L  O  T  O  N  O  E  O  H  O
N  E  E  I  V  T  B  I  A  L  T  T  M  O
D  X  R  E  N  N  O  O  O  O  B  O  R  K
V  I  O  Y  L  G  P  Y  E  Y  W  B  N  A
```

Solution is on page 369.

Your basic canoe trip requires only three things—a CANOE, PADDLES, and strong arm muscles! But for the advanced rower who likes extended river trips, there is much more equipment to carry and many different paddle strokes to learn. Listed below are some terms related to river canoeing.

AIR MATTRESS

BACK FERRY
(moving across
swift currents)

BOW

CANOE

CANTEEN

CAP (headgear)

CROSSDRAW
(stroke for dodg-
ing through
shallow rocks)

DRAW (stroke)

FLASHLIGHT

FLOTATION
(needed for
rapids)

HIGH BRACE
(paddling)

J-STROKE (used
in white-water
canoeing)

KAYAKS (Eskimo
canoes)

KNEE STRAPS

LIFE JACKETS

LOW BRACE
(paddling
technique)

MAPS
PADDLES
PRYAWAY (stroke)
ROPE
SCULLING STROKE
(continuous stroke)

SLALOM (type of
white-water racing)
SPLASH COVERS
(for fighting waves)
STEER (for still water)
TENT

```
N V R S S E R T T A M R I A C
E S W T A Q N Q E Q T E D R U
K T E O N A C E S L A L O M R
O E T I B O J N E B D S Q D E
R K H M I S P A R T S E E N K
T C G E Q E E S C D N D C O O
S A I S E P C K R Z T A L I R
G J L O W B R A C E P Q C T T
N E H O S F W Y R Q P B R A S
I F S T N E T A A B U O D T J
L I A P N D L K Q W H R R O V
L L L Q A Q S D U Q A G H L O
U A F R U M I U D W U Y I F R
C W Y R R E F K C A B T M H L
S R E V O C H S A L P S R Y T
```

Solution is on page 369.

Here's a Tanglewords with a mystery word. First solve as a regular Tanglewords (solving directions on page 11.) Then, after you have entered all 38 listed words into the diagram, you should find that there is just one blank space remaining. Fill in this blank with the one letter that, when entered, will form the longest possible word that is not included in your list.

ACADEMIC
AMBROSIA
ASSET
BELL
BISCUIT
BONDAGE
CORE
CRUMBLE
DELUSION
ELITE
EMBRACE
ENGAGED
EPICURE
FAME
GAMETE
GLUTEN
ICICLE
IMPACT
ISSUED
ITEM
LAND
LONGITUDE
MAGICAL
MAGNET
MEDIA
OPERATE
PEDESTAL
PENNANT
PROSAIC

REACT
RETICENT
RETREAD

SCALP
SERGEANT
TARP

TRAMP
TRIBE
WISE

Mystery word: _____

Solution is on page 369.

New Year's Day begins a new year, but what was the origin of New Year's Day? If that's a puzzling question, this puzzle will give you a brief answer.

```
A M J G N I T T E L S I J Y
D T Y N S A C R I F I C E S
T O W H O M E A C B S X R A
R W Z O R W B L E G N H U C
O G L C F A T H E R O L T R
M N H D B A T T E A I O U I
A I W Y C T C P A S T Y F F
N K Q H A Y L E Q N U R E I
X O R N A A L K D E L T H C
T O U B C T H N G W O S T E
W L O E R S E U O D S A X S
O N D D U L R M A D E L N R
N I N N Z G A Y D J R I Q A
E T A R B E L E C Q B T T E
W J H L Y A D S R A E Y H Y
T I M E H A S A W S U N A J
```

Solution is on page 369.

Janus was
a two-faced
Roman
deity
to whom
sacrifices
were
made
on what
we now
celebrate
as New
Year's Day.
Today
Father
Time has
replaced
Janus
in looking
at the
past,
a baby
heralds
the future,
and our
only
sacrifice
is letting
go of
last
year's
unkept
resolutions.

Be TRUE to your LOVE this Valentine's Day. Send a CARD and a BOUQUET of flowers. We've listed a number of terms relating to this FEBRUARY holiday.

ADMIRER
AMOUR
ARDOR
BALLOONS
BE MINE

BEWITCH
BOUQUET
BOW AND ARROW
CAKE
CARD

CHERUB
CHOCOLATE
COUPLE
CUPID
DANCE
DATE
EROS (god of love)
FAVOR
FEBRUARY
HEART
HUGS AND KISSES
LACE
LAPIS (lazuli)
LOVE
MOOD
MUSIC
NEST
OPEN IT
PARTY
POEM
POETRY
RHYME
ROMANCE
ROSES
SONG
SOUL MATE
ST. VALENTINE
SWEET
TEARS
TREAT
TRUE
VASE
VERSE
WISHES

```
R S N O O L L A B S W E E T
O P E N I T N E L A V T S E
V E R S E B N A A E T A D A
A H R P S I P E C N A M O R
F H O O M I D E E V O L O S
E E N E S T K R C I S U M E
M A B O W A N D A R R O W T
Y R E R C I D A N C E S T A
H T W S U I S C E A J O E L
R R I K P A L H H L S N U O
U E T U E U R T E E P G Q C
O A C P A R T Y S S R U U O
M T H Y R T E O P R A U O H
A R D O R E R I M D A V B C
```

Solution is on page 369.

If you've run out of ideas about what to give your Valentine, maybe we can help. You can come up with one sure-fire gift idea after you find CANDY hidden 38 times below.

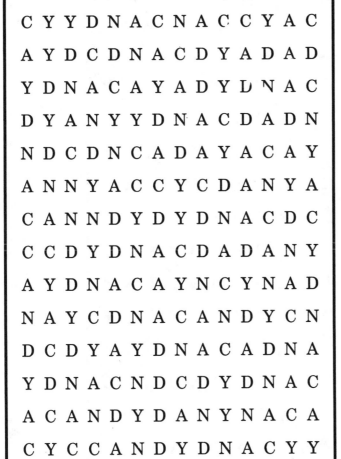

```
C Y Y D N A C N A C C Y A C
A Y D C D N A C D Y A D A D
Y D N A C A Y A D Y L N A C
D Y A N Y Y D N A C D A D N
N D C D N C A D A Y A C A Y
A N N Y A C C Y C D A N Y A
C A N N D Y D Y D N A C D C
C C D Y D N A C D A D A N Y
A Y D N A C A Y N C Y N A D
N A Y C D N A C A N D Y C N
D C D Y A Y D N A C A D N A
Y D N A C N D C D Y D N A C
A C A N D Y D A N Y N A C A
C Y C C A N D Y D N A C Y Y
```

Solution is on page 370.

Silver is a color associated with the holiday season in many ways. Many ornaments may be silver, and the word "silver" is included in many titles of books, movies, and songs about Christmas, as in the song "Silver BELLs." Find the terms below, all of which can be preceded by "silver," or are otherwise related.

AGE	BELL	CERTIFICATE	DOLLAR
ANNIVERSARY	BERRY	CHLORIDE	FIR
BARS	BROMIDE	COIN	FISH
			FOIL
			FOX
			HAIRED
			HAKE
			INGOT
			IODIDE
			JEWELRY
			LINING
			MAPLE
			MEDAL
			MINE
			NITRATE
			PERCH
			PIN
			PLATE
			POINT
			SCREEN
			SMITH
			SPRING
			STANDARD
			STAR
			WARE
			WEED
			WORK

```
G K A H T I M S E C R R E P
A N S H X J C K D E E W T R
L I I C E R A W M M T L A Y
F I X R E H J A R J A L R X
O E O E P R P N S T L P T J
X T N P G S T N I O P X I L
S C O I T A T I D G I I N N
T H U O M S D V F N F F I T
A L A D E M T E D I M O R B
K O X I J S R R R N C J I E
D R A D N A T S B I F A A L
S I O E E L P A M L A I T L
L D N W W A R R R I S H S E
B E R R Y S J Y R L E W E J
```

Solution is on page 370.

"White" is another word that has a special place in the holiday season. In addition, it is a word which precedes many other words to form new terms, as shown below.

ANT
BAIT
BASS
BLOOD CELL
BREAD
CAP
CHAPEL
CHRISTMAS
CLOVER
COLLAR
CORPUSCLE
FIR
FLAG
FLY
FOX
FRIAR
GASOLINE
HEAD
HEADED
HEAT
HOPE
HOUSE
KNIGHT
LEAD
LIE
MAGIC
MATTER
METAL
MOUNTAINS
NILE

NOISE
OAK
OUT
PAPER
PEPPER

PINE
POPLAR
POTATO
RIVER
SALE

SEA
SMITH
SNOW
SPACE
SPRUCE

TIE
WALL
WASH
WATER
WINE

```
X L S E N I L O S A G F E C
H E A D E D L D R L E I O T
A A M T D A E H A E T R S X
C D T J E N C T O E P B O C
L U S W R M D E C U R P S H
O S I Y A M O F S A S B E A
V N R A L L O C L M P E L P
E O H Z P F L U O A A I I E
R W C R O E B E N T G G N L
X H R E P A P R E T A W I E
B S L V X O K A H E A T S C
A A O I H F R I A R A I O A
S W I R T T P N K D O L N P
S M I T H G I N K N B T X S
```

Solution is on page 370.

As midnight approaches on New Year's Eve, Father Time leaves the scene. Time has been measured for thousands of years, but not very accurately. Today's timepieces are not only accurate but give us the day, month, moon phase, and year. Can you find the 35 different clocks hidden in the diagram below?

ACORN
ALARM
ANNIVERSARY
AUTO
BANJO
BEEHIVE
BOX
BRACKET
CALENDAR
CANDLE
CARTEL
CHAMBER
CUCKOO
DESK
DIGITAL
DUTCH
GALLERY
GRANDMOTHER
LANTERN
MANTEL
MARINE
MIRROR
OGEE
PEDESTAL
PILLAR
PYRAMID
ROUND BELL
SHELF
STEEPLE

STICK
TABLE
TALL

TRAVEL
WAG-ON-THE-WALL
WALL

```
R L L A W E H T N O G A W M
E W P Y N B A N H R J T A L
H B Y I R L E N R E T N A L
T R R R A E L L D O T B A E
O A A R A L L I P E C T F B
M C M C A S G L L E S A L D
D K I W A I R M A E E L E N
N E D J T R E E D G M T H U
A T L A S V T E V O C T S O
R T L D I T P E M I R R O R
G Z A H N J I Y L A N K T K
X R E B M A H C V L C N U S
O E K S L X C E K U A W A E
B R A D N E L A C H C T U D
```

Solution is on page 370.

Here is a selection of possible Christmas presents. Some of them come in big boxes and some of them come in little boxes. (If you are buying any of these, you might check to see if you have the right size box.) When you have circled all the entries, the leftover letters will spell out an appropriate comment.

Big Boxes

BICYCLE
BLANKET
BOOTS
COAT
DOLLHOUSE
GLOBE
MICROWAVE
QUILT
SKATES
STEREO
SUITCASE
TELEVISION
TOWEL SET
VCR
WAGON
WOK

Little Boxes

BELT
BRACELET
CHARM
COMPACT
CUFF LINKS
EARRINGS
KEY CHAIN
NECKLACE
PEN
PIN
RARE COIN
RING
TICKETS
TIE TACK
WALLET
WATCH

```
S M A L T E L E V I S I O N
T I C K E T S H M R A H C L
S E T A K S C G G L O B E
C I F T N T S W N N B I L L
S O D R A R E C O I N B O I
U K A W L K S T C R R F Y D
I T N T B T E Y E A B R O T
T C O I O S C Y C L E L A I
C A U O L L N E C K L A C E
A P B E E F L R H H T A E T
S M W R N E F N O G A W W A
E O A E T R Q U I L T I O C
T C P T T I S R C V P I N K
S B I S G E V A W O R C I M
```

Solution is on page 370.

Collard greens are known as good-luck food in the South. Served at New Year's Day dinner, its color symbolizes money and rising fortunes. You wouldn't want to miss out on this, so solve the puzzle, then try the recipe.

ADJUST	FRESH	POUNDS	TABLESPOON
BUNCH	GREENS	PUT	TOUGH
CHOP	HAM HOCK	ROOT	TRACE
CLEAN	IF NEEDED	SALT	TWO
COLLARD	LEAVES	SAND	VINEGAR
CUT OFF	LUKEWARM	SINK	WASH
DOWN	MORE	SIX	WATER
ENDS	PEPPER	STEMS	WILTED
FILL	PLACE	STIR	YIELD
FINAL	PLUNGE	SUGAR	

Collard Greens

1 bunch (about three pounds) collard greens
1 (½-pound) ham hock
1 quart water

1 tablespoon salt
1 tablespoon sugar

Clean fresh greens by discarding wilted leaves. Cut off root ends. Chop the collards, removing tough stems. Fill bowls of a double sink with lukewarm water. Plunge greens up and down in one sink and then place into the other one. Wash until no trace of sand remains in final rinse water.

Wash ham hock and put in a large pot. Stir in 1 tablespoon of salt, more if needed. Add greens and remaining ingredients. Bring to a boil. Stir well. Reduce heat. Cover and simmer for two hours. Adjust the seasoning and serve hot with pepper vinegar. Yield: Six to eight servings.

```
R P L R K C O H M A H L R G
C H E N J B V I N E G A R T
R U I P U L P L Q C M E O I
M S T N P O U N D S E O D F
R L C O H E T A H N R J R N
A H R C F F R E S H X A A E
W A T E R F A L A L G C L E
E D S J I L C C W U D D L D
K J A L S T E M S E L Q O E
U U L L A G Z L T E C L C D
L S T Q N N S L I N V A N R
O T O U G H I Y R D W A L H
H W L R Z W X F J S S O E P
L P T A B L E S P O O N D L
```

Solution is on page 370.

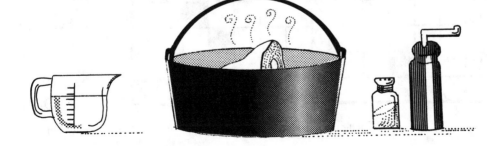

As with the puzzle on page 11, you write the missing letters in the blank diagram spaces, creating a finished grid as you fill in the 45 listed words.

ARCHAIC   DEVIATE   IMITATE   MARIGOLD
ASTRAL   DOMESTIC   INNUENDO   MESA
BLUEPRINT   GIGANTIC   INSERT   MUSED
CACAO   GLAD   JEWELER   NEUTRAL
CAPITULATE   HALO   LATENT   OMITTED
CHEAT   HEIGHT   LOGISTIC   OPAL
DETER   HINGE   LUCID   ORGAN
                                                PALATIAL
                                                PAYOLA
                                                PEAL
                                                REBUTTAL
                                                RECURRENT
                                                RETRIEVE
                                                RUNG
                                                SEMBLANCE
                                                SOUL
                                                STRATA
                                                TACITURN
                                                TELECAST
                                                TORNADO
                                                TRUISM
                                                UNICORN
                                                WIDTH
                                                WISE

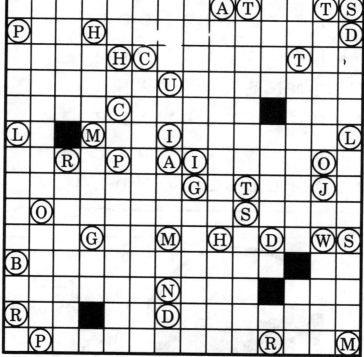

Solution is on page 370.

There are 51 terms hidden in this puzzle, and they all can be formed using the letters in the phrase "Happy New Year." When you have found all the terms, you will have used every letter at least once.

ANEW	ARENA	HARE	HYPHEN	NEWER
ANYWAY	ARYAN	HARP	NAPE	PAPA
ANYWHERE	AWARE	HEAP	NAPERY	PAPER
APER	AWAY	HEAR	NEAP	PARE
APPEAR	AWRY	HEWN	NEAR	PAWN
AREA	HAPPEN	HYENA	NEPHEW	PAYEE

PEAHEN
PEEN
PEEP
PRAWN
PRAY
PREEN
PREPAY
REAP
RENEW
WANE
WARN
WARP
WARY
WEAN
WEAR
WEARY
WHEN
WRAP
YARN
YEAN
YEARN

```
N E H P Y H N E P P A H
W E A Y P E N A R R W Y
A E R A E W E E E A A
R N P E A N E P A P A W
P E E P H N A R N A A Y
R A E E W Y R R Y Y N
A R A H P A Y Y A R N A
E Y W E N A E N W E R P
P R A Y E A Y A A E H E
P A R W R E W E N E R R
A A E N A E Y A E A W Y
W W E H P E N E H A E P
```

Solution is on page 370.

Solve this puzzle like the one on page 22, but this time search for words that begin with the LETTERs "LE." We've given you lots of LEEWAY here because the terms can be found on all three sides of the cube.

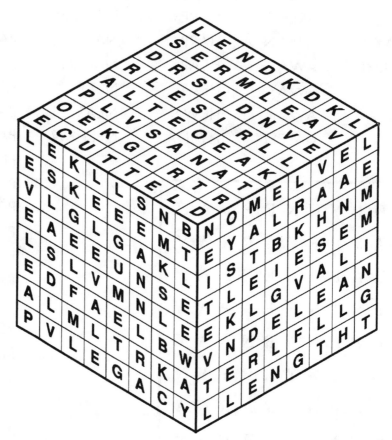

Solution is on page 370.

LEAD
LEAF
LEAGUE
LEAK
LEAN
LEAP
LEARN
LEASE
LEASH
LEAST

LEAVE
LED
LEDGE
LEEK
LEEWAY
LEFT
LEG
LEGACY
LEGAL

LEGEND
LEGIBLE
LEGUME
LEMMING
LEMON
LEND
LENGTH
LENS
LENTIL
LEOPARD

LEOTARD
LESSON
LET
LETTER
LETTUCE
LEVEE
LEVEL
LEVER
LEVITY

Now that you've had one lesson in "LE" terms, how about another one? This puzzle's just as SIMPLE, only all the words end with the letters "LE." Make sure your loops are LEGIBLE. (That's one that could work in both puzzles—hmm. . .)

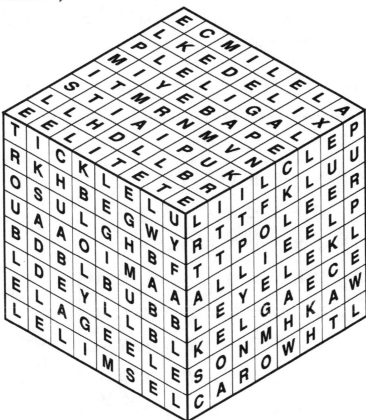

Solution is on page 371.

AGILE	DALE	ORACLE	TABLE
AMPLE	DIMPLE	PALE	TACKLE
ANGLE	EXILE	PILE	TICKLE
AXLE	FABLE	POLE	TILE
BABBLE	GALE	PURPLE	TRIFLE
BALE	IDLE	RILE	TROUBLE
BATTLE	ISLE	RULE	TURTLE
BAUBLE	LEGIBLE	RUMBLE	UNCLE
BOGGLE	LITTLE	SADDLE	WHALE
BRITTLE	MALE	SIMPLE	WHILE
BUBBLE	MILE	SMILE	
COLE	MULE	STYLE	

There are hundreds of different grasses growing on Earth's surface; most of them are used for food and forage. Here are the names of 40 types of grasses—some edible, some not. Can you find them all? We've circled TIMOTHY to start you off.

ALKALI   BEACH   BROOM SEDGE   CRAB
BAMBOO   BERMUDA   BUFFALO   DARNEL
BARLEY   BLUE   BURRO   FESCUE
BARNYARD   BROME   CHESS   FOXTAIL

GAMA
GOOSE
GRAMA
HAIR
JOHNSON
JUNE
LOVE
MAIZE
MILLET
OATS
ORCHARD
QUACK
REDTOP
RICE
RYE
SALT
SANDBUR
SUDAN
SUGAR CANE
SWITCH
~~TIMOTHY~~
WHEAT
WITCH
ZOYSIA

```
G O O S E M O R B U F F A L O
A A F S N A S B V E O M N Q R
M N O S U I A E A X A A R U C
A O X E J R L R T R D C S A H
F S T H C E T M G U N T H C A
E N A C R A G U S Z A Y T K R
S H I H I R E D T O P I A Y D
C O L S C S T A E H W O E R Y
U J Y A E T A R L S J I A H D
E O R E E G N E K M U T A G
Z O Y L L Q U E D C A O R C H
I E L O U R U L A B M L O A H
A I V Y E R A R B I U L I R A
M E O O B M A B T E O R R U B
```

Solution is on page 371.

The continent of South America is home to a fascinating variety of animals including the TAPIR, an ancient, pig-like animal that lives in forests and near rivers; the GUANACO, a soft, woolly member of the camel family, and other animals that can also be found in other parts of the world. Find some of the animals from South America below.

AGOUTI
ALPACA
ANTEATER
CAPYBARA
CAVY
CAYMAN
COATI
CONDOR
COYPU
FLAMINGO
GREEN BOA
GUANACO
IGUANA
JAGUAR
LIZARD
LLAMA
MACAW
MANATEE
MARGAY
MARMOSET
MEERKAT
MONKEY
PARAKEET
PARROT
PECCARY
PIRANHA
RHEA
SAPAJOU

SLOTH
TAMANDUA
TAPIR
TAYRA

TOUCAN
UAKARI
VICUNA
YAPOK

```
O G N I M A L F J A G U A R
C U A G O U T I Y E K N O M
A O M R E T A E T N A W P P
N J Y X V H Y M T A V C E A
A A A P T J R M H A O Q C R
U P C O U E A H V N P C C A
G A L A W Q S M D I X I A K
R S Y A P O K O A Q C T R E
E I A T Y Y R J M C O U Y E
E R G O L W B X V R A V N T
N A R U L I Z A R D A W Q A
B K A C A P L A R C X M E N
O A M A M N P I R A N H A A
A U D N A M A T A K R E E M
```

Solution is on page 371.

Laverne DeFazio and Shirley Feeney are Milwaukee brewery workers who live at 730 Hampton Street, in the series "Laverne and Shirley." Penny Marshall portrayed Laverne, and Cindy Williams, Shirley.

```
2 5 1 1 4 9 8 0 9 1 7 2 6 8
0 0 9 8 8 9 0 1 1 8 3 7 8 2
5 0 8 0 8 1 7 2 6 0 7 5 5 3
9 6 9 7 7 9 1 3 6 4 3 7 1 4
4 9 0 6 7 0 6 4 9 9 0 4 6 8
7 7 6 8 9 8 0 3 5 4 9 1 4 0
2 4 1 3 9 0 2 3 1 3 8 5 5 8
6 8 3 5 3 6 4 4 8 3 2 3 2 7
5 7 6 2 4 1 5 9 3 5 6 4 6 9
2 5 1 8 6 6 5 3 7 1 9 7 3 7
3 2 0 4 0 3 7 1 2 2 5 2 4 8
2 7 3 9 5 0 6 2 6 1 1 4 0 2
1 1 4 4 9 5 8 1 7 5 8 5 1 9
3 6 0 2 0 4 1 2 4 0 3 9 3 6
```

0269	5324
0768	5541
0997	5966
1336	6020
1533	6274
2216	6305
2494	6400
2634	7100
3007	7574
3232	7791
3372	8447
3644	8677
4099	8738
4116	8776
4322	9358
4614	9812

Solution is on page 371.

We've hidden 48 words, from AGATE to WARBLE, in the diagram below. After you've found them all, the uncircled letters, when read from left to right down the diagram, will spell out the name of the queen who reigned for over 60 years over the British Empire.

AGATE	AUSTERE	CEDAR	GROWN
ALLOW	BALLAD	DECADE	HAZEL
AMBER	BLANK	DOOR	HEAVY
APIARY	BRAND	ENGAGE	IMAGE
APPLE	BRAVE	FAITH	LABEL
ARROW	BRIDAL	GARNET	LEAD
ATLAS	CANDOR	GRAIL	MEDAL
			NAVAL
			ORBIT
			ORNATE
			PARADE
			PLEAT
			REALM
			REBATE
			SALAD
			SMALL
			STALK
			STALL
			SUAVE
			SUNDAE
			TIDAL
			TRADE
			TURBAN
			VALOR
			WALTZ
			WANDER
			WARBLE

```
E O V I P R E A L M T L R R
C R T L D N A R B E I E O A
D N E Y R A I P A D B Z O D
F A I T H B E D P A R A D E
T T L R S R N O T L O H L C
T E I A E U G E C L E A I A
S E L D S T A L L A M S A D
R T N E A Z G V V B N R R E
A A A R T L E Y E A R D G V
W O L L A A E R V O L A O A
B L A N K G G A W I M O W R
N W O R G A L A D I R B R B
```

Solution is on page 371.

109

You might want to roll up your French CUFFs before you eat that French TOAST, and before you solve this puzzle filled with terms that will form new words or compound phrases when preceded by, or are otherwise related to the word "French."

BREAD

BULL DOG

CANADIAN

CHALK

CHIEF

CHOP

COMMUNITY

CONGO

COOKING

CUFF

CURVE

DIP

DOOR

DRESSING

ENDIVE

FRIES

GUIANA

HEEL

HORN

ICE CREAM

INDIA

MAN

MOROCCO

PASTRY

POLISH

POLYNESIA

PROVINCIAL

REVOLUTION

SEAM

SOUP

SUDAN

TOAST

WINDOW

WOMAN

```
E M P T Y O H C C N C P L S
N I M L T S N A D U S R C E
D C N A I D A N A C R O L I
I O G L N O I T U L O V E R
V H O P U O S F M K P I E F
E P D R M L F A I O R N H S
M D L C M B E N H T N C M P
W R L H O R G C M P S I O N
L E U I C E H N A E S A R W
C S B E C A I S E N Y L O P
A S C F L D T N S T A D C T
N I F K N R O H D S N M C T
G N N C Y R A N A I U G O P
O G N O C A M O W D A S U W
```

Solution is on page 371.

You'll see stars and stripes forever if you take in a night of FIRE WORKS displays. Celebrate Independence Day with a fantastic display of your own by solving this puzzle. Find FIRE and WORKS, both hidden 21 times below.

```
S W F F S F I R E R I F S
K E I K S K R O W I E K K
R W R F F F R F O W R I R
O O E I W I E O I O I W O
W I R R F R R F W R F O W
O E I E I E W E E K E R S
E R F F E W O R K S F K W
W I K I O F I E W E R S F
O F I R E F S K R O W I W
R I K E F K O I W O R O F
K S W I R I F I R E R K E
S K R O W O R K S K I W S
K E W O R K S E S K R O W
```

Solution is on page 371.

THE BANKING INDUSTRY

Banking was practiced by the ancient Egyptians and Greeks long before bankers began to offer personalized checkbooks in designer colors and styles. Later, the Italians became large-scale bankers, investing in and financing their profitable wool trade. The first bank in the United States was founded in Philadelphia, in the year 1781. Find all the terms below relating to the banking industry.

ACCOUNT

AGENT

ALARM

ANNUITY
(fixed yearly payment)

BALANCE

BANK NOTE

BOND

BOX (safety deposit)

CHARTER (government
authorization)

CHECK

CREDIT

DATE

DEBIT
(account entry)

DEPOSIT SLIP

DISCOUNT

DRAFT
(written payment order)

EXCHANGE
(debt paid by draft)

FUNDS

GUARD

INTEREST

LEDGER

LOAN

LOCK

MANAGER

MONEY

MONEY ORDER

PASSBOOK

PATRON

PEN

RATE

SAFE

SAVINGS

STAFF

STAMP

STATEMENT
(itemized financial account)

TELLER

TRUST
(account with designated
beneficiary)

VAULT

WINDOW

WITHDRAWAL

```
Q S T A F F Z R E G D E L Z L D
C D L K U D R A F T X Z T Q E I
W P E N B X C Z Q C V P T B T S
I T D P O C Q B H Y A S I Q A C
N S R B O P M A T S E T Q Z D O
D R A U G S N O S R Q N M N C U
O N N Q S G I B E T Q O O H Z N
W T Q Z E T O T N N N B A M Q T
E Q A B C O N E S E A R Q L Y Z
T T G H K I M V Y L T O M O T S
O Z E J Q E C O A E I A L C I G
N C N L T Q R N R U N P R K U N
K Q T A L D C Z K A L A R M N I
N Z T Q E E K Q G P A T R O N V
A S Q R L C R E D I T Q Z N A A
B Q L A W A R D H T I W E F A S
```

Solution is on page 371.

Ralph Waldo Emerson, an American poet and essayist, was a leading proponent of transcendentalism, a school of thought that believed in the mystical unity of nature. The list below is an excerpt from one of Emerson's many writings. Words listed together in the word list will be found together in the diagram.

```
C A R E O F O U R H A L B
W W W F O O R R U O T E H
Y E A H L Z V I Q X S N I
C L M N O Y R W E T A K E
L A E A T P C R J N N Z H
O Y L S K I R T D E D E T
T U Y H I E N O A I C S A
H P V T L W U G V C J L H
I K T L C R E M T I G H T
N N A A U H T O I F D F E
G H T E B T O N J F M E S
S N W H D U L E H U I S S
P R O P E R T Y T S R C E
```

Solution is on page 371.

We take
care of our
health,
we lay up
money,
we make
our roof
tight
and our
clothing
sufficient,
but
who provides
wisely
that he
shall
not be
wanting
in the
best
property
of all—
friends?

There are 62 terms in this puzzle, and they all have four or more letters. Words entirely within other words are not included. When you've finished the puzzle, every letter will have been circled at least once.

ABSORBED
ADULTS
AGED
ALIT
ALIVE
ALMOST
AMATEUR
ANTE
ARDENT
ARRIVALS
BASIL
BORING
BRAVE
CRONIES
CYAN
DECORATORS
DRAMATIC
DROSS
DWELL
ENTIRE
FALSE
FLOSS
GADGETS
GUTS
HAIR
ISLES
LATE
LEANS
LESS
LIENS

LOAVES
MARkY
MARVEL
MIRE
MULL
NAIL
NEVER
OBOE

ORDER
PEACE
RAGES
REMOTE
ROAD
ROBINS
SAGE
SAUNA

SAVINGS
SEER
SHALE
SHARED
SHREDS
SILKY
SINCE
SLUMPS

SPIRAL
STANDARD
STILL
SWEET
TUMULT
VENDOR
VEST
WRINGING

```
F A L S E E R I T N E D R A
L Y K L I S A B S O R B E D
O S A V I N G S H A R E D U
S H W N S T E G D A G C R L
S R C E L S S N L N I E O T
P E A C E T A L I T V R D S
I D I V S T U G A E S S N L
R S A N S M N M N V N E E U
A O A O O I A O U I I V V M
L E M A R R Y B B L R R A P
L L E W D E C O R A T O R S
A M A T E U R E M O T E B A
```

Solution is on page 372.

KITES IN FLIGHT

Kite flying can be a complex exercise in aerodynamics as well as a breezy-day pastime. For over 200 years scientists have used kites to study the weather and to help solve problems of aircraft construction. Can you find all the kite terms hidden on the opposite page?

AIRBORNE

ALTITUDE

ANGLE

BALANCE

BIRD (kite)

BOW

BOWLINE

BOX KITE

BREEZE

BUTTERFLY (kite)

CENTIPEDE (kite)

CLIMB

CLIMBER

CORD

DELTA WING

DIAMOND (kite)

DIHEDRAL

DRAG

DRAGON (kite)

EDDY (kite)

FALL

FIGHTER (kite)

FISH (kite)

FLAT (kite)

FLIER

FLOAT

FLY

GUST

HARGRAVE
    (box kite)

HOIST

JALBERT (parafoil)

KEEL

LANDING

LAUNCH

LIFT

LINE

LONGERON

LOOP

NONRIGID

PARAFOIL

PARAWING

PULL

REEL IN

RIP

SEMIRIGID

SLACK

SNAG

SOAR

STABILITY

STRING

TAIL

TANGLE

TEAR

TETRAHEDRAL (kite)

TRIANGULAR
    (box kite)

VELOCITY

WIND

WING

ZENITH

```
M B G Y D D E R E T H G I F Y H F J S S
R G A N S R D A T R N N H O I S T N E G
A T B L I V A H L I W I N D C I A M T N
E A P O G W T G R T R W I E Z F I F C I
L I U N W I A T O L I A N O N R I G I D
G L L G N L S R I N M T L E I L U U R N
N D L E B X I O A O I L U G N S J A A A
A H Z R V I F N N P W E I D T I G S E L
B N C O L A R D E H I D B K E W L T T A
O K E N R P R D R O C A R N F L O A T H
X N C A U E E G K Y L F R E T T U B F J
K P P A B A E T R A E O L E P N L I A I
I O F M L A L L N A B Z Y T I C O L E V
T O I L N S G C I R H M E S L L B I A O
E L G N A T E W I N G X I E O E F T R F
C W Y T E T R A H E D R A L R A E Y I L
T E L G R A L U G N A I R T C B R K P Y
```

Solution is on page 372.

This is a Word Search in reverse. Circled letters are the initial letters of one or more words in the list. Starting with a circled letter, fill in each word in a straight line without crossing any black squares; when you're done, every square will be filled. ABSOLVE has been entered to start you off.

~~ABSOLVE~~	BUSHEL	EPIC	INNING
ACCLAIM	CONGENIAL	ERROR	INTEREST
BONNET	CULOTTE	GENERAL	LOGIC
BRASS	EASEL	INACTIVE	MARATHON
BURRO	EMBROIL	INGOT	MERRIER

NEBULOUS
NICHE
ORIGINATED
PLUMB
POEM
POTENTIAL
RABBIT
RECENT
REMINDER
STEROID
SUBSTITUTE
SUBURB
THEATER
TOURNAMENT
TRELLIS
TRIANGLE
UPON
VAPOR

Solution is on page 372.

118

Many of the female singers below are known for their unique stylistic approaches to music and singing. One such singer, Natalie COLE, used the style of her late father, Nat "King" Cole, in recording her latest hit song, "Unforgettable." Can you find Ms. COLE, Bette MIDLER and the other females hidden in the diagram?

ABDUL (Paula)
BAEZ (Joan)
BAKER (Anita)
CAREY (Mariah)
CASH (Rosanne)
CHER
COLE (Natalie)
CLINE (Patsy)
DAYNE (Taylor)
FLACK (Roberta)
FORD (Lita)
FOX (Samantha)
GAYLE (Crystal)
GIBSON (Debbie)
GRANT (Amy)
GUY (Jasmine)
HOUSTON (Whitney)
IAN (Janis)
JETT (Joan)
JOPLIN (Janis)
JUDD (Wynonna)
LEE (Peggy)
LENNOX (Anne)
LYNN (Loretta)
MADONNA
MCENTIRE (Reba)
MIDLER (Bette)
OSLIN (K.T.)
PARTON (Dolly)
PATTI (Sandy)
RAITT (Bonnie)
ROSS (Diana)
SADE

SIMON (Carly)
SLICK (Grace)
SNOW (Phoebe)
STREISAND (Barbra)

SUMMER (Donna)
TUCKER (Tanya)
TURNER (Tina)
WARWICK (Dionne)

```
N N O T S U O H D F O X Q C
J A G I B S O N O A R Q O Z
Z Y I J T N A R G A Y L E N
R E M M U S D L J R E N I X
W R M I I Q L O A B I L E E
O A N E D Z P I X L S K T P
N C R J J L T Q C O Z S X P
S T E W I T E R E K A B O A
S T N N I P M R R D F K N R
Y E R A A C Q E E L Y N N T
U J U T L B K H A U O O E O
G U T Z Q C A C P D Z M L N
K I D D U J K E A B X I K L
E R I T N E C M Z A H S A C
```

Solution is on page 372.

A HOUSE, an IGLOO, a TEEPEE and the other listed terms show the great variety that exists in dwellings. After you find all 30 homes below, read the uncircled letters from left to right to answer this riddle: Why didn't the homeowner pay for his new roof?

```
D E L T S A C E G A T T O C
L O F T D I S A T T C O O P
E T R O K T W O L A G N U B
S E B M A C W I B L D W A A
U E S T I N A I G O I M E P
O P E O H T N H M W A V S A
H E A O O N O I S N A M U R
T E U L A N N R S T F M O T
N S H G A I E E Y H L N H M
E O O I U C R E L I A R T E
P H U M T N E T S M T U H N
E L E T O H O U S E B O A T
```

ADOBE
APARTMENT
BUNGALOW
CABIN
CASTLE
CONDOMINIUM
CO-OP
COTTAGE
DORMITORY
ESTATE
FLAT
HOGAN
HOTEL
HOUSE
HOUSEBOAT
HUT
IGLOO
LOFT
MANOR
MANSE
MANSION
PALACE
PENTHOUSE
SHACK
TEEPEE
TENT
TOWNHOUSE
TRAILER
VILLA
WIGWAM

Solution is on page 372.

James HOBAN, William PEREIRA, Frank Lloyd WRIGHT are some of our master builders. These gifted men gave America some of its most enduring legacies; capitol buildings, stately homes, museums and skyscrapers.

ADLER (Dankmar)
BERTOIA (Harry)
BREUER (Marcel)
CARRERE
  (John Merven)
COBB (Henry N.)
CRAM (Ralph
  Adams)
DINKELOO (John)
ELMSLIE (George)
FREED (James Ingo)
GEHRY (Frank)
GRAVES (Michael)
GREENE
  (Henry Mather)
GROPIUS (Walter)
HOBAN (James)
HOOD (Raymond)
HOWE (George)
HUNT
  (Richard Morris)
KAHN (Albert)
LAFARGE (John)
LOOS (Adolf)
MEIER (Richard)
MIES VAN DER
  ROHE (Ludwig)
NEUTRA (Richard J.)
OBATA (Gyo)
OTIS (Harrison Gray)
PEREIRA (William)
PURCELL
  (William Gray)
RAUCH (John)
RENWICK (James)
ROCHE (Kevin)
ROGERS
  (James Gamble)

ROOT (John Wellborn)
SAARINEN (Eero)
SKIDMORE (Louis)
SOLERI (Paolo)
STEIN (Clarence S.)
STONE (Edward Durell)

SULLIVAN (Louis H.)
VAN BRUNT (Henry)
WANK (Roland A.)
WEST (Benjamin)
WRIGHT (Frank Lloyd)
WURSTER (William)

```
E H O R R E D N A V S E I M
Y W K A N O A O H R I M A K
R E U E R B O C O L T I D C
H O E R O I U T S H O U L I
E R C H S A E M S T T S E W
G S T H R T L R R T U N R N
R E P H E E E E I O E H E
A V U L G W B R P P I N N R
F A R W O I W O E E K I E O
A R C H R C R A M R E R B M
L G E E U G M W N T R A B D
O O L E K N I D S K T A O I
O O L W D H T N H A K S C K
S T N U R B N A V I L L U S
```

Solution is on page 372.

Who lives at 535 Hudson Street? That is the Greenwich Village, New York, address of the comic strip character Mary Worth.

```
0 9 6 9 4 5 4 0 9 1 9 1 7 9
5 8 6 9 3 0 1 2 8 8 3 4 4 4
3 4 2 7 3 1 3 1 0 9 8 3 2 5
4 7 8 5 2 8 0 9 6 7 0 8 6 0
9 1 7 8 5 2 7 2 0 3 7 1 5 2
3 6 1 3 0 2 9 9 9 1 9 2 4 5
6 7 2 1 9 7 5 8 1 8 9 2 0 1
8 0 3 7 6 6 2 5 6 4 3 3 3 1
2 5 0 6 8 7 5 1 4 0 0 3 6 4
4 9 8 0 9 1 9 0 5 1 3 2 4 3
6 8 9 1 7 6 6 4 2 9 1 8 2 7
7 4 8 5 9 7 8 4 2 4 9 2 4 0
7 8 5 6 7 6 3 0 4 7 5 3 6 8
9 5 0 3 4 0 7 6 2 5 7 3 1 5
```

0181	3736	6807
0305	4249	7243
0608	4552	7662
0676	4886	7886
0795	4980	8178
0956	5116	8246
1760	5378	8334
2430	5446	8845
2633	6452	9130
2883	6540	9844
3004	6763	

Solution is on page 372.

Just as wise men followed the star in the East to Jerusalem, we all use guidance of some kind to steer us to where we want to go. Find and circle the kinds of guidance below to reach your own successful conclusion to this puzzle.

ARROW
AUGURY
AUSPICE
BEACON
BEARING
BLAZE
BODEMENT
BUOY
CAIRN
CLUE
COURSE
CUE
DIRECTION
EVIDENCE
FLAG
FLARE
FORECAST
HARBINGER
HEADING
HINT
LANDMARK
LIGHT
MARK
MILEPOST
OMEN
POINTER
PORTENT
PRESAGE
PROPHECY
SIGN
SIGNAL
TIP
TOKEN
TORCH

```
C D I R E C T I O N G E H L
H M L J H N N L C S N D U W
M B O D E M E N T N I M X C
I Y W G Q D T M E G D G L B
L A N D M A R K O C A U N U
E L Q A C Y O K J L E T E O
P G R M P T P R O P H E C Y
O K N I B R H O Q G D G I O
S Y T I E E C A I R N M P Y
T G S S R D A L W N H J S Z
Y R A F L A G C L H T I U C
W G C D H G E C O I G E A O
E O E C H A R B I N G E R U
H M R Y R U G U A T D H Q R
J O O R C F B L A Z E G L S
T D F L A R E V I D E N C E
```

Solution is on page 372.

Caution! Before you begin solving this puzzle, let us warn you that there are dozens of creatures roaming about. There's a SWARM of bees, a CRASH of rhinoceroses, a SKULK of foxes, a LITTER of pigs, and many more. So enter at your own risk and find the 43 animal groups hidden below. Words in parentheses indicate the animal for which the group name applies.

BAND (gorillas)
BED (clams)
BEVY (swans)
BRACE (ducks)
BROOD (chicks)

CETE (badgers)
CHARM (goldfinches)
CLAID (gnats)
CLUTCH (chicks)
COLONY (ants)

COVEY (quail)
CRASH (rhinos)
CRY (hounds)
DROVE (cattle)
FLIGHT (birds)
FLOCK (sheep)
GAGGLE (geese)
GAM (whales)
HERD (elephants)
HORDE (gnats)
KNOT (toads)
LEAP (leopards)
LEASH (greyhounds)
LITTER (pigs)
MOB (kangaroos)
MUSTER (peacocks)
MUTE (hounds)
NIDE (pheasants)
PACK (wolves)
PAIR (horses)
POD (whales)
PRIDE (lions)
SCHOOL (fish)
SEDGE (cranes)
SHOAL (fish)
SKULK (foxes)
SLEUTH (bears)
SWARM (bees)
TEAM (horses)
TRIBE (goats)
VOLERY (birds)
WING (plovers)
YOKE (oxen)

```
E B E M A V T H S A R C A C
D B A N D G O F M G O L D E
R G I E C H N L A V C A D R
O A B R C G K D E D F I C E
H R E T T I L Y T R N D M T
C S U D H B R A Y O Y O B S
B L A D G C C S A V B O C U
C F O E I A C E T E E H K M
K P A E L M G D C E O B C E
S C L F F U B G O O C P B G
K A A L H T U E L S J A N B
U X O P D E A D O E D I R P
L C H A R M R C N D W R C B
K A S W A R M D Y D O O R B
```

Solution is on page 372.

BEES are everywhere, buzzing around flowers and trees. You'll also find them buzzing about below. There are 44 "BEES" in the first diagram, the word "BEES" appears only once in the second. Don't get stung searching for these busy BEES.

1

```
B  E  E  S  S  S  E  E  B  S
B  E  E  S  E  E  B  E  E  S
S  E  E  E  E  E  S  E  E  B
B  E  B  E  B  B  B  E  S  S
B  E  E  B  E  E  S  E  E  B
E  E  E  B  E  E  E  E  E  B
E  E  E  S  S  B  B  S  B  S
S  E  E  S  E  E  E  E  E  E
S  E  E  E  E  E  E  E  E  E
B  B  S  B  B  S  B  B  S  B
```

2

```
B  E  E  B  E  S  E  E  E  B
E  E  E  E  B  E  B  E  E  E
B  S  E  E  E  B  E  E  E  S
E  E  E  B  E  E  E  B  E  E
S  E  S  B  E  S  B  E  E  E
S  E  E  E  B  E  E  E  E  S
B  E  B  S  E  S  B  E  S  B
B  B  E  E  B  S  E  E  S  E
E  S  E  B  E  E  B  B  S  E
E  E  B  E  E  B  E  E  B  E
```

Solutions are on page 373.

ROYAL PLANTS

The Palace Gardens at London's beautiful Buckingham Palace contain hundreds of varieties of plants, some fifty of which are found nowhere else in London. Take a stroll through the Queen's backyard by finding the names of 43 plants of Buckingham Palace hidden in the diagram on the opposite page.

ALLSEED	FLAG	RUSH
ARUM	FOXTAIL	SAGE
BRACKEN	GEAN	SEDGE
BRAKE	GOLDENROD	SHEPHERD'S PURSE
BROOM	HEART'S-EASE	SORREL
BUGLE	HEMP	SPURGE
CATKIN	HENBIT	TARE
DAFFODIL	LORDS AND LADIES	THISTLE
DAISY	MADDER	THRIP
DANDELION	MINT	VARRO
DARNEL	NETTLE	VIOLET
DILLENIUS	PANSY	VIRGIL
DOCK	PIGNUT	WALL RUE
DODDER	RADISH	
FAT HEN	RED LEG	

```
S U I N E L L I D O F F A D
E E P M E H M F M O L R E X
S V I R G I L M A D D E R M
A I R D N N D C O T S D Y O
E O A T A D A R A L H L E O
S L D B A L N E L T T E N R
T E I I U E D A G T K G N B
R T S E D G E N H H D I F R
A Y H L T C L R A I W O N A
E E O E U E I E Y S X T C C
H G R A N P O S F T D A B K
S A R R G B N W A L L R U E
U S A U I A I I H E A E O N
R D V M P Y L T M K R G L L
E S R U P S D R E H P E H S
```

Solution is on page 373.

A patriarch, according to the Bible, is the father and ruler of a family or tribe. In this puzzle are the names of some patriarchs, many of whom may be familiar to those acquainted with the Old Testament. ABRAHAM, for example, was the founder and first patriarch of the Hebrews; and METHUSELAH, another leader in the line of ENOCH and SETH, is reputed to have lived for 969 years!

```
E N O C H A L E S U H T E M
L C H A J S E L O M M A A M
E J N A S A L S N N A H O R
E O V S L S C X E E A S J N
L E V I X A X O B R E Q A R
A L I N I V D E B S U Z E T
L V T N A M R A M S G G R E
A X A K K M R R M H H X T R
H N J M O P E L E G T R H A
A M A A H B V X W C O E V H
M J K A A A K J E C C J S J
A J X K T V L A M E C H S H
M A M L H X J A A Q E X V M
D E R A J A R M S M L M O S
```

Solution is on page 373.

ABRAHAM
ADAM
AMRAM
ARPHAXAD
CAINAN
EBER
ENOCH
ENOS
ISAAC
JACOB
JARED
KOHATH
LAMECH
LEVI
MAHALALEEL
METHUSELAH
MOSES
NAHOR
NOAH
PELEG
SALAH
SERUG
SETH
SHEM
TERAH

You should have no problem solving this puzzle if you've ACED the one that appears on page 115. See that page for solving directions.

ACED
ALONG
ANTI
APPEARANCE
ARMORY
ASTERS
CANINES
CHESS

COOL
DAMP
DEBIT
DERIVE
DREAM
EASY
EITHER
ENTIRE

FAIR
FLEE
GASP
HISTORY
HULA
LAUGH
LETTER
LIMITING

LONGS
LOTION
MANIC
MENTAL
NARROW
NICE
OLID
PILOT

PRIMP
QUIET
QUILTS
RECIPES
RESPECT
RETORT
SCALD
SCREAMS
SEQUEL
SIRE
SLIM
SOLAN
SOPS
STONE
STRETCH
TENSE
TERSE
THERE
TOILS
TRIVIA
TUMBLER
UNDERTOW
UPSIDE
WARNS
WENT
WISHFUL

```
A L U H C T E R T S S E H C
S Y R O M R A U C H G U A L
T E N S E I M A E C I N P A
E N P H V B L G P R I M P T
R O T I L D N S S N A N E N
S I R E C I A C E D Y S A E
E T R O T E R S R L R L R M
Q O L I D E R I V E O I A A
U L M I A L O N G S T O N E
E I S M U F W A R N S T C R
L P S A G Q U I E T I B E D
U N D E R T O W I S H F U L
```

Solution is on page 373.

THE DIXIE OVERLAND HIGHWAY

One of the most direct routes from the Atlantic Ocean to the Pacific through the southern United States is on the "Dixie Overland Highway," which is actually a series of several different highways running from Savannah, Georgia, to San Diego, California. We've hidden the names of 40 towns along the Dixie Overland Highway in the diagram opposite. How many can you find?

BENSON (AZ)	MINEOLA (TX)
BORACHO (TX)	MONROE (LA)
BOSSIER (LA)	MONTGOMERY (AL)
CAMBRAY (NM)	NEWTON (MS)
CISCO (TX)	ODESSA (TX)
CUBA (AL)	PELAHATCHEE (MS)
DALLAS (TX)	ROBERTA (GA)
DOUGLAS (AZ)	RODEO (NM)
DUBLIN (GA)	ROSCOE (TX)
EL CENTRO (CA)	SAN DIEGO (CA)
EL PASO (TX)	SAVANNAH (GA)
GENEVA (GA)	SELMA (AL)
GILA BEND (AZ)	SEPAR (NM)
GLADEWATER (TX)	SHREVEPORT (LA)
GRAYMONT (GA)	SIERRA BLANCA (TX)
KENT (TX)	STANTON (TX)
LAS CRUCES (NM)	SWEETWATER (TX)
MACON (GA)	TERRELL (TX)
MESA (AZ)	TOMBSTONE (AZ)
MINDEN (LA)	VAIL (AZ)

```
A C N A L B A R R E I S S O B
E Y B M L S A C D O C S I C E
L U R L S L V N N E D N I M N
C L L E R R E T A W T E E W S
E R D S M B N W M L E E O E O
N O T R A O E O S H N Z C L N
T Q U L E V G M C O D U S R E
R H I Z A T O T T A R M O D W
O G E I D N A S N C M N R A T
P N L C R H B W S O O B L L O
E O I O A M T A E T M O R L N
V S E L O H L T N D E Y Q A A
E A E T B G H A N N A V A S Y
R P J P U U T L I E T L E R M
H L C O A S D M R J K M G L G
S E D A T R E B O R A C H O R
```

Solution is on page 373.

Here's a different type of puzzle for you to solve. Instead of just words or numbers, the list below contains numbers, letters, and symbol combinations. Each combination consists of one number and one letter plus three different symbols.

/ 5 A + &
B – @ 7 :
% = 2 C ?
! 6 / @ D
3 E + ? !
: % 8 F =
– & G / 1
H ? – 2 %
@ 7 & = I
+ J : 9 /
= ! 3 K @
& 9 % : L
M + 1 ! –
3 : N % +
? O = & 5
P @ ! 4 :
– 6 ? ! Q
@ 4 R – &
= / 7 S %
8 T – ? /
! : U @ 4
1 & = V –
W 6 / % +
? 5 @ : X
% Y ! 8 =
/ ? Z & 2

I	:	5	&	=	O	?	+	%	1	–	/	J
%	W	:	/	2	H	&	=	%	+	1	7	%
&	@	7	@	&	R	2	D	@	/	6	!	Y
9	S	@	H	Z	C	Q	=	G	&	6	/	!
%	J	–	?	?	I	=	&	7	@	P	W	8
:	2	B	/	/	–	–	B	–	6	@	=	=
L	X	C	9	!	Q	2	6	V	R	!	=	P
/	3	X	:	@	5	?	%	:	3	4	T	A
D	5	U	J	K	!	/	+	K	%	:	@	!
?	@	A	+	Q	Y	?	@	%	9	8	?	8
4	X	M	+	1	!	–	!	+	N	+	F	O
L	:	4	!	&	E	T	Z	F	E	:	@	=
–	V	=	&	1	–	8	5	3	N	%	3	Z

Solution is on page 373.

Solve the puzzle below, which tells how we came to observe Flag Day on June 14. When you've finished, the uncircled letters, when read from left to right, will spell out the title of a 1906 song, written by George M. Cohan, dedicated to the US flag.

On June seven, first thirteen
fourteenth, it was flag stars and
seventeen decided would stripes
seventy- that the have representing
the original
colonies.
After
that,
a new
star
was added
for each
new state
of the
union.
New York
State
was the
first to
observe
Flag
Day in
eighteen
ninety-
seven.

```
Y W G N I T N E S E R P E R T
H C A E R O F W G O U K R D H
F Y F S E N A O F A R A G N I
I T T R A S E I N O L O C A R
R E E G T D R V Y J A F E S T
S N R H A S D W E E U N V R E
T I E A T L E E T S D N R A E
N N W T N N F A D E O L E T N
E N O N E E T N E V E S S S D
E E U D V S W H F E L R B A E
T V L D A Y I N A N A G O O D
H E D W H T N E E T R U O F I
G S T R I P E S S Y T A H T C
I I L A N I G I R O E H T H E
E T A T S W E N O I N U E E D
```

Solution is on page 373.

KNEE-DEEP IN DIAMONDS ────────────────

A diamond, the hardest mineral substance known, is valued both for industrial use and, of course, for the beauty of the gem. The earliest sources of diamonds were India and Borneo. In the nineteenth century, Brazil and South Africa became important diamond-producing countries. Although diamond mining has never been as important in the United States as it is in Africa or in the Commonwealth of Independent States (formerly the U.S.S.R.), there have been a number of major diamond finds in the US. Eighteen of these diamonds are hidden in the diagram at right.

Name of diamond	Year	Carat weight
BIRMINGHAM	1900	4.25
BURLINGTON	1893	2.11
CLINCH RIVER	1889	3.00
DEWEY	1884	23.75
DOWAGIAC	1895	10.87
EAGLE	1867	15.37
EISENHOWER	1957	3.11
GARRY MOORE	1960	6.43
MILFORD	1879	6
MORROW	1877	4.50
OREGON	1893	3.87
PUNCH JONES	1928	34.46
SAUKVILLE	1881	6.57
SEARCY	1926	27.21
STANLEY	1900	4.875
STAR OF ARKANSAS	1956	15.33
THERESA	1886	21.25
UNCLE SAM	1924	40.23

```
R B J C T R K A C D F I E L C
O Y N G C S R O O E Y M M Y E
K S E A K O E W R K R A R W L
J A K L M R A N W E H R O C L
U S W O N G L W O G G R X N I
M N G F I A H I N J R O N U V
G A C A L B T I S O H O N R K
S K C S R U M S M F J C K C U
E R E V I R H C N I L C N R A
A A N I I L Y W A E L O Y U S
R F G B N I R M S S Q F C T P
C O A L R N P A O R E Y O W R
Y R E A E G M U H O E R Q R K
H A H I Y T O G A W R C E I D
U T R E W O H N E S I E S H N
K S F K S N T D T H A R E A T
```

Solution is on page 373.

The diagram below is filled with a variety of 49 terms. After you've circled them all, the uncircled letters will reveal the name of a 1971 film for which Jane Fonda won an Oscar. Donald Sutherland also starred in this thriller.

ALERT
ARISE
ASTIR
AUTHOR
BADGE
BERET
BROWN
CRISIS
DESERT
DIVER
DIZZY
DOZEN
DREAM
EMPIRE
ENTER
FREEZE
GAVEL
GOSPEL
HAPPY
HEDGE
HEFTY
HEIR
HURDLE
ISSUE
JEWEL
KHAKI
KINDLE
LUNAR

OASIS
OCHER
ORDER
ORIOLE
PERCH
PRINT
RAVINE

REVERE
RHYTHM
RIDDLE
SERVE
SHIELD
SHOAL
SIZZLE

SWIPE
TINSEL
VALUE
VARIETY
VISIT
WHIRL
WISHING

```
E R H Y T H M K Y T F E H G
G O S P E L E L O I R O A L
D N H P R U U A Y R E V I D
E R I A R I S E T Z E T O E
H W E H T I N S E L Z Z I S
S P L A S I T T I M E I E E
H E D I M I S S R N P L D R
O R R O K B W I A O D I E T
A C U V R A D H V N H V R R
L H H O E D H E I R E T N E
J E W E L G E K N R A N U L
E N B E R E T R E U L A V A
```

Solution is on page 373.

Hidden below are 34 six-letter words. Each word contains a letter that repeats itself two additional times, for a total of three times. In the example shown, ELEVEN contains three "E"s. Solve this puzzle for three-of-a-kind fun!

YOUR WORD LIST

```
B R E L G G I G A G G L E Y
E I D N O N N A C E E D F V
Z D K N G I G G L Y L F D E
E E F I L N B U B B U H E N
E D E B N N A E A L L O E E
R C E B P I H Z F N L V P E
F H B O P O A E A G E H E R
D E L B B A B E S L D G N E
E E E I R U A H E E E L T R
L S D O D C S W A O E A R E
D E D D A P A P A Y A M E C
D A E C I E C B A B L M E E
A D I Z A K T S E T T A C D
T A T T L E E S T E E M D E
```

Solution is on page 374; list, page 397.

MEMORIAL TROPHY WINNERS

James E. Sullivan (1860-1914) organized the Amateur Athletic Union in 1888 to help maintain the standards of amateurism in sports. The trophy in his honor is awarded annually by the A.A.U. to the athlete who "by his or her performance, example and influence as an amateur, has done the most during the year to advance the cause of sportsmanship." Below are the names of those who have won the award, the sport in which they participated, and the year they won.

ASHENFELTER (Horace, track; 1952)

BAUSCH (Jim, track; 1932)

BEATTY (James T., track; 1962)

BERLINGER (Barney, track; 1931)

BLANCHARD (Doc, football; 1945)

BONTHRON (Bill, track; 1934)

BRADLEY (Bill, basketball; 1965)

BUDGE (Don, tennis; 1937)

BURK (Joe, rowing; 1939)

BUTTON (Dick, skating; 1949)

CUNNINGHAM (Glenn, track; 1933)

CURTIS (Ann, swimming; 1944)

DAVIS (Glenn, track; 1958)

DILLARD (Harrison, track; 1955)

DODDS (Gilbert, track; 1943)

JOHNSON (Rafer, track; 1960)

JONES (Bobby, golf; 1930)

KELLY (John B., Jr., rowing; 1947)

KINSELLA (John, swimming; 1970)

LASH (Don, track; 1938)

LEE (Sammy, diving; 1953)

LITTLE (Lawson, golf; 1935)

MACMITCHELL (Leslie, track; 1941)

MATHIAS (Robert B., track; 1948)

MATSON (Randy, track; 1967)

MCCORMICK (Patricia K., diving; 1956)

MEYER (Debbie, swimming; 1968)

MORRIS (Glenn, track; 1936)

MORROW (Bobby Joe, track; 1957)

O'BRIEN (Parry, track; 1959)

PENNEL (John T., track; 1963)

RICE (Greg, track; 1940)

RICHARDS (Robert E., track; 1951)

RYUN (Jim, track; 1966)

SCHOLLANDER (Don, swimming; 1964)

SPITZ (Mark, swimming; 1971)

TOOMEY (Bill, decathlon; 1969)

TUCKER (Arnold, football; 1946)

WARD (Wilma Rudolph, track 1961)

WARMERDAM (Cornelius, track; 1942)

WHITFIELD (Mal, track; 1954)

WILT (Fred, track; 1950)

```
L K I N S E L L A N O S N H O J
L E O H A D E Y E L D A R B O B
Q L E C I O D M D R A W R N E D
S L A S H D O A A E F I E L D L
C Y M U T D M H S D E S T R A E
Z Z O A A S C G H N R T W W V I
I Q R B M I C N E A I E I O I F
M Z R E R U O I N L E L M R S T
A T I A R R R N F L T E Y R O I
T I S T H R M N E O E U J O A H
S P I T U O I U L H N N M M E W
O S N Y E C C C T C A E N A N K
N O T T U B K O E S Y O L E A R
B E R L I N G E R E G D U B P U
Y D R A L L I D R A H C N A L B
X M A C M I T C H E L L Z Q R S
```

Solution is on page 374.

139

"STAR TREK" WRITERS

The original "Star Trek" TV series starring William Shatner and Leonard Nimoy and created by Gene RODDENBERRY, followed the exploits of the Enterprise crew as they tried to "boldly go where no man has gone before." Listed below are the names of 45 people who wrote or co-wrote at least one episode in the classic series, which remains popular in syndication.

ADAMS (Stanley)

ARMEN (Margaret)

AROESTE (Jean L.)

BIXBY (Jerome)

BLACK (John D.F.)

BLOCH (Robert)

BURNS (Judy)

CARABATSOS (Stephen W.)

COON (Gene L.)

CRAWFORD (Oliver)

DOLINSKY (Meyer)

ELLISON (Harlan)

ERWIN (Lee)

FONTANA (D.C.)

GERROLD (David)

HAMNER (Robert)

HARMON (David P.)

HEINEMANN (Arthur)

INGALLS (Don)

JOHNSON (George C.)

KANDEL (Stephen)

LAKSO (Edward J.)

LEWIS (Shari)

LUCAS (John M.)

MANKIEWICZ (Don M.)

MATHESON (Richard)

MUSKAT (Joyce)

RALSTON (Gilbert A.)

RICHARDS (Chet)

RODDENBERRY (Gene)

SABAROFF (Robert)

SCHNEIDER (Paul)

SINGER (Arthur H.)

SLAVIN (George F.)

SOBELMAN (Boris)

SOHL (Jerry)

SPIES (Adrian)

SPINRAD (Norman)

STURGEON (Theodore)

TARCHER (Jeremy)

TRIVERS (Barry)

VOLLAERTS (Rick)

WALLACE (Art)

WILBUR (Carey)

WINCELBERG (Shimon)

```
A B Z I D Y D J T C Q A M O X E L P
F L O U R L S T A R C H E R Y L S J
Q O S H O N M R E V I E C A L L A W
Z C N R F H A R M O N V U N L I F J
I H R T W B D G A V O T E A O S N O
K E U S A B A R O F F E G R H O W H
G L B T R N R E D I E N H C S N C N
R H S E C T A B B N I W R E A Z P S
A O S T R E A L L O V M H U J R I O
S S D C S H K E R K S T U R G E O N
R A K D Y E W C A U A D S S K N E L
Z C I W E I K N A M B O R H K M G E
W U I R S N D I I L B L N A R A N T
A L L E N E B W Q E B I I A H H T S
J W I G L M W E L O V N M W O C Z E
S P I N R A D M R A L S T O N C I O
S R Y I Z N A J L R D K P I Q U A R
L A K S O N A S K E Y Y B X I B X A
```

Solution is on page 374.

During the 1800s, thousands of prospectors and merchants—with their families—moved West in search of gold. They set up small towns known as tent cities virtually overnight, and continued moving further West after they had mined each area of its gold. The 30 gold rush settlements listed below are not on the map; we know of them only through history books and old diaries. Search for ELKO, SKIDOO, and others.

ALTA
BODIE
CHEROKEE

COLUMBIA
COPPEROPOLIS
DOBLE

DOWNIEVILLE
ELKO
ELY
FORBESTOWN
FOREST
FRENCH GULCH
GEM
GENOA
HART
HELENA
HIGHGRADE
HORNITOS
IONE
MIDAS
NEVADA CITY
OHIO
OPHIR
PROVIDENCE
SEGO
SKIDOO
SONORA
STEDHAM
TUMCO
VOLCANO
WEAVERVILLE
YREKA

```
A T W O C M U T E A K E R Y
F R E N C H G U L C H B F T
C A A L T A N E L E H O O I
D H V P F B O D I E R P G C
C H E R O K E E V B G H E A
D I R O R A O N E G E I S D
A G V V E E F S I G M R E A
I H I I S M T O N A C L O V
B G L D T O A H W I B A O E
M R L E W O I H O O E R D N
U A E N O K L E D L L O I O
L D M C M I D A S E Y N K I
O E S E N H O R N I T O S N
C O P P E R O P O L I S T U
```

Solution is on page 374.

Driven by dreams of fortune, the first Western settlers lived lives very different from those of people back East. They coined new words and phrases specific to their new lifestyles. Solve the puzzle below, which has terms associated with the wild, wild West.

AMBUSH
BAR J (ranch)
BARN
BED ROLL
BELL
BOOTS
BUGGY
BUNK (house)
CARDS (poker)
CATTLE
COWBOY
DEPUTY
DRIFTER
DRIVE (cattle)
DUDE (ranch)
DUEL
GUNFIRE
GUNSMITH
HAND (ranch)
HAT
HERD
HORSE
INDIAN
JERKY (dried beef)
LAWMAN
MARM (school)
MULE (pack)
OUTLAW

PALE (enclosure)
RANCH
RANGE
RANGER
RIDER (out)

ROPE
RUT (wagon)
SADDLE BAGS
SALOON
SETTLER

SHERIFF
SPURS
STAGECOACH
TRAIL DUST
WAGON

```
N Y G G U B F F I R E H S S
U H S U B M A E V I R D A E
S H A N D N A M E S R O H T
R P T F A N A M W A L B R T
E I U I J R L A C D E A U L
T C D R M N H E R D I R G E
F N A E S S O K R L T N L R
I B D T R U N O D E P U T Y
R U D A T U L U L B M A H K
D E N S B L S T G A E T L R
N C P T L T E L A G S L A E
H C A O C E G A T S Y N L J
S M O O R V U W N O G A W A
E Y O B W O C D R E G N A R
```

Solution is on page 374.

Did you know that Stanley and Blanche Kowalski lived at 632 Elysian Fields in the Tennessee Williams play *A Streetcar Named Desire*?

0093	4313	5899
0096	4319	6151
0971	4436	6371
0979	4466	7282
1679	5511	7320
2931	5513	8871
3246	5610	8877
4136	5613	8932
4139	5736	8939
4263	5794	9360
4267	5897	

```
0  4  7  6  4  1  3  9  7  7  9
0  1  4  2  6  7  2  9  7  6  1
9  2  9  3  1  1  2  8  1  9  3
3  1  6  3  6  5  8  1  9  7  4
6  2  1  9  7  6  3  7  3  3  6
4  9  7  5  0  1  9  2  1  2  9
4  1  7  3  6  0  2  3  7  1  9
4  3  3  6  7  2  9  9  7  1  1
6  2  1  6  2  9  3  8  3  1  7
6  1  6  6  8  1  8  2  5  6  9
3  1  5  5  2  6  1  5  1  3  0
```

Solution is on page 374.

In his two terms as US President, Ronald Reagan appointed a total of 32 people to the thirteen Cabinet positions. Here are the members of his Presidential Cabinet from 1981-1988.

BAKER (James)

BALDRIGE (Malcolm)

BELL (T.H.)

BENNETT (William)

BLOCK (John)

BOWEN (Otis)

BRADY (Nicholas)

BROCK (William)

BURNLEY (James)

CARLUCCI (Frank)

CAVAZOS (Lauro)

CLARK (William)

DOLE (Elizabeth)

DONOVAN (Raymond)

EDWARDS (James)

HAIG (Alexander)

HECKLER (Margaret)

HERRINGTON (John)

HODEL (Donald)

LEWIS (Andrew)

LYNG (Richard)

MCLAUGHLIN (Ann)

MEESE (Edwin)

PIERCE (Samuel)

REGAN (Donald)

SCHWEIKER (Richard)

SHULTZ (George)

SMITH (William)

THORNBURGH (Richard)

VERITY (C. William)

WATT (James)

WEINBERGER (Caspar)

```
T S O Z A V A C C X S W Y T
H T L O Z N P A L B C E T B
O R S E P T E R A V H A A L
R B R A D Y L L R H W K E R
N A V O N O D U K C E W B Y
B O W E N R H C H R I K R E
U H T P I Y T C N S K M O L
R R C G T B A I D R E P C N
G W E I N B E R G E R R K R
H Y R G S I A L S L Y N G U
V E I M A W R E L K C O L B
V A I T D N S R E C R E I P
H T T E N N E B E E L O D R
H W X M C L A U G H L I N S
```

Solution is on page 374.

EATWELL, USA

A chef could certainly cook up a fine meal using the names of the US towns listed below as items on the menu. Begin with OYSTER, VA, continue with SALMON, ID, or LAMB, KY, accompanied by ROLL, AZ, and BUTTERS, NC, and have as dessert PIE, WV, or HONEYDEW, CA. Take a gourmet tour of the nation without leaving home!

Le Menu

BACONS (DE)

BASS (AR)

BEAN (City, FL)

BERRY (KY)

BUTTERS (NC)

CHERRY (IL)

CHICKEN (AK)

CHILI (WI)

CLAM (Falls, WI)

COCOA (FL)

CORN (OK)

DUCK (WV)

FIG (NC)

FRIES (VA)

HADDOCK (GA)

HAMBURG (LA)

HERRINGS (NY)

HOMINY (OK)

HONEY (Creek, IN)

HONEYDEW (CA)

LAMB (KY)

MANGO (FL)

OLIVE (MT)

OYSTER (VA)

PIE (WV)

PIKE (NH)

PINE APPLE (AL)

RAISIN (CA)

REDWINE (KY)

RICE (KN)

ROE (AR)

ROLL (AZ)

SAGE (AR)

SALMON (ID)

SALT (Gap, TX)

SANDWICH (MA)

STRAWBERRY (AR)

TOAST (NC)

TOMATO (AR)

TOPPING (VA)

TORTILLA (Flat, AR)

TROUT (LA)

TUNA (PA)

TURKEY (KY)

```
L H A M B U R G H O M I N Y
P M S I W A Y E N O H S H M
I D C T C B R Y N I S I A R
N P U H R R E R P A P L D Y
E N I C I A D R B I C P D C
A L E N K L W E D Y E N O H
P O G N A M I B T A A R C T
P S A L M O N K E L N E K O
L C U G R Z E E T R A T I R
E G A S Y E K R U T R S O T
S A N D W I C H O F R Y T I
T N K E P C I N R E R O L L
R O O J O N H M T R M I A L
I H A C M A C T E A G M E A
C R O S A E U H T N B I J S
E A H M T B C O L I V E F A
```

Solution is on page 374.

VENTURESOME VEECK ————————

Bill Veeck (1914-1986) was probably regarded as the most flamboyant of all baseball club owners, and was known for his penchant for publicity gimmicks, such as the one described below. After you have circled all the terms hidden on the opposite page, the uncircled letters will spell out how Bill Veeck was referred to by people in baseball circles.

Prior to	They	doing so
a White	collared	well, they
Sox–Indians	Luis	"decided
game in	Aparicio	to let
nineteen	and	them
fifty-	Nellie	stay." One
nine, a	Fox, and	of the
helicopter	said	midgets was
landed	they'd	Eddie
in the	come	Gaedel, who
outfield at	to take	pinch-
Comiskey	their	hit for
Park and	"compatriots"	Veeck's
four	home,	Browns
midgets	but since	eight
dressed as	the	years
spacemen	two	before.
emerged.	were	

```
T S R A E Y D H N E D O I N G S O
D T H E I R N D E Y P H I O I T E
N E E D S P A C E M E N A T E E H
B N D D S S X T T D E K A R M G T
U O H I T F O R E A N T S O O D F
T Y Y E C Y F X N A P A R I C I O
S A W S T E G D I M L D L R M M C
I T O F M S D R N N R L B P A O P
N S I O K O H W L E D E A G M I C
C F H C R D I A S T F I N P N U T
E O E M O N E S D H O F A C S E O
W E L L T H E Y T E U T H N F M T
V T U L T D E L E M R U W B S E A
A I S N A H H E L I C O P T E R K
S H I S T R E E O I R B F A H G E
O W T H G I E T T B E L L E R E W
G A M E I N S D N A K R A P B D Y
```

Solution is on page 374.

One of many lessons of Bible study is to memorize all 66 Books of the Bible from both the New and Old Testaments. Search the diagram below, which has 34 of these ancient books.

AMOS
ESTHER
EXODUS
EZEKIEL

EZRA
HAGGAI
HEBREWS
HOSEA

ISAIAH
JAMES
JOEL
JOHN
JONAH
JOSHUA
JUDE
JUDGES
KINGS
LUKE
MARK
MATTHEW
MICAH
NAHUM
NUMBERS
PETER
PROVERBS
PSALMS
ROMANS
RUTH
SAMUEL
THE ACTS
TIMOTHY
TITUS
ZECHARIAH
ZEPHANIAH

```
J O N A H A B Y H T O M I T
A O R O M A N S O C E A I H
M L S D S U G E S F D T G E
E U I H M T H G E R U T H A
S K J B U K G L A S J H H C
M E E N H A I A S I O E A T
A R G R A N Q P M L B W I S
S M S D N H R L E R T U R M
M Z O Y U O X O E T W V A S
L I A S V J J W Z I E R H U
A B C E G C S D R E K R C D
S K R A J N I H A G F E E O
P B L M H A I N A H P E Z X
S A M U E L N K R E H T S E
```

Solution is on page 375.

BIBLICAL NAMES ─────────────── 119

Here's a list of notable names that appear in the Bible. After finding them below, read the uncircled letters to learn the answer to this riddle: What promise did Adam and Eve make after they were cast from the Garden of Eden?

ABDON
ABEL
ABIHU
ABRAHAM
AHAB
CAIN
ELEAZAR
ELI
ELIASHIB
ESAU
EZEKIEL
GOLIATH
HANNAH
HIRAM
ISAIAH
JETHRO
JOAB
JOB
JONAH
JUDAH
KOHATH
MACHIR
MANASSEH
MANOAH
MARK
MATTHEW
MOSES

NAOMI
NATHAN
NEBAT
NEHEMIAH

NOAH
RUTH
SAMUEL
SAUL

SHEBA
URIAH
ZEDEKIAH
ZIBA

```
H A I K E D E Z E K I E L T
A N E B A T I M O A N H A K
O T N S A B S H A N N A H O
N N O E A H T H T H A E R H
A E A L Y U A D E A H H T A
M H H I R A M U R B T T E T
A E L A B D O N N E A A L H
C M U S H A D U J L N I E E
H I A H O V S A M U E L A S
I A S I I H A I A S I O Z S
R H I B E B R B O J E G A A
A A B R A H A M N E W S R N
K R A M U O L N I A C E O A
H A N O J A F W E H T T A M
```

Solution is on page 375.

151

MOVIE FILL-INS

Here's a puzzle designed to test your knowledge of the cinema. Each film listed below has one word missing from the title. To solve, supply the missing words, which will be in alphabetical order, then circle those words in the diagram on the opposite page. Numbers in parentheses denote word length. If you need help, you'll find the word list on page 397.

1. Bill and Ted's Excellent _____ (9)

2. Her _____ (5)

3. The Fabulous _____ Boys (5)

4. No Holds _____ (6)

5. Memphis _____ (5)

6. Uncle _____ (4)

7. Tango and _____ (4)

8. Who's Harry _____ ? (5)

9. Indiana Jones and the Last _____ (7)

10. Driving Miss _____ (5)

11. _____ of Dreams (5)

12. Great Balls of _____ (4)

13. My Left _____ (4)

14. Back to the _____ (6)

15. All Dogs Go to _____ (6)

16. Turner & _____ (5)

17. Born on the Fourth of _____ (4)

18. Licence to _____ (4)

19. Steel _____ (9)

20. _____ League (5)

21. The Little _____ (7)

22. The Hunt for Red _____ (7)

23. Phantom of the _____ (5)

24. Dead _____ Society (5)

25. When Harry Met _____ (5)

26. Honey, I _____ the Kids (6)

27. Look Who's _____ (7)

28. Teenage Mutant Ninja _____ (7)

29. Quigley Down _____ (5)

30. Joe Versus the _____ (7)

31. Star Trek IV: The _____ Home (6)

32. Lethal _____ (6)

33. _____ at Bernie's (7)

34. Bird on a _____ (4)

35. Pretty _____ (5)

```
Y F F A B B E D A I S Y J T
F U I U A M R I N Q M O X N
I N O R T H E A V E N S P O
E D R V E U M M E J K T V P
L E W O K O R R O P E R A
D R A Y W C U E I Z E O E E
R E K A B T H M W D W P E W
E M A G N O L I A S J I N G
Y O P E H B N S S H R U N K
L M V S A E U A O E K I L L
L D A L F R M O C L K A B Y
A C I J C O C S E L T R U T
S B W I O H O P A E O I C H
I X B M U R C T A B Z V K E
```

Solution is on page 375; list, page 397.

The films listed below share one common element. While they each begin with the letter "R," they are not necessarily rated "R." So your entire family can enjoy watching some of them. Whether or not you decide to see these "R" films, this puzzle is suitable for your entire family.

RABID
RACERS (The)
RACK (The)
RACQUET
RAGE
RAID (The)
RAIN
RAMBO
RAMONA
RAMPAGE
RAPTURE
RAVEN (The)
RAYMIE
REBECCA
REBEL
REDS
REMBRANDT
REMEMBER?
RESCUE (The)
RHAPSODY
RHINESTONE
RHODES
RHUBARB
RIOT
RIPPER (The)
RISK (The)
RITUALS
RITZ (The)
RIVER (The)
ROAR
ROBERTA
ROCAMBOLE
ROCKY

RODAN
RODEO
ROLLERBALL
ROMERO
ROOF (The)

ROONEY
ROPE
ROSE (The)
ROSIE!
ROUNDERS (The)

ROXANNE
RUBY
RUCKUS
RUMBA
RUNNING

```
Y R R H O D E S E N N A X O R
E U C S E R R G R E B E L R A
B B H O A I A S D E R E L I O
R Y K I B P C M I E C G A V R
A A D Y M P K S B L S A B E E
B Y V A U E O F O O R R R R M
U E R E R R E S V B E O E G O
H N I K N R U Z L M D D L N R
R O S E U K R T Z A N E L I A
O O K T C E Q I N C U O O N C
B R P U B I L R W O O T R N Q
E A R E B M E M E R R S I U U
R O C K Y Y Y D O S P A H R E
T C D I B A R E M B R A N D T
A N O M A R H I N E S T O N E
```

Solution is on page 375.

Put your pencil into high **GEAR** to solve this puzzle! Our expert found all 31 words that often follow "high" in just three and a half minutes. Perhaps you can beat the score if you solve at high **SPEED**.

AND DRY	BOY	COMMAND
AND LOW	BUSH	COMMISSIONER
BAR	CHAIR	DUTY
BEAM	COMEDY	GEAR
		GRADE
		JUMP
		LAND
		LEVEL
		LIGHT
		NOON
		OCTANE
		PITCHED
		RISE
		ROAD
		SCHOOL
		SEA
		SPEED
		TABLE
		TEST
		TIDE
		WATER
		WAY
		WIRE

```
R E T A W A Y E C N Q B J
E S L T D A O R W H A C Z
N B H E Q E S I R R S E E
O L E V E L C H R C R U L
I P Q A D E H C T I P H B
S B J U M P O D W M A J A
S H T C W C O N L I G H T
I Y W S A O L A G Y M N C
M D Q E E C L L R R O H T
M E S Q A T L D W O A D M
O M B C Z A D B N C Q D T
C O M M A N D R R A E G E
Y C S Q A E D I T Z B M C
```

Solution is on page 375.

PING-PONG is a table tennis game that can be played indoors or out. Using a paddle, players hit a PING-PONG ball across a small net that spans the width of the playing table. You are a sure winner if you use your pencil to find PING, hidden 33 times, and PONG, hidden 34 times, in the puzzle below.

```
P G N O P G P G G P I N G O
P O N G O I N G N I P N P P
P I N G N N G O I O I I O I
G P I G G N I P P P G N N
N O P O N G I P G N O P G G
I N P G N O P O N G N O P N
P G N I P I P I N G G N G O
O G P O N G I G O P N G N P
N P N G·N G N I P O I I O I
G G N I P O G N N N P G P N
N G N O P P P O N G N O P G
I O N O G I P I N G N I P N
P G N I P N P I N G N O P O
I G N O P G N O P G G N I P
```

Solution is on page 375.

Solve this puzzle EXACTLY as you did the one on page 115. We hope we've given you ENOUGH terms to find in the diagram below. TAKE a shot at it.

AGONY	CLOSET	ELBOW	GLOSS	MOTTO
ALTER	COAT	EMPTY	GRAND	MOUTH
ANGRY	CRATE	ENOUGH	JAUNT	NAME
BABY	DARE	ERMINE	JOIN	NOTED
BEEN	DEEMED	EXACTLY	JUICE	OBJECTION
BOLD	DEER	EXUDE	JURY	OGLE
CAMP	DISTORT	GLADE	MASTER	PAGAN

PATCH
PIRATES
PLIERS
POROUS
PROMOTION
RAID
REPAY
REPEAL
ROOM
RUSH
SCARAB
SEASONAL
SETA
SPATIAL
STREAMLINE
TAKE
THREE
TRIO
USHER

```
E N I M R E H S U O R O P B
X X B O L D E M E E D A R E
U B A B Y A Y T P M E E O E
D T O C P L I E R S T K M N
E W R M T G A T P L O A O I
E S A O G L E J A U N T T L
R C E T T O Y N T P H Y I M
H A C T E S O L C A S N O A
T R I O A S I R H G U O N E
U A U D A R A D N A R G I R
O B J E C T I O N N R A O T
M A S T E R E P A Y R U J S
```

Solution is on page 375.

A diller, a dollar, a ten-o'clock scholar,
What makes you come so soon?
You used to come at ten o'clock,
But now you come at noon.

30246	79229	84246	86414
30460	82014	84969	88101
33044	82690	86140	88242
33496			
36046			
36960			
39042			
39690			
50469			
50694			
51406			
51442			
55060			
55406			
59026			
59614			
73690			
73902			
75210			
75919			
77190			
77240			
79060			

```
6 8 5 5 4 0 6 4 9 0 3 2 6 7
2 2 1 9 2 1 8 2 0 2 3 0 4 5
4 6 0 5 0 6 9 4 6 1 4 6 9 9
0 9 6 9 9 0 2 2 2 1 9 4 0 1
8 0 0 6 5 7 9 8 5 4 6 3 1 9
1 6 9 2 7 6 9 8 0 0 6 0 5 5
4 4 4 3 0 4 6 0 4 9 4 2 6 1
8 2 0 1 4 4 2 4 6 7 5 2 1 0
1 0 6 2 4 5 1 0 9 0 3 1 9 0
0 9 8 6 9 4 9 6 2 6 4 6 3 7
9 9 8 6 4 4 0 0 8 1 4 2 9 4
6 4 1 2 1 0 9 2 6 2 2 2 0 0
9 4 0 7 0 3 6 4 0 9 2 1 4 0
3 6 1 9 7 3 1 3 0 9 4 6 2 9
```

Solution is on page 375.

STAMPs and ROCKs may come to mind when someone mentions collecting as a hobby. Actually, a collection may consist of a number of different kinds of items that are of special interest to the individual collector. Collectors search far and wide to find the rarest, most unusual, oldest or even newest edition for a particular collection, which is part of the challenge of the hobby. Search for the items below.

BADGE
BEER CAN
BIBLE

BOTTLE
BUTTERFLY
BUTTON

CAMEO
CHARM
CIGAR BOX
COIN
COMIC BOOK
COOKBOOK
DOLL
FLAG
FOLK SONG
HORSESHOE
LETTER
LICENSE PLATE
MATCHBOOK
MUGS
OIL PAINTING
POSTER
PUPPET
RECIPE
RECORD
ROCK
SEASHELL
SHAKERS
STAMP
SWORD
TEACUP
TRAIN

```
Q Z N E T A L P E S N E C I L Y
G O I L P A I N T I N G Q N L Z
W A Q G L A V Z S W W Z I F Q B
L C L C L B U T T O N A R Z I Q
Z I Q F O Q A N A C R E E B Q W
M G N Q D M S Q J T T E L Q W K
L A L Z P Q I G W T Z E C P O Q
L R T W M L Z C U V Q K C O Q B
L B Z C Z C Z B B M C J B S R A
E O E O H S E S R O H K Z T B D
H X L A L B P B I E O D L E M G
S J R C O U O N V O T K R R L E
A M K E P T R O C K R T N O Z Q
E N M P T S R E K A H S E N W V
S A E L N F O L K S O N G L N S
C T E A C U P Q N L E P I C E R
```

Solution is on page 375.

THE PRODUCE STAND

You can buy lots of fresh produce in season at a roadside stand. Spend no money, and you may have all the fruits and vegetables listed below by circling them in the diagram on the opposite page.

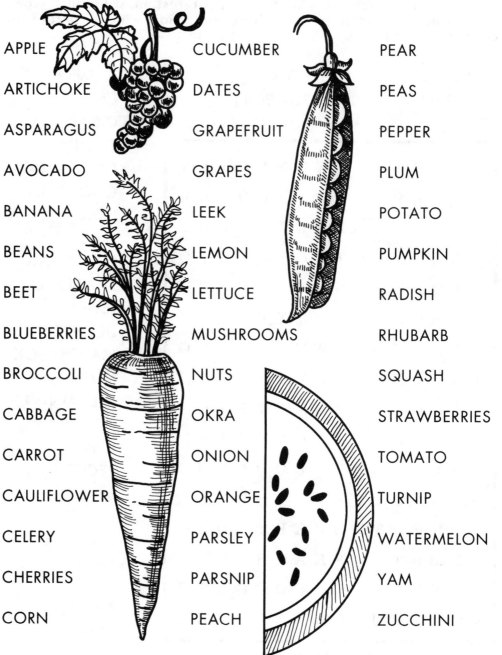

APPLE

ARTICHOKE

ASPARAGUS

AVOCADO

BANANA

BEANS

BEET

BLUEBERRIES

BROCCOLI

CABBAGE

CARROT

CAULIFLOWER

CELERY

CHERRIES

CORN

CUCUMBER

DATES

GRAPEFRUIT

GRAPES

LEEK

LEMON

LETTUCE

MUSHROOMS

NUTS

OKRA

ONION

ORANGE

PARSLEY

PARSNIP

PEACH

PEAR

PEAS

PEPPER

PLUM

POTATO

PUMPKIN

RADISH

RHUBARB

SQUASH

STRAWBERRIES

TOMATO

TURNIP

WATERMELON

YAM

ZUCCHINI

```
L E T T U W P R E W O L F I L U A C
E T O R R A C T O M A T O T A T O P
M C E L R T P A K S L E S Y R A R L
O E T S S E I R R E H C E E O N A U
N L L P A R S U A E L P P A K A D M
A E P E P M Q M R E S P A R S N I P
Y R D A T E S I E F E U R I R A R S
S Y T R E L L K O P E M G O N B E M
E A T I R O T U R N I P C N O I H O
I W M E C N Z U C E N K A I R C S O
R Z U C C H I N I P G I P R D A H R
R L O N U T O C H E I N E N G V R H
E R T N C J A K C A B B A G E O H S
B H S A U Q S B E S W E C R N C U U
E Y O C M T O E P A P A H R O A B M
U A A V B P S E R P E N H S I D A R
L D O M E C U T T E L S O R N O R G
B E R Y R A S P A R A G U S O Y B E
```

Solution is on page 376.

England's famous hero-king, Richard the Lion-Hearted (1157-1199), actually spent only six months of his ten-year reign in England, preferring the battlefields of foreign wars to politics at home. His valor was recognized even by his enemies, as this true story shows.

England's King Richard I fought in the Crusades against the Turks. The Turkish commander Saladin so admired his enemy that he once sent Richard fresh horses when his own were killed in battle, and fresh fruit when Richard became sick.

```
S E N G L A N D S C H U H H
A G A I N S T O R U Y S K O
L H S C N E H W R A I G H R
A K I K A N L C A K H K I S
D I C S R T R T R W Y C H E
I L C H O U Q U T H H R I S
N L K Y S W T I S A Z E V R
B E C A M E N E R B B D N I
U D D Y H T R D H K I N G C
S E Q T H F I F Y T C A I H
S I A E R E W E D E Q M V A
S H C U C H I S E N E M Y R
T V I K D E R I M D A O S D
Y T H G U O F L Y O N C E K
```

Solution is on page 376.

The words listed below may well have been used to describe Richard the Lion-Hearted, just as they're used to describe many of today's movers and shakers. Search the diagram for this list of lion-hearted adjectives.

AUDACITY
BACKBONE
BLOOD
BOLDNESS
BRAVADO
BRAVERY
CHUTZPAH
COURAGE
DARING
DASH
DERRING-DO
ELAN
FIRE
FORCE
GAMENESS
GRIT
GUMPTION
GUSTO
GUTS
HEART
KICK
METTLE
MOXIE
OOMPH
PANACHE
PITH
PLUCK
PROWESS
SAND

SNAP
SPIRIT
SPUNK

STAMINA
STARCH
STYLE

VIM
ZEAL
ZEST

```
P I T H C J X O D A V A R B
D K S T Y L E H M Q N G L O
B A C K B O N E C I F O J L
D U H U V Q T X M R O I H D
L D Q J L T D A C D A L R N
N A L E L P T Q Z D H T T E
R C J E C S G A M E N E S S
G I H G M O G X A R A Q E S
N T Z U Q Q U R T R Z L Z P
I Y P S T G T R E I X O M U
R R A T V Z S H A N R T G N
A N N O I T P M U G C I H K
D J A Q M A Q A Y D E R P L
K I C K N Y Z N H O H G M S
C D H S S E W O R P Y Q O C
Y R E V A R B L J E C R O F
```

Solution is on page 376.

RECIPE: CANADIAN GREEN BEANS ────────────

Canadian Green Beans is a savory side dish flavored with Canadian BACON and ONIONs. The terms in the list are taken directly from the recipe and are hidden in the diagram on the opposite page.

ADD

BACON

BEFORE SERVING

BUTTER

CAN

CASSEROLE

COOK

COVER

CUP

DASH

DICED

DRAINED

FRY

GREEN BEANS

HIGH

LARD

LET SET

MARGARINE

MINCED

MINUTES

MIXTURE

MUSHROOMS

ONION

OPTIONAL

OUNCE

PEPPER

PLACE

POUND

REMOVE

SALT

SERVES

SNAPPED

TABLESPOON

TEASPOON

WATER

CANADIAN GREEN BEANS

1 pound green beans, snapped
1 teaspoon butter
¼ cup water
½ teaspoon salt
dash of pepper

2 tablespoons lard or margarine (optional)
⅓ cup Canadian bacon, diced
2 tablespoons onion, minced
4-ounce can mushrooms, drained

Place beans in casserole dish. Add butter, salt, pepper and water. Cover and cook in microwave for approximately 8 minutes on high, or place in pot, bring to a boil, then simmer for approximately 10 to 12 minutes until done. Meanwhile, fry bacon for two minutes. Add onions and mushrooms and fry in bacon fat until onions are yellow and transparent. (If there isn't enough bacon fat, add lard or margarine.) Remove beans from microwave, add mushroom mixture, cover and let set for 3 minutes before serving. Serves four.

```
Q R J J L E N I R A G R A M T
T G R E E N B E A N S K C H A
E Q G N I V R E S E R O F E B
S C R E V O C M I X T U R E L
T A E E L A R D L L R E Y Y E
E T T P T L D N E Z P E Q E S
L E T B L A D U J P V L J L P
A A U Q A A W O E O P Q D O O
N S B L S C C P M U N A E R O
O P J H R E O E C A J L N E N
I O N I O N R N C O O K I S Q
T O B G L Q Q V J N L J A S O
P N Q H J D I C E D U Q R A J
O M U S H R O O M S Q O D C N
D E C N I M I N U T E S R Q D
```

Solution is on page 376.

Diving, whether done competitively or just as a refreshing way to begin a swim, requires grace, precise timing and skill. Why not put your searching skills to use by plunging into the diagram below and coming up with the 25 swimmer's dives listed below?

ARMSTAND
BACK
BUTTERFLY
FALL-IN
INWARD
ISANDER
JACKKNIFE
MERCURY
PIKE
PLUNGE
PORPOISE
ROCKER
RUNNING
SAILOR
SEAL
SITTING
SOMERSAULT
SPANKER
STATUE
SWALLOW
SWAN
TIP-IN
TUCK
TURTLE
TWIST

```
S O M E R S A U L T C G C E
W O L L A W S R E W N N O V
D R E K N A P S M I L I T O
P R A R I Z J N N S Y L Z S
O L A L N Q V N I T T L W K
R P O W S E U T P K S A E Y
P R L K N R T I P I N F N K
O F N U Q I O N K O K E T D
I E F I N K K C A J U E U O
S J T G A G S L K T S L R N
E Y R U C R E M A E A V T Z
C K Q O C B U T T E R F L Y
V A B A C K S I S A N D E R
```

Solution is on page 376.

Do you know which Robert starred in the Broadway musical and hit film *How to Succeed in Business Without Really Trying*? It was Robert MORSE, whose name appears below along with 34 other Roberts.

BLAKE
CONRAD
CULP
CUMMINGS

DE NIRO
DONAT
DUVALL
EVANS

FOXWORTH
GOULET
GUILLAUME
HAYS
HOOKS
KLEIN
LANSING
LOGGIA
MERRILL
MITCHUM
MONTGOMERY
MORLEY
MORSE
PRESTON
REDFORD
REED
RYAN
SHAW
STACK
STERLING
TAYLOR
URICH
VAUGHN
WAGNER
WALDEN
WALKER
YOUNG

```
E H C I R U D M U H C T I M
R M A I G G O L P L U C O E
E C U M M I N G S D V N W R
N D M A Y X A I E Y T W Z R
G U O J L K T N L G A A K I
A V R R Q L I B O R D H C L
W A L K E R I M D E E S A L
A L E S O E E U M D N T T A
L L Y K N R D O G F H T S N
D R X O Y I R G H O G A N S
E Y N O T S E R P R U Y A I
N A U H E K A L B D A L V N
L N C O N R A D K M V O E G
G N M H T R O W X O F R N T
```

Solution is on page 376.

JUMBO JUST WORDS

If you VALUE puzzles that are just loaded with words, then this puzzle, packed with 63 words of five or more letters should make you feel JOLLY. Have fun!

ADVISE	HELMET	OCTET	SYMBOL
ARGUE	IMPACT	OPERA	TELLER
ARTIST	JOLLY	ORNATE	TORCH
ASTER	JOVIAL	PARCEL	TOTEM
ATOLL	KERNEL	PLANT	TRILL
BEACON	KINDLE	PLUMP	TROUT
BRINK	LAVISH	PUPPET	UPDATE
CALICO	LOCUST	QUORUM	VACANT
CEDAR	LUMBER	RATIO	VALUE
DAINTY	MELODY	RIPPLE	VOICE
DINER	MERRY	ROOST	WARBLE
DRAWL	MODERN	ROYAL	WONDER
FACET	MOTTO	SALMON	WRIST
FILTER	NESTLE	SPICE	YIELD
GINGER	NORTH	SQUEAK	ZENITH
GRANT	NOTCH	STAIR	

```
K A E U Q S Z J O L L Y R R E M
E A L O C U S T E L D N I K D E
L D R A W L O Y I S E P M X B T
B L Q T K C C R N A P T P E N O
R E G N I G T E U L H E A A J T
A I E L T S E N E M J C C D L P
W Y A W R A T I O O O A T L P M
E C T T O T K D X N V F O O M U
U E P N S N E Z E N I T H O N L
L D W O I R D K P L A N T R T P
A A O R N A T E F I L T E R E A
V R B T I O D R R L O B M Y S R
I O X H R S O N O G M P L T I C
S P I C E Y T E P U P P E T V E
H N H C A R E L L E T R H R D L
Y D O L E M E U G R A N T C A W
```

Solution is on page 376.

IT'S ON THE MAP

"It matters not how far you roam, the cartographer's map will bring you home." This little ditty honors mapmakers who help us get where we want to go. Currently they are hurrying to complete a new map to show the global changes that have taken place in all the countries of Eastern Europe. The words below describe various geographical features found on many maps.

ACRE

ARCHIPELAGO
(large group of islands)

ARCTIC

AREA

ATOLL

BAY

CAPITAL

CHART

CITY

DEGREES
(of latitude or longitude)

DESERTS

EARTH

ESTUARY
(where a river meets the sea)

FJORD (steep, narrow
inlet of the sea)

FOREST

ICE CAP

ISLAND

ISLET

LAGOON

LAKE

MERCATOR (map projection)

OCEAN

PARKS

PLAIN

PLATEAU

PRIME MERIDIAN (0° longitude)

REEF

REGION

STATE

STRAIT (narrow marine passage)

TOWN

TRACT (area of land)

TROPIC

VELDT
(grassland of South Africa)

```
D R O J F E F Q K S I B X F
Y L M C Y A R E A C K G O L
N A I D I R E M E M I R P Q
S T R A I T A C T R E O A D
Y I V C S H A U A S D K E P
R P Z M H P F J T E W G A U
O A P Y D I B Y S S R T M L
T C U L N N P E V E E R L H
A E R C A G R E E P X O N N
C R T E L T I S L E T P O A
R J C N S O E A D A Q I O H
E O A T I W I A T H G C G B
M Z R Y I N C W U E V O A I
R S T G H C H A R T H Y L U
```

Solution is on page 376.

You can choose your friends, but you can't pick your relatives! However, in this puzzle, you can choose to circle 24 different words for "cousin."

BRATRÁNEK (Czech)

COUSIN (French)

CUGINO (Italian)

DODAN (Hebrew)

DVAYÚRNI BRAT
(Russian)

EXÁDELFOS (Greek)

FAETTER (Danish)

FETTER (Norwegian)

IBN AM (Arabic)

ITOKO (Japanese)

KUSIN (Swedish)

KUZEN (Turkish)

KUZO (Esperanto)

KUZYN (Polish)

NEEF (Dutch)

PATRUELIS (Latin)

PRIMO
(Spanish, Portuguese)

SAUDARA SEPUPU
(Indonesian)

SCHVESTERKIND
(Yiddish)

SERKKU (Finnish)

SESTRIC
(Serbo-Croatian)

UNOKAFIVÉR
(Hungarian)

VAR (Romanian)

VETTER (German)

```
K K B K N C O U S I N T R Y
J U U R U V R I F P A E J S
O Z S G A E A A R R V N C E
O Y I I T T E R B I C E S S
Z N L T N T R I F M I E O T
O B E S T E N A D O D F G R
K F U E L R K I N H L K Q I
O Q R R U O B B N E Z U K C
T R T Y N C V N D F K L A S
I S A U D A R A S E P U P U
I V P I P U X M U K K R E S
D N I K R E T S E V H C S H
```

Solution is on page 376.

Perry Mason has been one of the world's favorite fictional lawyers for many years. When he puts his mind to work for a client you can be sure of the result. This puzzle deals with a Perry Mason-style setting in the courtroom. Can you solve it?

BAIL

BENCH (warrant)

BLIND (justice)

BOND

BRIBE (an informer)

BURGER (Hamilton)

CASE

CLUE

COURT

DEFEND

DELLA STREET

DOCKET

DROP (the charges)

FAIR (trial)

GARDNER
  (Erle Stanley)

GAVEL

GUILTY (verdict)

HALE (Barbara)

JUDGE

JUROR

JURY

JUSTICE

LAWYER

LEGAL

LT. TRAGG

ORDER (in the court)

PAUL DRAKE

PERRY MASON

PLEA

PLED

RAYMOND BURR

ROOM (court)

TRIAL

WARRANT

```
D L G G A R T T L H Q X Z J
K N E T E K C O D R O R U J
Q T I G N O S A M Y R R E P
X R R L A N E K T O Y U U A
E U L C B L Q L E K R B Z U
B O E S A C I O E M X D D L
T C L W W U E B R D O N E D
P N Y P G B B E T E E O Q R
O E A D I O N N S L C M R A
R W R R N D A C A P I Y I K
D P B D R E K H L Q T A A E
T R I A L A F L L S S R F Z
T H G P I T W E E F U V U L
Y G A V E L E G D U J Q Z X
```

Solution is on page 377.

Here's a puzzle to solve like the one on page 118. See that page for complete directions.

ACTUATED	CARAT	ELFIN	INTEGER
ALARM	CAVERNOUS	ERADICATE	JUMPING
ANCESTOR	CIRCUS	FLARE	LIMIT
BEND	CULT	FRUGAL	MAJESTIC
BROGAN	DORMANT	GREMLIN	MILITIA
BRUNT	DRUDGE	GRIP	MOPE

NEST

NOVELIST

PATIO

PELICAN

PRUDENCE

RELIC

RETRACT

SATIN

SCOLDING

TACITURN

THEORETIC

THERE

UNICORN

UNNERVE

VIRTUOSO

WHARF

Solution is on page 377.

Three blind mice, see how they run!
They all ran after the farmer's wife,
Who cut off their tails with the carving-knife;
Did you ever see such a sight in your life
As three blind mice?

21404	23077	25401	36057
21540	23606	25717	36501
22451	24570	30140	37070
22560	24765	30576	37104
			38041
			38765
			39061
			39614
			80104
			80176
			82176
			82410
			84140
			84767
			86445
			86771
			88014
			88141
			91011
			91756
			93165
			93218
			95256
			95456
			97101
			97646
			99067
			99760

```
2 5 4 0 1 8 0 1 4 3 9 6 1 4 5
8 4 6 7 6 5 6 1 3 9 0 5 4 1 0
2 7 7 2 1 4 0 4 7 6 1 4 0 8 3
1 0 4 6 0 9 1 6 4 7 1 7 5 2 6
7 1 0 7 5 1 0 4 5 5 5 0 1 1 5
6 9 5 6 6 0 3 8 6 7 0 6 5 2 2
3 3 6 5 0 1 0 1 6 4 5 5 7 6 5
1 4 4 7 6 1 5 2 7 7 1 3 9 8 9
5 5 1 0 0 5 7 3 1 2 4 7 7 9 3
9 6 4 4 0 8 6 9 0 3 1 0 0 7 1
9 8 1 2 7 4 2 0 8 0 6 7 1 6 7
0 7 8 5 2 7 1 4 1 7 7 0 1 4 7
6 0 0 0 7 6 4 1 1 7 4 0 6 6 6
7 6 4 6 1 7 5 4 6 0 4 1 0 3 8
3 5 0 7 5 4 2 8 8 1 4 1 4 5 2
```

Solution is on page 377.

This puzzle is solved like the one on page 132. Instead of finding words, you will find a combination of letters and symbols. Reading down, the initial letters spell out four different nuts.

```
C  =  /  %  #  A  T  ?  C  /  N  ?  +
-  :  L  @  &  A  P  +  E  A  #  C  -
I  *  &  :  &  =  :  *  A  %  U  P  =
D  ?  #  -  M  +  H  -  -  &  =  =  D
=  +  *  :  @  E  A  C  +  N  ?  ?  ?
M  S  -  &  #  M  T  ?  /  %  *  /  +
S  I  *  U  %  H  -  @  ?  E  @  &  %
+  #  A  T  ?  C  :  %  D  *  /  #  @
W  %  P  =  ?  -  *  -  I  W  -  =  E
=  L  &  #  ?  =  &  A  =  /  H  +  @
A  +  N  -  /  &  W  #  C  %  S  *  :
%  ?  =  /  A  W  #  &  L  &  N  U  *
```

Solution is on page 377.

P = ? / &
E @ : * +
C − % # ?
A + & @ /
N % = − :
W # * & @
A : − + %
L & # ? =
N / @ : −
U * + = #
T ? / % *
C : & − @
A # % / =
S + ? * :
H − / @ *
E % = ? +
W & * : −
M @ # % ?
A = ? & #
C / − # %
A * : = &
D ? / + −
A / = ? %
M + # : &
I * @ / ?
A − & % +

This summer millions of students will be looking for ways to earn money during their summer break from school. The list below may give them some ideas, since it contains places that just might hire them.

```
C L K R A P L L A B E S A B O B Y
O O D D R I V E I N M O V I E V R
N O N N O I T A T S S A G O Q E O
S P U S C V X N P O O Q Y D T V L
T G O X E R V Z A Q H N X N L I R
R N R W Y R U Q R R A T E N B Z A
U I G D B K V O K P U C R R Q J P
C M Y Y Z U C A M P N A A O G Q M
T M A B X O L O T O M R T K S L A
I I L E F V C C I I Y B K S Z E E
O W P F W G A T Y M O T E L E B R
N S I O N R A M A R I N A A C R C
T C F I W E Z S Q D T W C K C S E
E G V A R Y J D L Z V N Q O U H C
A O S C B H C N A R E D U D R Y I
M H E D X P P U O R G R U O T P X
H R I D I N G S T A B L E P C Q S
```

Solution is on page 377.

BASEBALL PARK
BEACH
CAMP
CAR WASH
CONSERVATION CORPS
CONSTRUCTION TEAM
COUNTRY CLUB
DRIVE-IN MOVIE
DUDE RANCH
GAS STATION
ICE CREAM PARLOR
LIBRARY
MARINA
MOTEL
MOVING COMPANY
OFFICE
PARK
PLAYGROUND
RECREATION CENTER
RESORT HOTEL
RESTAURANT
RIDING STABLE
SWIMMING POOL
TOUR GROUP

To win the Grand Slam, a tennis player must win all four major tennis tournaments in the same year. So it is no surprise that in January the attention of tennis fans everywhere was focused on the Australian Open. Some of the men who have won this tournament include Boris BECKER and Rod LAVER. Find their names and those of 30 other men who have won the Australian Open.

ASHE (Arthur)
BECKER (Boris)
BOROTRA (Jean)

BOWREY (Bill)
BUDGE (Don)
CONNORS (Jimmy)

COOPER (Ashley)
EDBERG (Stefan)
EMERSON (Roy)
GEMMELL (Rhys)
GREGORY (John)
HAWKES (John)
HOAD (Lew)
KRIEK (Johan)
LAVER (Rod)
LENDL (Ivan)
MCGRATH (V.B.)
MCGREGOR (Ken)
MOON (Gar)
NEWCOMBE (John)
OLMEDO (Alex)
PAILS (Dinny)
PERRY (Fred)
ROSE (Mervyn)
ROSEWALL (Ken)
SAVITT (Richard)
SEDGMAN (Frank)
TANNER (Roscoe)
TEACHER (Brian)
VILAS (Guillermo)
WILANDER (Mats)
WOOD (Pat)

```
B C Y D L L A W E S O R T C
G O R N A M G D E S L T M O
C R R V L B S R J B I M L M
R L E O X O E Q E V U M L C
E R P B T W K J A G E D O G
D G L V D R W S T D O O G R
N E C I I E A R O A P R K E
A M L L P Y H O E E N R Y G
L M Q A D T W N R H I N L O
I E I S A Z J N B E C K E R
W L N R O N Q O K X L A O R
S L G D H L O C Z L Q S E R
R C L C L J N O S R E M E T
M L F N E W C O M B E H S A
```

Solution is on page 377.

178

Margaret Smith COURT won the Women's Australian Open eleven times. In the puzzle below, find her name and those of 29 other women who have won this tournament.

AKHURST (Daphne)

BOLTON
(Nancye W.)

BOYD (Esna)

BROUGH (Louise)

BUNDY
(Dorothy M.)

BUTTSWORTH
(Coral)

CARTER (Mary)

CAWLEY (Evonne
Goolagong)

COURT (Margaret
Smith)

EVERT (Chris)

FRY (Shirley)

GRAF (Steffi)

HART (Doris)

HARTIGAN (Joan)

JORDAN (Barbara)

KING (Billie Jean)

LANCE (Sylvia)

LONG (Thelma)

MANDLIKOVA
(Hana)

MOLESWORTH
(Mall)

MORTIMER (Angela)

NAVRATILOVA (Martina)

O'NEILL (Chris)

PEMROSE (Beryl)

REID (K. Melville)

REITANO (Mary)

RICHEY (Nancy)

ROUND (Dorothy)

SELES (Monica)

WADE (Virginia)

```
A V O L I T A R V A N O V C
L K H A R T I G A N N C L Y
C L H U Q D G L X E G J E B
A D O U Y Z N J I R S H O U
V C L O R M O L A E C L C T
O L B C W S L F L I T W J T
K J Y C A R T E R O X K O S
I L D Z D W S B N Y I L R W
L A N C E O L A R N J C D O
D L U L R C T E G O Q N A R
N I B M Q I L Z Y T U C N T
A L E V E R T L Q O R G L H
M P L R E M I T R O M A H C
C V L M O L E S W O R T H L
```

Solution is on page 377.

Known for its earthquakes and vineyards among other things, California is a state of many faces. Travel with us now to the small towns which dot the countryside of our 31st state.

ADIN
AMBOY
ARTOIS
AVENAL
BANGOR
BIGGS
BRAY
CAPAY
CIMA
CLAY
DALES
DARWIN
DEVIL'S DEN
DOS RIOS
ETNA
EXETER
FRIANT
GRENADA
HEBER
HELM
JAMUL
JENNY LIND
KELSO
LAWS
LOTUS
MILTON
NAVARRO
NORD
ONYX
PEANUT
PIXLEY
POSEY

RAISIN
RICE
RYAN
SAN ARDO
SEARLES

TOBIN
TWAIN
VIOLA
YERMO
ZENIA

```
N Y O B K E L S O L U M A J
B O M I L T O N T G S P E E
I B R C F I I N S U I N C C
G M E D R B A A T X N I H I
G A Y S O Y N O L Y R A D M
S I O T R A L E L N J W E A
E D K N R R Y I S O G T V P
L N I D A B N P E C T E I O
A L O I V D S R A L N X L S
D M S Y A P A C R A A E S E
Z I S R N T I N L Y I T D Y
N Z W C E T N A E K R E E D
B I A R E B E H S R F R N F
N M L E H X Z W R O G N A B
```

Solution is on page 377.

Depending on the structure of a sentence, the word "STUDY" may be used in place of the word "look." This means that it is synonymous with "look." SCAN the diagram for other synonyms of "look."

ADMIRE
ANALYZE
ATTEND
BROWSE

COMPARE
EXAMINE
EYE
FIND

FOCUS
GAZE
GLANCE
GLARE
GLIMPSE
GLOWER
INSPECT
JUDGE
PEER
PERUSE
PICTURE
PORE
READ
REMARK
REVIEW
SCAN
SCRUTINIZE
SEE
SKIM
SPOT
SQUINT
STARE
STUDY
SURVEY
VIEW
VISUALIZE
WATCH

```
A S U R V E Y T C E P S N I
E G Y I Y A R E Z A G R W E
A R L E M E F I N D Y M A S
H J O I E R L B M D Q W R J
P O K P M A E J U D G E I E
I S M A U P H T E R A L G Z
C V I S E D S T A R E B M I
T R I R A T T E N D R R T N
U V U E I N N C A J A O K I
R S R N W I S N L K P W R T
E I A U M U U A Y S M S A U
H C T A W Q C L Z I O E M R
S O X I U S O G E U C I E C
R E W O L G F W E I V E R S
```

Solution is on page 377.

Walter PLUNKETT designed Vivien Leigh's splendid *Gone With the Wind* wardrobe; Edith HEAD fashioned Dorothy Lamour's famous sarong; and the colorful costumes in *The Wizard of Oz* were fashioned by ADRIAN. These are three of the 32 Hollywood costume designers listed below. Look for them all in the diagram below. We've circled MABRY to start you off.

ADRIAN
BANTON (Travis)
BEAR (Jack)

BEATON (Cecil)
BEST (Marjorie)
FURSE (Margaret)

FURSE (Roger)
HAFFENDEN (Elizabeth)
HEAD (Edith)
HUBERT (René)
IRENE
JEAKINS (Dorothy)
JEAN-LOUIS
JOHNSTONE (Anna Hill)
KEYES (Marion Herwood)
KIAM (Omar)
LEMAIRE (Charles)
MABRY (Moss)
ORRY-KELLY
PALMER (Adele)
PLUNKETT (Walter)
POWELL (Anthony)
RENIE
ROSE (Helen)
SHARAFF (Irene)
SHOUP (Howard)
STEVENSON (Edward)
TRAVILLA (William)
VALLES
VAN RUNKLE (Theadora)
WALTON (Tony)
WEST (Vera)

```
J V E W E S T E V E N S O N
E E P A L M E R F Q Z K A E
A E A K I N E R F I U I E D
N R O K U N O E A I R A L N
L I A Z I S O T R D Y M K E
O A L E E N W B A N T O N F
U M L G Z A S E H E S R U F
I E E L L U H T S E B R R A
S L W T I R B R L N S Y N H
S H O U P V A L L E S K A U
D N P I C E A H S R E E V B
U V Y R B A M R U I Y L O E
S P L U N K E T T L E L O R
Y E N O T S N H O J K Y D T
```

Solution is on page 378.

The men listed below are our nation's first patriots. They fought the British in a successful attempt to gain independence from our ruling country. Thanks to these early leaders, the United States has remained one of the freest nations of the world.

ADAMS (John)
ADAMS (Samuel)
ALLEN (Ethan)
ARNOLD (Benedict)
CLARK (George Rogers)
DEANE (Silas)
FRANKLIN (Benjamin)
GATES (Horatio)
GREENE (Nathaniel)
HALE (Nathan)
HANCOCK (John)
HENRY (Patrick)
JAY (John)
JEFFERSON (Thomas)
JONES (John Paul)
KNOX (Henry)
LEE (Charles)
LEE (Henry)
LIVINGSTON (Robert)
MARION (Francis)
MASON (George)
MORRIS (Robert)
MOULTRIE (William)
OTIS (James)
PAINE (Thomas)
PUTNAM (Israel)
REVERE (Paul)

SALOMON (Haym)
SCHUYLER (Philip J.)
STARK (John)
ST. CLAIR (Arthur)
WARD (Artemus)

WARNER (Seth)
WARREN (Joseph)
WASHINGTON (George)
WAYNE (Anthony)

```
S M A D A M S E N O J R P S
B A R T A E R E V E R I U Y
W A R R E N T O F E L A T R
W X I M Z E J F T V L L N N
X O N K O E E L W I K C A E
N N Q B O R A Q V P S T M H
I R U O S G R I M Y X S O A
L E N O T G N I H S A W U N
K N N R U G O A S I T J L C
N R B A S A L O M O N A T O
A A A T M E D E N A E D R C
R W O L S J G A T E S N I K
F N E S C H U Y L E R O E Y
F P Z E N I A P A W A Y N E
```

Solution is on page 378.

Jane Goodall's book, *In the Shadow of Man,* is an account of her ten years of living among and studying chimpanzees in the wild. Listed below are some of the subjects of her research. After you find all of their names, the uncircled letters, when read from left to right down the page, will spell out the place where her fascinating studies were conducted.

BEATLE

CINDY

DAVID GRAYBEARD

EVERED

FABEN

FIFI

FIGAN

FLAME

FLINT

FLO

GILKA

GOBLIN

GOBLINA

GOLIATH

HUMPHREY

HUXLEY

LEAKEY

MARINA

MELISSA

MERLIN

MIFF

MIKE

MR. MCGREGOR

MR. WORZLE

OLLY

PASSION

PEPE

POM

POOCH

RODOLF

SNIFF

SOREMA

WILLIAM

```
N E L Z R O W R M O P G O D
O P M B L H L E A K E Y A E
I O E L N U N A K T I V O N
S O Y P F M A I L L I W A N
S C R L E P G L I D I F I F
A H I O P H I E G O B L I N
P N A R G R F R V K R F I N
T T I Y B E A T L E F A C M
E A N L E Y R Z M I R B I E
M K O A B L N G N A I E N L
I L I E A O X S C A R N D I
F L A M E F G U R M I I Y S
F R G O L I A T H C R A N S
D R O D O L F S O R E M A A
```

Solution is on page 378.

Here is a picnic table to use at your summer picnics. Search the table to find the word PICNIC, hidden 19 times. When you have circled all the terms, the uncircled letters will spell out a comment about picnics.

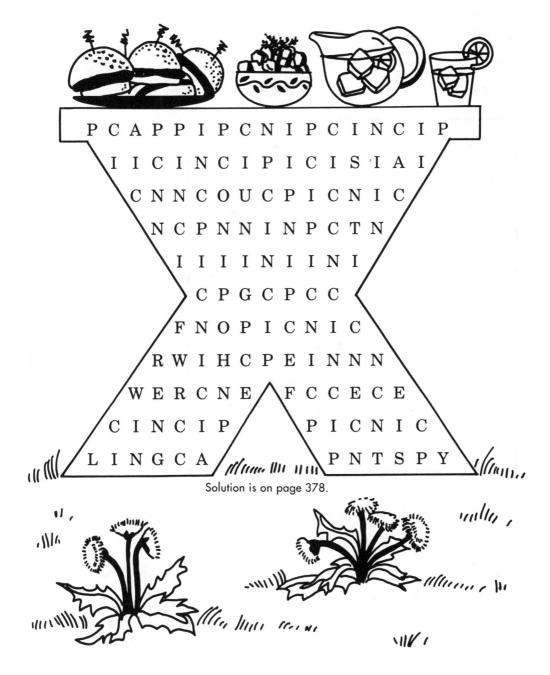

```
P C A P P I P C N I P C I N C I P
  I I C I N C I P I C I S I A I
  C N N C O U C P I C N I C
  N C P N N I N P C T N
  I I I I N I I N I
  C P G C P C C
  F N O P I C N I C
  R W I H C P E I N N
W E R C N E   F C C E C E
C I N C I P     P I C N I C
L I N G C A       P N T S P Y
```

Solution is on page 378.

Did you know that 22 was the number of Burt Reynold's football jersey at West Palm Beach High School and at Florida State? He also wore this jersey number in the films *The Longest Yard* and *Semi-Tough*.

3310	3910	4419
3384	3922	4459
3612	4282	4601
3691	4298	4699
		5012
		5098
		5501
		5598
		5708
		5781
		5928
		5981
		6489
		6499
		6609
		6621
		6828
		6898
		7182
		7190
		7515
		7590
		7780
		7798

```
9 2 8 0 1 2 4 8 3 3 8 0 1 2
9 0 1 9 3 6 7 1 9 8 7 9 2 0
6 8 0 1 0 8 9 7 1 1 9 8 5 0
4 4 9 1 0 5 1 2 9 9 0 1 9 5
5 7 8 1 1 2 1 0 8 8 5 1 0 2
5 8 2 9 6 3 6 1 2 7 2 8 2 1
9 9 0 6 8 1 0 5 9 8 1 2 1 0
2 1 2 2 7 9 9 9 2 8 9 8 2 5
3 8 9 8 5 2 0 6 1 3 9 0 7 2
6 3 0 1 9 8 4 9 3 8 2 0 1 9
4 0 1 8 0 2 2 4 9 7 8 1 0 0
9 1 9 0 9 4 1 4 8 1 8 2 8 6
9 8 2 8 8 1 0 5 5 8 4 1 2 6
6 7 7 8 0 9 0 9 9 2 0 4 9 8
```

Solution is on page 378.

In honor of all labor, take a rest on Monday, September 7, the day we observe Labor Day. The puzzle below tells how the holiday began. After you circle all the terms, the uncircled letters will reveal the name of a song written by John Lennon that is an appropriate dedication to those who labor for our welfare.

When American laborers were working long hours for low wages, unions were formed to improve conditions. In eighteen eighty-two, a union suggested that a day be set aside to honor Labor, and a parade took place in late summer. Twelve years later, Congress proclaimed the first Monday in September Labor Day.

```
E C D W R E B M E T P E S N I
D O O E V O R P M I O T R K K
A N S U M M E R I W N N H O G
R D E C S R E R O B A L O N G
A I G L A T O L E O C T U T E
P T A N A N R F W W I O R H B
R I W L I O E T S E R H S A Y
O O T C F K Y E V S E O R T A
C N H O H T R L T D M N O A D
L S E N H A E O I H A O B U R
A R F G E W N S W R G R A N O
I A I R T Y A D N O M I L I B
M E R E W T E C A L P O E O A
E Y S S E T A L N I W H E N L
D E T S E G G U S N O I N U I
```

Solution is on page 378.

We've hidden 56 words in the diagram below. There are no proper nouns, or words that end in "s." When all the words have been circled, a symmetrical design will be formed. Our list of words is on page 397.

4 Letters

_____ _____ _____ _____
_____ _____ _____ _____
_____ _____ _____ _____
_____ _____ _____ _____
_____ _____ _____ _____

_____
_____

5 Letters

_____
_____
_____
_____
_____
_____
_____

6 Letters

_____
_____

7 Letters

_____
_____
_____
_____
_____
_____
_____

```
C O M P A C T A M N E S T Y
I O A G A N T W D I O B T T
R U A S E O T M I O S I C I
E I T T I S K D U N C T N B
N L F D O N N E O S I L E O
E I I R A O A E I L I A A R
G O F R U L B D A M P C L P
M O M M I R G E R I W Y L P
E I O E O I L S P A R A A R
R L R S R L U L D I N I E E
M O B B E C E E A T R P D C
A P M M L U Y F I O M I Y E
I U W R U U R X O A L Z F P
D E F L A T E T H G U O H T
```

Solution is on page 378; list, page 397.

Each number from one through ten will be found spelled out in this puzzle as many times as the number represents. That is, ONE will be found once, TWO will be found twice, three will be found THREE times, etc. When you've circled them all, the uncircled letters will spell out a message. To help you keep track, place a check next to each number below each time you find it.

ONE

TWO

THREE

FOUR

FIVE

SIX

SEVEN

EIGHT

NINE

TEN

```
E T H G I E T E N E X I S T
T V N I N E N E E I G H T N
P E I G H T E E S G N E N T
R N N F O I H E T H N E T H
U S S W N E I G H T I E N R
O L E E I E N I N N L E E
F I V E B G T E N E F I V E
U E E E R H T T V Y F N E T
S N N O X T M E W O O O S T
T H G I E R S S F O U R U H
E T S E N H A E I N R O N R
S E V E N I N N V X E I I E
S I X D O W T I E E N I N E
F X I S M E S E V E N N E T
```

Solution is on page 378.

A LONG, HOT SUMMER

Summer has arrived once again, bringing with it the unmistakable signs of the season that we're all familiar with. So sit back and indulge yourself in a little summer reverie as you solve your way through this puzzle, filled with terms associated with the season.

AIR CONDITIONING

BASEBALL

BEACH PARTIES

BLUE SKIES

CLAMBAKES

COOK-OUTS

FANS

FISHING

FRESH VEGETABLES

HAMMOCKS

HAYRIDES

HEAT

HIKING

HOT DOGS

HOT SUN

HOT WEATHER

HUMIDITY

ICE-COLD DRINKS

ICE CREAM

ICED TEA

LEAFY TREES

LEMONADE

LIGHT CLOTHING

LOAFING

MOSQUITOS

NO SCHOOL

PICNICS

SAILING

SALADS

SANDALS

SHORTS

SIGHTSEEING

SUNBURNS

SWIMMING

TANS

TENNIS

THE BEACH

VACATIONS

WATERMELON

WATER SKIING

```
U J J L C V X W A T E R M E L O N T G
U M W J O D P S Y T H Z C F B H Z Y F
Q O I K O W U H O T W E A T H E R H R
K S T Q K I E I F J O N B F H I S U E
V N P H O T H K N R S G Z E S C X G S
S S K S U S E I T R A P H C A E B K H
W O G N T M C N G Z Q G I E W C C L V
I L T O S E I G N R N N Q J R O H O E
M J V I D M I D P I C S D V M L H A G
M I S T U T N R I I S I A M O D D F E
I X E A F Q O K P T Q G A I G D A I T
N A D C L H S H R S Y H C U L R N N A
G K I A I R C O N D I T I O N I N G B
N J R V E E H H M A P S T Z B N N C L
I B Y T G S O S P L M E O K W K S G E
H Y A D K T O S Z A Z E B F M S U E S
S W H S S B L U E S K I E S G Z N B O
I L C U E A F R E D A N O M E L B A Y
F Z N Z D B C O E A E G D H L Z U B T
W A M N L E A F Y T R E E S A D R X A
L M A M C N C L A M B A K E S Y N R P
B S L I G H T C L O T H I N G X S C C
```

Solution is on page 378.

Hamburger lovers, did you know that the IQ of Popeye's friend, J. Wellington Wimpy, is 326? Now that's food for thought!

4032	4232	4520
4082	4310	4592
4121	4398	5601
4181	4430	5683
4212	4432	5701
		5799
		5803
		5898
		5909
		5913
		6032
		6098
		6232
		6282
		6401
		6432
		6691
		6698
		6801
		6833
		7131
		7192
		7301
		7399
		7501
		7532
		7710
		7733
		7938
		7988

```
4 1 8 1 3 5 6 0 9 8 2 1 6 2
1 3 3 8 5 7 6 8 0 1 9 3 4 2
2 1 1 9 7 8 9 8 9 1 8 7 0 3
7 2 2 3 0 1 9 3 3 9 8 9 1 4
8 3 3 2 1 6 2 9 3 2 3 8 5 6
7 9 8 0 6 5 8 4 2 3 2 8 1 2
5 3 3 7 6 6 7 9 3 1 9 6 6 3
0 2 0 7 1 0 9 9 1 8 8 3 3 0
1 3 5 1 1 1 8 2 9 2 3 8 8 8
8 3 9 0 0 1 3 4 5 5 6 9 1 5
2 1 0 3 4 4 9 3 9 2 2 9 5 4
9 0 2 5 4 1 7 0 9 1 9 8 2 3
1 2 3 1 3 2 9 8 3 4 0 8 2 9
7 1 9 8 4 2 1 2 7 8 2 3 2 6
```

Solution is on page 379.

This is another Word Search in reverse. Circled letters are the initial letters of one or more words, and any letter may be part of more than one word. Fill in each word in a straight line without crossing any black squares; when you're done, every square will be filled. KNEAD has been entered for you.

AFGHAN

ARDOR

ARSENAL

BALANCE

BITE

CONFORMED

CROWD

DETAIL

DETRIMENT

EDGED

ENTRUST

EXCAVATION

GRASP

IRIS

IRKED

ISOTOPE

KNEAD

LISTEN

LOGO

MOONLIT

NAUSEA

OBLIGATED

PERUSE

PROFIT

PROPRIETOR

RESTRICTED

SHED

SHRIEK

SILICONE

SUBLIMATE

TERRIFIC

TITANIUM

TODAY

VINTNER

VOLLEY

WHEREIN

WHET

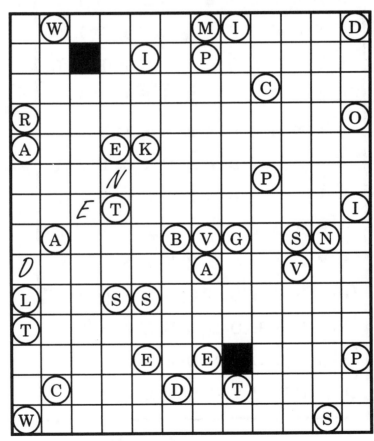

Solution is on page 379.

Solve this puzzle by forming a chain of circled words in which the last letter of one word is the first letter of the next. The number in parentheses tells you the length of the word you're looking for. We have provided MIND to start you off.

MIND _____ (4)	_____ (4)	_____ (4)
D _____ (4)	_____ (4)	_____ (5)
_____ (4)	_____ (5)	_____ (4)
_____ (4)	_____ (5)	_____ (6)
		_____ (6)
		_____ (5)
		_____ (5)
		_____ (5)
		_____ (5)
		_____ (6)
		_____ (6)
		_____ (5)
		_____ (5)
		_____ (5)
		_____ (4)
		_____ (6)
		_____ (5)
		_____ (4)
		_____ (6)
		_____ (4)
		_____ (4)
		_____ (5)
		_____ (7)
		_____ (4)
		_____ (6)
		_____ (4)
		_____ (5)
		_____ (4)
		_____ (6)
		_____ (7)
		_____ (6)

```
S P E A K E R L R R E B M E
R E Z V T E S D I A R Z V
E X P E L S A Q R N E Q B O
L Y J O A Q D Z E G R E A L
B W Q U L Y E R A L E X X E
B W N M B E R E M E D Y L X
A A H L M D M A E T N D Z I
D I V I L L E Z T S O H G L
W H B O Y A Q A I O Y V N E
L R D Z W C U Z N Z S S I L
D I S C B S L Q G H S Q W I
N J B R R O U Z E L A A E M
I H Z O O Y N D E B R I S I
M N P W H Y G L I B G N A T
```

Solution is on page 379; list, page 397.

Take time out now to gaze at the STARs. Don't worry if it's not dark yet, because there are plenty of STARs hidden below. Find the word STAR, hidden 34 times, and TREK, hidden 29 times. This puzzle's for Trekkies and for those who aren't necessarily such big fans of "STAR TREK" too.

```
S E K R K K R A T S K E R T
T T R E K E R T R E T R E K
A R A A R R R A T S T A R T
R E T R T T E T T S T A R S
A K S K R S R K E R T E T T
T R E K E R T E R S K A R A
S T A R E T A R K R R E R R
T T R E K R S T A R K A R A
A R A T S E T T S S A E T T
R K E R T K S A K T R T R S
T R E T R A T S E A A T S T
R T R A T S A T R R T R R R
E E T R E K R A T S S E S E
K S T A R S T R E K K K T K
```

Solution is on page 379.

September 5 marks the Hindu festival honoring Ganesh, the god of luck, son of Shiva and Parvati. Ganesh's image is hung above many doors in India, and on this day people ask for his help before beginning any new project. Ganesh has the head of an elephant. Read on to find out why.

Ganesh so provoked his father one day that Shiva cut off his head. Parvati begged her husband to replace it, and since an elephant was close by, Ganesh received an elephant head. In spite of his unusual head, Ganesh proved to be a distinguished god.

```
D H N A E C N I S A P B E T
A D I O F H I S T D R N C A
Y B E S O L C H G A O F D H
O T A H T H I S H I V A H L
M F N S S T N E P T E R A L
D D F E V I N N H D U A Q
E F N N D D U A U T S R E P
G A W A O X H G H U Y S B R
G T E G T P E B N P P Z O O
E H C D E I A U F I E G T V
B E M L W L D K T J T L I O
N R E C A L P E R O T S E K
D N A B S U H P T U V Q I E
A W V R H E R E C E I V E D
```

Solution is on page 379.

"Father Knows Best" was a popular series based on the premise that when things go wrong in the family, the father's always there to help straighten them out. In addition to television, fathers have long been given attention in movies. Some of the actors who have portrayed fathers in films are listed below. Can you find them? The movies in which their father portrayals are featured are listed on page 397.

1. AIELLO (Danny)
2. BRYNNER (Yul)
3. CAAN (James)
4. CANDY (John)
5. CONNERY (Sean)
6. COOPER (Gary)
7. COSBY (Bill)
8. DAILEY (Dan)
9. DANIELS (Jeff)
10. DUVALL (Robert)
11. FALK (Peter)
12. FONDA (Henry)
13. GLOVER (Danny)
14. GRANT (Cary)
15. HEARD (John)
16. HOFFMAN (Dustin)
17. IVES (Burl)
18. JULIA (Raul)
19. KEATON (Michael)
20. LYNDE (Paul)
21. MARTIN (Steve)
22. MORANIS (Rick)
23. NELSON (Craig T.)
24. NIVEN (David)
25. NOLTE (Nick)
26. PACINO (Al)
27. PARKER (Fess)
28. PECK (Gregory)
29. PLUMMER (Christopher)
30. POWELL (William)
31. RYAN (Robert)
32. SCHEIDER (Roy)
33. SCOTT (George C.)
34. SHEEN (Martin)
35. STONE (Lewis)
36. TRACY (Spencer)
37. WEBB (Clifton)
38. WINFIELD (Paul)

```
M L T D L E I F N I W L M Y
S Y Y S I N A R O M V T R N
P T B N L A J Y L L R E J E
O N O S D K E A T O N U S L
W A L N O E Y N E N L C S S
E M O P E C K C O I O X L O
L F L G Q E R C A T L R E N
L F D R A E H R T R P J I I
A O L A N Z R S E A T V N C
V H A N I E B E R M E L A A
U N Y T V L B K P N M N D P
D R A O L L E I A O D U R T
B K L A F R W Y R Y O T L M
L G R S C H E I D E R C M P
```

Solution is on page 379; films, page 397.

MATH FUN

Here's a puzzle where you first complete each of the simple arithmetic problems in order, from left to right. Then write the answer in the space provided and search for that word in the diagram. We've done number 11 to show you what we mean. Warning: If you're looking for six, be careful not to circle part of sixty of sixteen! Answers may be repeated.

1. $15 \times 5 + 20 =$ _____

2. $144 \div 18 \times 2 =$ _____

3. $22 \times 6 \div 44 =$ _____

4. $48 + 33 - 15 =$ _____

5. $13 \times 15 \div 39 =$ _____

6. $8 \times 17 - 71 =$ _____

7. $24 \times 4 \div 8 =$ _____

8. $43 + 19 - 56 =$ _____

9. $2 \times 2 \times 10 =$ _____

10. $36 - 15 + 8 =$ _____

11. $45 \times 30 \div 90 =$ **FIFTEEN**

12. $9 \times 18 \div 54 =$ _____

13. $61 - 13 - 39 =$ _____

14. $11 + 21 - 28 =$ _____

15. $8 \times 36 \div 32 =$ _____

16. $52 - 4 + 12 =$ _____

17. $21 \times 8 \div 2 =$ _____

18. $27 + 19 - 39 =$ _____

19. $195 \div 5 - 34 =$ _____

20. $134 \times 3 \div 6 =$ _____

21. $16 + 52 - 48 =$ _____

22. $200 \div 25 \div 4 =$ _____

23. $54 - 19 - 29 =$ _____

24. $28 \times 4 \div 8 =$ _____

25. $16 \times 8 - 38 =$ _____

26. $11 + 56 - 48 =$ _____

27. $4 \times 120 \div 6 =$ _____

28. $92 - 36 - 52 =$ _____

29. $34 \times 6 \div 12 =$ _____

30. $13 + 13 + 65 =$ _____

31. $56 \times 4 \div 16 =$ _____

32. $44 \times 14 \div 88 =$ _____

33. $7 \times 8 + 13 =$ _____

34. $25 - 11 - 12 =$ _____

```
E V I F L A N D S S I T I S
F T E N O Y T E N I N E I E
T O W E R U V E E X O X A E
O E R E A E R C A T T E V N
N F E T N I N E T Y F I V E
E V O R Y T W O S S F I L E
E V O U H O Y I E E O E F T
T L I O R T X N I V N W W E
R U O F Y T H G I E L E T N
U S A T Y O H R E N N E O I
O N I N E T Y T E T E E W N
F R I X Y O X O Y E A W I T
R N L I T I I I R E V N A V
E M O S S Y S L S N E V E S
```

Solution is on page 379; list, page 397.

RECIPE: MONTEREY ZUCCHINI

If you're planning a luncheon or a light supper, this protein-filled casserole can be your menu's main feature. At the bottom of the page you'll find the recipe for Monterey Zucchini. In the list below, and hidden in the diagram on the next page are terms taken from the recipe.

APPROXIMATELY
BAKE
BEAT
BOWL
BUTTER
CASSEROLE DISH
CHEESE
CHOPPED
DICE
EGG MIXTURE
EGGS
GARLIC SALT

GRATE
MELT
MINUTES
ONION
OPTIONAL
OVER THE TOP
PEEL
PEPPER
PINCH
PLACE
POUR
SEASONINGS

SERVINGS
SET ASIDE
SKILLET
STEAM
STIR
TABLESPOONS
TO TASTE
UNTIL TENDER
WARM
WELL BLENDED

MONTEREY ZUCCHINI

2 tablespoons butter
¼ cup onion, chopped
1 lb. zucchini
4 large eggs

pinch of onion salt
   (optional)
pinch of garlic salt
pepper, to taste
2 cups Monterey Jack cheese

Grate the cheese. Set aside. Melt the butter in a small skillet, add the onions, and fry. While the onions are frying, peel and dice the zucchini; then steam for approximately 5 minutes or until tender. In a medium-sized bowl, beat the eggs. Add the seasonings and cheese. Stir just until well blended. Place zucchini and onions in a casserole dish, pour the egg mixture over the top, and bake at 350°F for approximately 20 minutes, or until the egg mixture is set. Serve warm. Makes 4–6 servings.

```
Y L E T A M I X O R P P A C L
D E D N E L B L L E W Q J A A
E T A B L E S P O O N S R S N
P A Q S B P I N C H K U G S O
P R J C E O O S T I R N E E I
O G B P H T T U L V I T G R T
H Q P E X E A L R N U I G O P
C E C J A H E S O N B L M L O
R I M M P T Q S I A A T I E N
D W R L L R A M E D K E X D I
R L A Q R E T T U B E N T I O
V C W J S V G L B Z P D U S N
E T S A T O T G E O Q E R H L
I S G N I V R E S M W R E Q J
J Q R G A R L I C S A L T L G
```

Solution is on page 379.

The popular ice cream sundae first came into being in 1904 as a reaction to a legal ordinance, then in effect in several American towns. The puzzle below describes its invention.

The mixture of soda and ice cream became a popular drugstore confection in nineteenth-century America. Many locales did not allow the sale of soda water on Sunday. To get around this law, shop owners offered a "Sunday soda"—ice cream topped with fruit, nuts, and syrup. The name was clipped to "sundae," and soon patrons were asking for this treat seven days a week.

```
E M A C E B I C E C R E A M
I D E P P O T I U R F D Y C
N T E G O T D D N U O R A X
N H L N S P R S U S D S D T
I E A S Y R U P T H E I N R
N M W N A N G L S L Y D U E
E I E A D O S Y A D N U S A
T X R A T S T C N R A J S T
E T E N H E O D D Q M A R Y
E U A D E L R O E F W M E R
N R S I A L E O N P X E N U
T E K C R E A M N C P R W T
H O I E T D I S K O Y I O N
I F N O I T C E F N O C L E
S A G D E R E F F O M A L C
S I H T I W A O F S O D A S
S H O P A T R O N S E V E N
```

Solution is on page 379.

Here's another puzzle like the one on page 193. If you use your INTELLECT, you will SUCCEED in solving this puzzle. Then you can say HURRAH!

AIMING

AMBIGUOUS

ANTHILL

BELOW

CHAIR

CHARISMA

COURAGE

ETHEREAL

FASCIST

FRET

GARNISH

GEODE

HURRAH

HUSTLE

IMBUE

INDOOR

INTELLECT

KNOWN

LICORICE

MAGICAL

NATURAL

NEON

NEWER

PARAMEDIC

REMNANT

RESTRICTION

SHROUD

STERN

STRAW

SUCCEED

TRANSITION

TRUCE

TWIRL

UPROAR

USUAL

WHEREOF

WITHOUT

Solution is on page 380.

All the terms in the puzzle below are indoor occupations. You'll find them hidden diagonally, horizontally or vertically on all three sides of the cube-shaped diagram. One term may be entirely hidden on one face of the cube or it may bend onto a second, or a third. TEACHER has been circled as a starter.

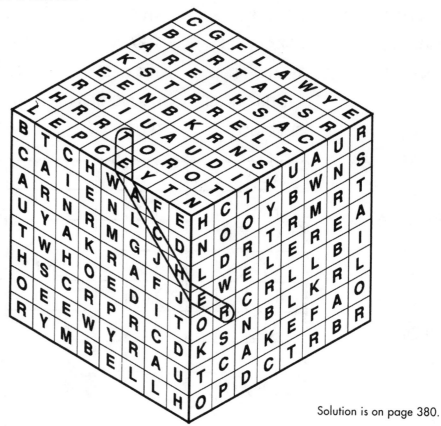

Solution is on page 380.

ACCOUNTANT	BELLHOP	DENTIST	NURSE
ACTUARY	BUTCHER	DOCTOR	PRINTER
AUDITOR	BUTLER	EDITOR	SECRETARY
AUTHOR	CASHIER	GROCER	TAILOR
BAKER	CHEF	JEWELER	~~TEACHER~~
BANKER	CLERK	LAWYER	TELLER
BARBER	DANCER	MAID	WAITER
BARTENDER		MECHANIC	

Solve this puzzle like the one on the opposite page. This time we've hidden 30 outdoor occupations. You don't need to be a PROSPECTOR to find the terms, or a TRAPPER to circle them.

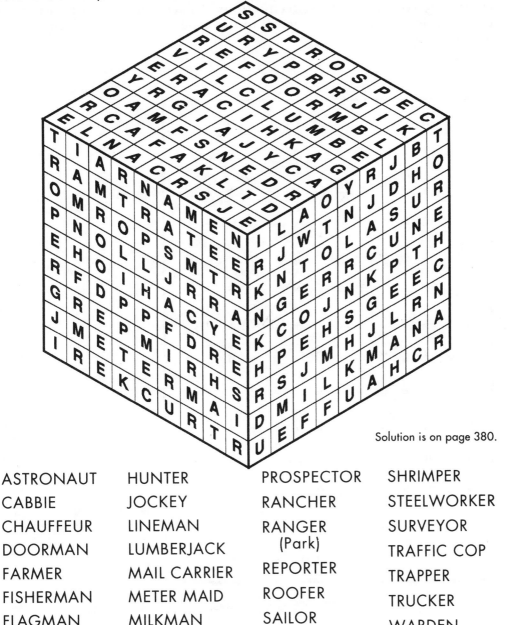

Solution is on page 380.

ASTRONAUT	HUNTER	PROSPECTOR	SHRIMPER
CABBIE	JOCKEY	RANCHER	STEELWORKER
CHAUFFEUR	LINEMAN	RANGER (Park)	SURVEYOR
DOORMAN	LUMBERJACK	REPORTER	TRAFFIC COP
FARMER	MAIL CARRIER	ROOFER	TRAPPER
FISHERMAN	METER MAID	SAILOR	TRUCKER
FLAGMAN	MILKMAN	SHEPHERD	WARDEN (Game)
GARDENER	PILOT		

We've hidden 30 arithmetic equations in this puzzle, forward, backward and diagonally, as usual. Each equation uses single digits only; that is, the numbers 0 to 9. As you read the diagram, you'll find some equations whose arithmetic is wrong, perhaps like 5 − 2 = 1. Don't circle those; circle only correct arithmetic equations. To start you off, we've circled the equation 7 − 2 = 5. Can you find the other 29? Our list of equations is on page 398.

```
5  =  8  −  8  +  3   6  =  3  −  9  +  8
5  +  1  −  4  =  3  +  1   7  +  3  2  =
=  1  4  =  2  =  5   0   6  =  −  +  1  3
1  =  1  =  2  7  5   =   4  −  6  3  −  +
4  7  1  +  9  −  =  6   2   =  9  =  =  5
6  −  5  =  1  1  4  6  8   −   =  6  =  4
3  8  +  =  6  =  +  3  +  0   7   2  9  −
1  =  4  0  3  9  1  9  =  1  +  8  2  6
7  −  7  =  0  +  −  =  +  6  2  1  +  2
9  +  5  2  3  1  +  6  7  0  =  4  −  4
−  −  4  −  =  0  =  +  =  1  =  5  +  +
8  +  0  2  =  5  1  3  −  2  =  9  −  2
=  =  9  −  9  =  0  9  −  7  =  2  8  =
3  −  5  =  8  6  +  2  =  4  −  1  =  6
```

Solution is on page 380; equations, page 398.

There are 49 terms in this puzzle, and they all have four or more letters. Words entirely within other words are not included. When you finish the puzzle, every letter will have been circled at least ONCE.

ADULATION
ADVISOR
APRONS
AQUA
ASPECT
AUTO
BIND
CAREER
CAVE
COINS
CRONY
EDIFY
ENGRAVE
FROG
GAPED
INVENT
LAZED
MANAGER
MAYHEM
MONTH
MOUSE
NATIVE
NUTRITION
ONCE
ONYX

ORES
PATH
PERFORMED
PICKET
PROPONENTS
PROSPER

QUAD
QUENCH
QUINCE
QUITE
QUOTED
RACKET

REBATE
REVISED
SAVOR
SCRAPS
SHAKE
SODA

SPECIAL
TREADS
TUNA
VIED
ZONE
ZOOM

```
P R O S P E R F O R M E D R
S R M D A U Q A D O S N E E
D E O E T S F U N H P G I E
A B O P H R X T I C A R V R
E A Z A O Y H O B N R A Q A
R T K G N N A R A E C V U C
T E N O Z S E M O U S E O K
C K R I N V E N T Q U I T E
E C N O I T I R T U N A E T
P I R S A V O R O S I V D A
S P E C I A L A Z E D I F Y
A D U L A T I O N A T I V E
```

Solution is on page 380.

In the puzzle field below, you'll find 36 words which will form new words or phrases when preceded or followed by the word "field." If you find yourself on a field OF HONOR, you know there'll be a duel starting soon. Whereas if you're walking in a cornfield, you are surrounded by countless stalks of CORN.

AGENT
ARTILLERY
CORN
DAY

EVENT
FARE
GLASS
GRADE

GOAL
HAND
HOCKEY
HOSPITAL
HOUSE
LENS
MAGNET
MARSHAL
MOUSE
OFFICE
OFFICER
OF HONOR
OF VIEW
OF VISION
PEA
POPPY
REPRESENTATIVE
SNOW
SOLDIER
SPANIEL
SPARROW
STONE
STOP
THEORY
TRAIL
TRIP
WINDING
WORK

```
L E M O H P T H E O R Y N K
A S D A Y O F F I C E R U R
T U N P R Y N O I S I V F O
I O P E E S S E U G D F F W
P M P K L Y H O R H L H F L
S A C T L G P A S G O A L O
O O C G I T G P L N S U S N
H E N O T S N E O M R P S S
N O W N R D I R A P O A P E
H F E H A N D G T T G A I T
E V I T A T N E S E R P E R
E I A P L E I T N R A A T I
N E S A T A W T O A D R I P
P W R E S N O W E F E L T L
```

Solution is on page 380.

Using the "E" in the word QUININE, the first word in our list, try to find the second puzzle word which begins where the first word ends. Each word thereafter will be formed in the same way. Sharpen your skills because there are more Tail Tags coming up!

QUININE ___(7)   _____(4)   _____(4)
_____(5)   _____(5)   _____(6)
_____(5)   _____(5)   _____(5)
_____(5)   _____(5)   _____(4)
                                   _____(4)
                                   _____(6)

```
Q U I N I N E Z Q D R O A N
S H R U B R M L U E G D H O
G B D O R D Z L D I A A J B
G Z W O Q B L R Z R H L Q L
E L R A D I O J N T C A X E
E S I R P R U S Z Y H S V Z
Q Z U M Q M D H Z Q T B W R
U W O R B H E J S U D O X E
A A Q E R Z R O B O T W R M
T T L H J M O E L N Z A A U
I E R T E N D O A Q W N N L
O R S A E R O I M E N O Z G
N A R R O W L L B E Z Q R Y
L A E U Q S D M R E L I E F
```

Solution is on page 380; list, page 398.

_____(6)
_____(5)
_____(5)
_____(6)
_____(4)
_____(4)
_____(6)
_____(5)
_____(5)
_____(8)
_____(8)
_____(6)
_____(4)
_____(4)
_____(6)
_____(6)
_____(6)
_____(6)
_____(4)
_____(4)
_____(5)
_____(4)
_____(4)
_____(4)
_____(5)

Do you have a time capsule buried in your backyard? In 6939 A.D. the 1939 New York World's Fair time capsule will be opened. It will have been buried for 50 centuries.

40357	96501	98350
40510	96735	98715
41071	97075	99075
41335	97573	99750
42073		
42877		
43035		
43210		
63012		
63730		
64703		
64750		
65303		
65717		
66012		
66023		
82033		
82567		
84030		
84102		
86175		
86232		
88010		
88301		

```
0 3 7 0 4 1 5 3 0 3 4 7 1 2
2 5 5 0 1 0 7 0 7 3 0 5 0 5
1 0 3 8 8 5 5 5 1 0 3 3 2 3
3 5 2 8 3 6 7 3 2 5 2 1 5 7
7 1 0 2 9 9 2 1 7 0 7 4 0 6
9 9 0 7 5 5 0 1 6 0 1 1 5 9
5 7 0 3 1 1 1 6 9 8 2 0 3 3
0 7 2 0 2 7 0 0 6 1 2 7 8 3
5 8 2 3 5 8 3 5 4 0 5 1 0 8
7 1 4 7 2 9 0 5 7 2 2 3 2 9
1 5 1 1 7 6 4 7 0 4 1 5 1 9
7 7 0 5 0 0 8 3 3 5 6 5 7 7
5 6 3 0 1 2 2 7 3 7 7 0 0 5
6 0 2 3 4 1 3 3 5 6 3 7 3 0
```

Solution is on page 380.

Here's another of our FEATURED Tanglewords puzzles. If you are FOND of Tanglewords, you'll be happy to know there are more on pages 222, 223 and 240. See page 193 for solving directions.

ALGAE	CAPTION	EDIT	HEAVILY
ASTRINGENT	CHINTZ	ELECTION	HOLD
BASIL	CRADLE	FANG	INTOLERANT
BOUNTIFUL	DIVERT	FEATURED	LAUREL
BUOYED	DOUBLOON	FOND	LOANER
			LOLLIPOP
			MASS
			MILITANT
			NEIGHBOR
			NONSTOP
			OILY
			OPERAND
			ORBITAL
			PUBLIC
			PUFFY
			RESISTANCE
			ROTOR
			SHOVE
			STUDIO
			TEACUP
			VEHEMENT
			WALNUT
			WOOLEN

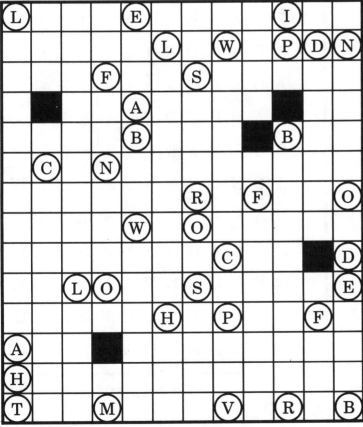

Solution is on page 380.

This puzzle contains 22 eight-letter terms, each with a number following it in parentheses. Each word will form a box, reading either clockwise or counterclockwise. FOREHEAD has already been outlined to start you off. As you find each term in the diagram, enter the letter in the middle of each box on the corresponding dash below the diagram. "O" has already been entered. When you have finished, the letters on the dashes will spell out a phrase relevant to the puzzle.

ACCOLADE (14)

AMBIENCE (17)

ANTELOPE (16)

BACHELOR (8)

BEHAVIOR (4)

CARELESS (11)

CAVALIER (5)

CHARISMA (1)

COSMETIC (13)

DEADBEAT (19)

ELEPHANT (10)

EXCAVATE (6)

FLAMBEAU (2)

~~FOREHEAD~~ (3)

HERMETIC (12)

IDEALISM (20)

ROOMMATE (15)

SPORADIC (22)

STOWAWAY (21)

SYMMETRY (7)

TOMAHAWK (18)

WATCHMAN (9)

```
B D E G I W A W L B I D E A
P H A A M O L A O O R I O L
E I N H E T S Y M U E M S I
L E T A W K Y P M A T S O M
M A C G N O R T E N I C C O
S A H M A V I A D F P A Q L
I R A Q H U O E O O L E D A
R S S S E B R H E R E H T V
B A C N L Y X A E B A C U W
T N A R E D T U R M M E T I
E A E L A H A F L A B M A C
L O P S D B E T A L I R E H
C R E C D I E D V N E N C G
L A D I F K X C A C R H J E
```

Solution is on page 381.

```
                O
___ ___ ___ ___ ___ ___   ___ ___ ___   ___ ___
 1   2   3   4   5   6     7   8   9     10  11

___ ___ ___ ___ ___ ___ ___   ___ ___ ___ ___
12  13  14  15  16  17  18    19  20  21  22
```

To solve this puzzle, insert a vowel into each of the circles in the diagram. This letter should be one that will let you form as many 5- and 6-letter words as possible. If you have entered the correct letters in the circles, you should be able to find 42 words in total. We've inserted an "O" to start you off. Vowels may be used more than once.

A	E	I	O	U

YOUR WORD LIST

```
C H I L C F N Q U E H N D E
N A M E C O D E R X Z R Y N
K I P H H N N L K P A S T O
E D O C E D S C L O D G E N
O S R M E E Y I H R T L O I
E U T M O R S C Z T A T V R
D P M R E D N O W Z C H O A
L O E T S O H T A K L R T M
H R E H P E M E U H S O L F
I S H R T A O R W A C S Y A
K O C O T E R I R O E H L O
A N L S M E M O C E B R L N
A I E H L B N H D E G G O R
D A K N P G A C L Y B I F B
```

Solution is on page 381; list, page 398.

DOUBLE PLAY

You're not really seeing double! The mini-diagrams on the opposite page are identical. Below are two word lists. First find the 31 five-letter words in Diagram 1; then find the 33 four-letter words in Diagram 2. We've circled a word for you in each diagram; there's some intricate searching here, but solving fun is guaranteed.

Diagram 1

ACUTE	RICER
CANAL	SANER
CHOIR	SNEER
EATER	STINT
EXCEL	STOAT
FERRY	STOUT
GIANT	SWEAR
IRATE	TACIT
IRONY	TEACH
MEANT	TEASE
OCEAN	TEPEE
RAISE	THERE
RANGE	~~TRADE~~
REALM	TRAIT
REFER	YEAST
RESET	

Diagram 2

ACHY	IRON
ANTE	MEAN
CITE	NOSE
CUTE	RANG
~~DART~~	RATE
DENT	REAL
DIET	RICE
EACH	SANE
EASE	SCUD
EAST	SEAL
FACT	SLAT
FERN	TINT
HEED	TOUT
HERE	TREE
HOWL	VASE
HURT	WEAR
ICER	

1

```
B F C Y T D S L A T
V Y A H U T E A S E
N A E C O O I N D P
R R S A T I R A T E
E A T E S E R C R E
F G I A N T E O T T
E D N S E U X I N H
R E T A E C C A O Y
R E C I R A E W S B
Y H U R T M L A E R
```

2

```
B F C Y T D S L A T
V Y A H U T E A S E
N A E C O O I N D P
R R S A T I R A T E
E A T E S E R C R E
F G I A N T E O T T
E D N S E U X I N H
R E T A E C C A O Y
R E C I R A E W S B
Y H U R T M L A E R
```

Solution is on page 381.

QUOTE ENDINGS ━━━━━━━━━━━━━━━━━━━━━

Below are 40 well-known quotes, each of which is missing the last word. Your job is to write this word on the dash provided and then circle it in the diagram. The words will be in alphabetical order when your word list is completed. The first word has been entered for you, and it has been circled in the diagram.

1. If at first you don't succeed, try, try ___AGAIN___
2. He who laughs last, laughs _____
3. A watched pot never _____
4. Too many cooks spoil the _____
5. A bird in the hand is worth two in the _____
6. A new broom sweeps _____
7. Uneasy lies the head that wears the _____
8. An ounce of prevention is worth a pound of _____
9. To err is human; to forgive _____
10. Well begun is half _____
11. Pride goeth before a _____
12. Leap out of the frying pan into the _____
13. Forgive and _____
14. All that glitters is not _____
15. Tall oaks from little acorns _____
16. Don't count your chickens before they're _____
17. The laborer is worthy of his _____
18. There's no place like _____
19. Look before you _____
20. Every cloud has a silver _____
21. Time and tide wait for no _____
22. Least said, soonest _____
23. No use crying over spilt _____
24. Better late than _____
25. A stitch in time saves _____
26. Empty barrels make the most _____
27. Opportunity knocks but _____
28. When the cat's away, the mice will _____
29. It never rains but it _____
30. It is more blessed to give than to _____

31. Hitch your wagon to a _____
32. Don't change horses in mid- _____
33. Experience is the best _____
34. A penny for your _____
35. Never put off till tomorrow what you can do _____
36. Birds of feather flock _____
37. Haste makes _____
38. All's well that ends _____
39. The early bird catches the _____
40. A soft answer turneth away _____

```
H Y A L P A E L D S L I O B
G N I N I L R M S R U O P U
R E M O H E I N E N R A T S
D C V F N L H H W N E L Z H
O N A I K C T O A O D V N T
N O V R E E R H M T R E E O
E I B E G C D A O T C G D R
D E N O L L E W M U O H E B
L M T E F R G R R T G D E H
O A A S T X O E X E S H A D
G N J S A W R E H C A E T Y
K H T A R W N O I S E Q B S
T E G R O F A L L N I A G A
```

Solution is on page 381; list, page 398.

Scan the grid in all directions for 60 familiar five-letter words, arranged in pairs. Each word in a pair crosses its partner through the center letter, forming either a "+" or an "x" shape. One pair has been circled to start you off.

YOUR WORD LIST

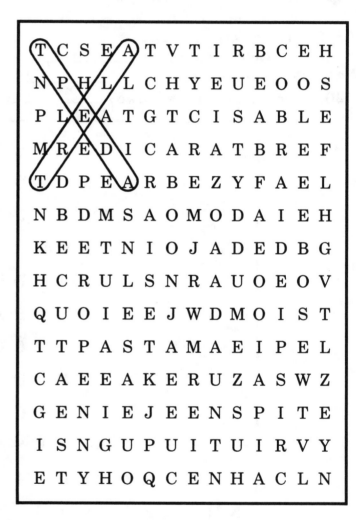

Solution is on page 381; list, page 398.

Here's another Full House for all ZEALOTS who QUEST for PLENTIFUL puzzling. Solve it as you did the one on page 207.

AVAIL
CEDAR
COMIC
DARK
EXCHANGE
EYER
FATE
FEET

FULL
GALE
GOGGLES
GRIT
HEAL
HERON
HUTS
ITCHY

KNIT
LASH
LOGO
METERS
MICE
MOTET
PAGE
PAPAYA

PILLOW
PIQUE
PLEASURE
PLENTIFUL
POKE
PREY
PROFESS
QUELL

QUEST
QUOTAS
RECALL
REMOTE
RENT
REUSE
REVEL
ROOT
SANG
SCHISM
SEES
SHREW
SORE
STRANGE
SURER
TASTED
TESTS
TOUGH
TRELLIS
TROOPS
WILLOW
WONDER
YELLS
YELP
YESTERDAY
ZEALOTS
ZESTY
ZITHER
ZUCCHINI

```
Y E L L S I L L E R T I N K
E H R E D N O W I L L O W W
S S C O M I C E D A R K O E
T E S T S H X M R E V E L R
E L T A I C G E H H S A L H
R G R Y H C R T O U G H I S
D G A A C U I E E Y E R P Y
A O N P S Z T R N T K O I T
Y G G A D E T S A T O U Q S
E O E P S S E F O R P M U E
L L E U Q U E S T O L A E Z
P L E N T I F U L L A C E R
```

Solution is on page 381.

YOU'RE COVERED

Better safe than sorry! Shop for the best RATES, check the company's solvency rating, and expect to hear many of the terms listed here when it's time to renew or purchase your next insurance POLICY. Can you find the 41 insurance terms hidden on the opposite page?

AGENT	EXCLUSIONS	OPTION
ANNUITY	FILE	PACKAGE
AUTOMOBILE	FIRE	PLAN
BENEFICIARY	FLOOD	POLICY
BENEFITS	GROUP	POLICY HOLDER
BOND	HEALTH	PREMIUM
CANCEL	HOMEOWNER'S	PROTECTION
CARRIER	HOSPITAL	RATES
CASH VALUE	INSURER	RENEWAL
CATASTROPHIC	LIFE	RIDER
CLAIM	LOSS	SUPPLEMENTAL
CLAUSE	MEDICAID	TERM
CONDITIONS	MEDICARE	TRAVEL
COVERAGE	MEDIGAP	

```
L B W N Y R A I C I F E N E B T L
A T M Q L C E N R L N M T E D E C
W S N O I T I D N O C S N N V Y N
E W S N O I S U L C X E U A M C O
N S Q F C N N Q O O F D R R R B I
E Y I R A L Y H P I H T L A E H T
R L W L S W S C T N Q Y S R T R C
E D P M H N E S I M M R C W R M E
L V O D V C T Y O L E I D I E T T
I A Y O A Y A L N N O I A D L V O
B D T W L M R T W B A P I L M O R
O M I N U F Q O A C E G A K C A P
M B U V E C E Y I S A T L A L N E
O D N O B M N D V P T D R V A B G
T C N Y O M E D I C A R E D U T A
U R A H V M R L T G I I O M S G R
A E Q N G R O U P E R D L P E C E
R L R L C G H V R P D E G N H N V
B M U I M E R P L M U R T R Q I O
C H L E F I L A T I P S O H B L C
```

Solution is on page 381.

WHILE you solve this Tanglewords, you can think AHEAD to the remaining Tanglewords in this book. Just a REMINDER—solving directions are on page 193.

ABSENTEE	CHAFE	ENTICE	HYPHEN
AHEAD	DEAL	FLOG	IDIOM
AJAR	DEBONAIR	FOURTH	INSURED
BAIT	DIABOLIC	GANGWAY	JUDGED
BOORISH	EFFICIENT	HENNA	JURY
CANOE	ELIGIBLE	HESITATE	KNOW
			LECITHIN
			MATURED
			MYRIAD
			NOMINEE
			OBSTINATE
			OPERA
			PAINT
			PARENT
			REMINDER
			REMOTE
			SEVENTH
			SPONGE
			STOLEN
			TAXI
			THATCHED
			THOROUGH
			TOUCAN
			WHILE
			WHOLE

Solution is on page 381.

Hello there, solvers! Tanglewords are USER-friendly. See page 193 for solving directions.

APERITIF

ATONE

BASTION

CANOE

CHROME

CLOT

DOMINATED

DRAFT

ENTITLE

ETUDE

EWER

FEATHER

FOREST

GARAGE

HALTER

HOMONYM

INTRICATE

JABOT

LACRIMAL

LITIGATION

METEORITE

MINT

MORNING

NEST

NUDGE

OILED

OMNIPOTENT

OPTION

PORK

PROMENADE

REUNION

ROTATION

SHIPMENT

STREWN

TALISMAN

TOPIC

USER

VOGUE

VOLUTE

WATCH

Solution is on page 381.

HIDDEN MEANINGS

This is a two-part puzzle. In Diagram 1 below, we've hidden 51 prefixes. Your job is to find them all, then search Diagram 2 on the opposite page for the words that define those prefixes. After you've found all the terms in both puzzle diagrams, see if you can match each prefix to its meaning. In the example shown, the prefix CRYPTO means HIDDEN, and both terms are circled in their respective diagrams.

1. ANTERO
2. ASTRO
3. CENTRI
4. ~~CRYPTO~~
5. CYANO
6. DENDRO
7. DENTI
8. DERMO
9. DEXTRO
10. DODECA
11. HELICO
12. HETERO
13. HOMEO
14. HYALO
15. HYDRO
16. LACTO
17. LEPTO
18. LEVO
19. LIGNO
20. LUNI
21. MYTHO
22. NEPHO
23. NEPHR
24. NOCTI
25. OBTUSI
26. ORTHO
27. OSTEO
28. PHILO
29. PHYSIO
30. PILI
31. PLATY
32. PLURI
33. POLY
34. PRETER
35. PSEUDO
36. PYRO
37. RETRO
38. RHIZO
39. SACRO
40. SAURO
41. SCHIZO
42. SCLERO
43. SEMI
44. SOMATO
45. SPORO
46. STENO
47. TAUTO
48. TETRA
49. TRANS
50. XANTHO
51. ZYGO

1

```
N O E T S O T U A T O R O P S
O Z I O N G I L A S A C R O A
C I Q A C E D O D E N D R O U
T H Y O R Y P L U R I A T O R
I C O R E T E H U Q I C R U O
P S E U D O O O R N A Y O T R
L H U G I T L C N L I L I P E
A Y O T R A A E V E O O S A L
T D H P B M Y N R O T P Y R C
Y R T R L O H T N S P S H T S
I O N E R S Z R E A E H P E O
T J A T E L Y I P S L M I T E
N X X E T E G O H T Y M I L M
E E V R R V O L O R E T N A O
D E R M O O H T R O C I L E H
```

A. ACROSS
B. BEHIND
C. BEYOND
D. BLUE
E. BLUNT
F. BODY
G. BONE
H. BROAD
I. CENTRAL
J. CLOUD
K. FALSE
L. FIRE
M. FOUR
N. FRONT
O. GLASS
P. HAIR
Q. HALF
R. HARD
S. ~~HIDDEN~~
T. HOLY
U. KIDNEY
V. LEFT
W. LITTLE
X. LIZARD
Y. LOVING
Z. MILK
a. MOON
b. MUCH
c. MYTH
d. NATURE
e. NIGHT
f. OTHER
g. PAIR
h. RIGHT

i. ROOT
j. SAME
k. SEED
l. SEVERAL
m. SIMILAR
n. SKIN

o. SLENDER
p. SPIRAL
q. SPLIT
r. STAR
s. STRAIGHT
t. TOOTH

u. TREE
v. TWELVE
w. WATER
x. WOOD
y. YELLOW

2

```
K L I M O R C R A L I M I S J
N B O D Y E A S Y B F L A H W
L E K R N T S T E J K L C R A
I L D T S A H Y N A T U R E T
T O R D L G O G D Y M H O D E
T A Y G I N F G I S L T S N R
L N C N D H I N K A T O S E S
E Q O L T B R I O M R O H L E
F O U R O W E V L E W T I S V
W D E N F U L O D O O W S H E
O E E A L I D L N H T P A I R
L E L E Z R A O A N I H G H A
L S F A A P O I U R L O G E L
E T R H O M R L A I P S K I N
Y D N I H E B L U E S T O O R
```

Both solutions are on page 382; matchups, page 398.

Some brides-to-be get engaged at an early age, but none can beat this record for youthful engagement, which was set in 1518. When you have circled all the terms, the uncircled letters will spell out a comment about love.

```
L F W D A U P H I N O F O E
T A R N E C N A R F R V E N
S W B A M A K E H F S I T G
H F O E N O E E N O W D N A
O E R W T C N E L E D N M G
A G H A O R E T H G U A D E
N R T S Y W O T O A R L P M
A U R V T S O T N Y D G R E
L H I E A T M O H N D N I N
L I B A E N G A G E M E N T
I S T L Y N O S L T D A C N
A T A S I B G S O L T F E P
N O E K O N N U M T E V S O
C R A T I N Y R H A I S S P
E Y L R E D O E O G R A T I
I S I C N A R F Z W W Y Z Y
```

Solution is on page 382.

One of history's smallest engagement rings was worn by Princess Mary, daughter of Henry VIII. To assure an alliance between England and France, Mary was betrothed at birth to the dauphin of France, son of King Francis I, and she was given a tiny engagement ring at the age of two.

Traditionally, a young couple goes on a honeymoon after the wedding, and at one time, this honeymoon period was a necessary precaution to secure the marriage, as explained below. When you have circled all the terms, the uncircled letters will spell out a comment about honeymoons.

The concept of a honeymoon being a period of seclusion for a newlywed couple had its origin in ancient times, when a young man often acquired his bride by abducting her from a neighboring tribe, and then took her into hiding until the girl's family gave up searching for them.

```
S E A R C H I N G A G H O N B E
A M O R F Y F M I N A O O R N I
S C T H N E O S I N Y L I M A F
K H Q O R O D R D T I D R E H T
F O P U E C O U P L E G R I N O
O T O D I B I M A B Y B I E E G
T R T T H R R N Y W O E I R E N
P I A G N I E B N E U C T H O I
E B I E B H P D G G N I D I H T
C E R I W M H E R A G O S D A C
N E W L Y W E D O L V U H S T U
O N O T O M F H F A L E T A S D
C S E T I O A T T C A I U N I B
E D N H R M T N E R D H T P H A
H I E A T B E S N A O U R N N T
T H E G I R L S H T O F A S U T
```

Solution is on page 382.

The words in the Bingo card make up your word list. Find as many words as you can in the diagram, crossing them off the Bingo card as you go. When you have found all the words you can find, use the uncircled letters to form the single five-letter word, which, when crossed off the Bingo card, will give you BINGO, which is five words in a row, across, down or diagonally. Hint: There will be 8 letters remaining after you find the Bingo word. ANVIL has been circled to start you off.

```
B  H  C  T  A  H  E  T  M
C  Y  O  S  H  C  U  O  C
L  I  V  N  A  N  H  R  D
R  E  A  C  H  A  R  E  M
E  O  H  H  O  R  S  E  A
G  E  M  A  L  N  R  D  D
A  M  O  R  A  N  R  Y  A
L  O  U  M  A  I  N  A  M
```

Bingo Word: _____ _____ _____ _____ _____

B	I	N	G	O
MADAM	HAREM	ALARM	CACHE	RANCH
MANIA	HASTE	ALOHA	CEDAR	REACH
MANSE	HATCH	~~ANVIL~~	CHARM	REBEL
MODEL	HAVOC	ARMOR	COUCH	REEDY
MYRRH	HORSE	AROMA	CRUST	REGAL

Solution is on page 382.

Keep your nose to the grindstone and solve this puzzle filled with 22 idioms. Instead of a straight line, each term will bend at an angle. We've outlined GET A MOVE ON to show you how.

BLAZE A TRAIL

CALL THE SHOTS

CARRY THE DAY

DIG IN

DO YOUR OWN
THING

FILL THE BILL

GET A MOVE
ON

GO AT

GO FOR

HOP TO IT

JUMP AT

LOOK ALIVE

LUCK OUT

MAKE A GO OF

MAKE YOUR
MARK

PACK A PUNCH

PEG AWAY

REV UP

SHOW OFF

STAY ON YOUR
TOES

TAKE A CHANCE

WHEEL AND
DEAL

```
G T R K G O A L A E D D N A L
N E I O F O G T E P L O N T E
I E B O Y T H E D A Y U S U E
H C L T R L A K O O L N C O H
T A A P R I L L I B E H K K W
N L Z O A V O T A P M T E A S
W L E H C E N I G E U L A H M
O T A T R A I L T I J L G C O
R H E S H O T S T A D I O N H
U M A K E Y O U M T P F O U S
O Y O D E G R O R E T A F P T
Y A W A G M V I N G D A C A A
P U V E A E O W O F F S K K Y
T E P R O H E C N A H C A E O
R N K N S E S E O T R U O Y N
```

Solution is on page 382.

Believe it or not, the sand that feels so soft underneath your feet at the beach is used to make GLASS—a hard, sharp substance which can cut you. The word "sand" can be used before the words listed below to form new words or phrases. Can you find them all?

BAG
BANK
BAR
BLAST

BLASTER
BLIND
BLUE STEM
BOX

BURR
CRACK
DAB
DOLLAR

DUNE
EEL
FISH
FLEA
FLY
FLY FEVER
GLASS
GROUSE
HILL CRANE
HOG
HOPPER
LANCE
LILY
LIZARD
LOT
MAN
MYRTLE
PAINTING
PAPER
PIPER
STONE
STORM
TABLE
TRAP
VERBENA
WASP
WORM
WORT
YACHT

```
R L G O D A B P A D N I L B
E N O T S U I L D P N T A Y
T N H X Z P N X U N A R E T
S R A N E B R E V E F Y L F
A E T R U E S U R I S Z F W
L P J R C T L E S U X T H O
B A G P O L P H Z G B V E R
W P J R A P L Y N G X U A M
N A M Z O R L I L Y E L R Y
E K S H X U T A H W L X V R
X C E P E N S H X O B F B T
B A N K I S A E D R A Z I L
R R A A Z I L B A T T L O E
A C P L L A B Y A C H T A X
```

Solution is on page 382.

According to Ralph Waldo Emerson, "Genius has no taste for weaving sand." However, Emerson may not have considered the genius of children of all ages who find pleasure in the building of a simple sand CASTLE. Search the CASTLE below for the word CASTLE, hidden 26 times. After you've finished, read the uncircled letters to learn a comment about a favorite summertime activity.

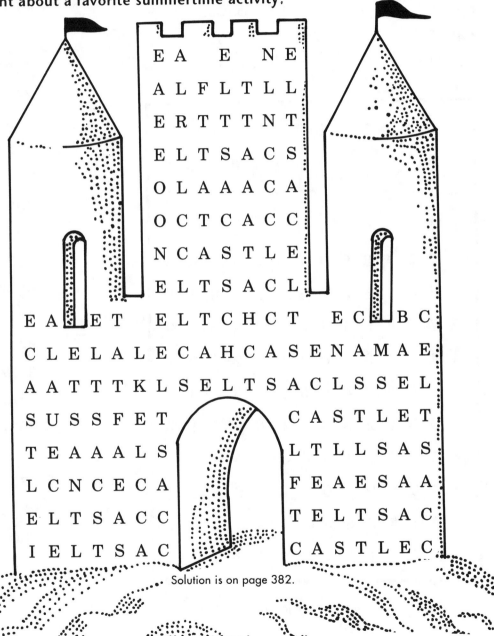

```
            E A   E   N E
            A L F L T L L
            E R T T T N T
            E L T S A C S
            O L A A A C A
            O C T C A C C
            N C A S T L E
            E L T S A C L
E A  E T  E L T C H C T   E C   B C
C L E L A L E C A H C A S E N A M A E
A A T T T K L S E L T S A C L S S E L
S U S S F E T       C A S T L E T
T E A A A L S       L T L L S A S
L C N C E C A       F E A E S A A
E L T S A C C       T E L T S A C
I E L T S A C       C A S T L E C
```

Solution is on page 382.

If you go to a baseball game, and are lucky enough to catch a foul ball, you'll find that there are 108 stitches on a regulation baseball.

63123	65010	71035
63430	65032	71345
64020	66301	73151
64541	66445	73234
		75031
		75415
		77450
		77501
		80345
		80510
		82012
		82345
		84134
		84501
		86345
		86441
		96345
		96430
		97235
		97450
		98044
		98450
		99012
		99305

```
7 5 4 1 5 4 1 0 5 7 7 4 4 3
1 5 3 0 3 3 5 5 4 1 3 2 0 5
4 1 0 2 1 0 1 0 3 2 4 0 1 0
5 4 1 2 0 8 5 2 3 1 0 4 1 5
4 3 5 4 3 6 9 7 0 3 4 5 6 4
6 9 2 1 6 3 2 1 4 3 0 9 5 8
2 7 3 4 6 4 4 3 3 8 2 9 1 9
4 4 4 5 0 5 6 4 5 0 2 3 0 2
1 5 8 0 3 4 5 5 1 1 3 0 3 9
0 0 5 2 2 3 5 2 5 0 0 5 1 7
3 1 3 1 3 1 3 4 1 4 5 5 7 2
4 4 0 8 9 4 0 0 3 2 6 4 2 3
6 9 1 3 5 8 5 0 7 1 5 4 8 5
9 2 7 4 1 6 4 0 2 0 3 5 0 1
```

Solution is on page 382.

This puzzle is solved in two parts. First, guess 30 words to complete the chart below. Beginning with each letter in the chart, there is an appropriate type of home, magazine, computer term, detective and musical instrument. Using the same words you used to complete the chart, begin the second part of this puzzle by finding them all in the diagram. If you can't find the word that you're looking for, you may have to guess another word that fits the chart. We've entered CORNET in the chart and circled it in the diagram for you. The completed chart is on page 398.

	C	M	T	B	P	D
Homes						
Magazines						
Computer term						
Detective						
Instrument	CORNET					

```
A  H  C  H  B  Y  T  E  D  I  S  R  E  T
B  U  H  C  A  L  J  R  E  N  E  E  R  A
A  M  A  R  G  O  R  P  A  V  B  L  T  B
C  H  T  E  C  L  O  R  O  I  M  P  R  U
L  M  E  H  T  P  I  C (C) O  L  O  S  T
A  D  A  T  A  O  S  H (O) P  W  E  R  H
N  N  U  N  M  I  T  O (R) N  E  P  R  W
I  D  R  O  D  R  U  M (N) O  E  L  O  B
M  A  N  S  I  O  N  C (E) T  C  L  P  A
R  W  R  A  S  T  L  H (T) R  A  C  Y  N
E  M  E  M  O  R  Y  I  N  G  L  H  T  J
T  P  E  R  M  Y  C  P  N  E  A  I  H  O
M  A  D  E  D  O  H  U  D  U  P  L  E  X
T  S  E  D  I  R  B  T  I  M  E  D  Y  E
```

Solution is on page 382; chart, page 398.

RECIPE: BARBECUE SAUCE

Who could go through summer without hosting or attending a backyard barbecue? And who could think of cooking on the grill without the tasty SAUCE that adds flavor to barbecued meats and veggies? Here's a recipe for just such an occasion. Solve the puzzle, then give it a try.

ADD	GARLIC	PLACE
BARBECUE	GRILLED	RED
BASTE	GROUND	REMAINING
BOIL	HEAT	
BROWN SUGAR	HOT	SAUCE
BUTTER	HOUR	SAUCEPAN
CATSUP	INGREDIENTS	STIRRING
CUPS	LARGE	TEASPOON
DRIED	LOW	
FINELY	MEAT	TENDER
FLAKES	MIX	TO TASTE
FREQUENTLY	NEVER	VINEGAR
FRESHLY	ONION	WATER

BARBECUE SAUCE

1 cup cider vinegar
½ cup water
4 tablespoons butter
2 teaspoons minced garlic
1 cup finely chopped onion
salt & freshly ground pepper
   to taste

2 cups catsup
2 tablespoons brown sugar
1½ tablespoons chili
   powder
½ teaspoon dried hot
   red pepper flakes

Heat butter in a large saucepan. Add garlic and onions. Cook, stirring, until onions are tender. Add remaining ingredients and mix well. Place over low heat for one hour, stirring frequently. Never let it boil. Baste meat with warm sauce as it is grilled.

```
W F C G N I N I A M E R M T
S L I S A U C E P A N R O W
B T R N O D L J V L L T R M
R N I N E E X I M E A T E D
O O I R F L A K E S R C E F
W O L E R L Y Q T G U I E R
N P I D V I N E G A R J L E
S S O N H R N F S D X A R Q
U A B E Q G D G R L E E L U
G E A T A N D J R E T A W E
A T H R U D N C A T S U P N
R L L O A O S P U C A H L T
L I R E U C E B R A B O L L
C G I N G R E D I E N T S Y
```

Solution is on page 383.

Solve this puzzle like the one on page 213. There are 50 five-letter terms hidden below. Use these consonants:

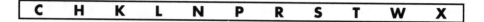

| C | H | K | L | N | P | R | S | T | W | X |

YOUR WORD LIST

```
T  S  E  K  P  E  H  V  N  B  F  M  R  U
S  ◯  I  N  E  M  R  I  I  E  U  W  E  M
C  A  E  W  O  I  C  H  A  ◯  M  L  I  E
S  N  I  N  T  ◯  I  C  K  E  T  A  ◯  S
P  K  I  B  E  C  P  Y  J  T  V  A  S  Y
I  H  N  E  L  R  L  T  W  Y  H  K  I  R
◯  O  P  E  D  A  A  I  L  S  V  E  R  R
E  E  E  S  R  U  ◯  I  A  R  G  E  F  A
I  E  G  A  C  E  E  K  T  E  L  B  A  ◯
R  E  ◯  D  I  R  U  E  E  A  H  T  S  A
C  L  E  A  E  A  T  A  ◯  E  D  U  W  P
Y  F  E  I  H  ◯  R  I  M  P  R  O  K  E
I  M  T  W  O  S  O  D  E  C  A  ◯  E  R
B  O  S  Q  U  M  I  H  T  Y  O  S  S  W
```

Solution is on page 383; list, page 399.

As on page 194, this puzzle can be solved by using the last letter of the given word as the first letter of the next. You will have successfully completed the puzzle if you continue in this manner. Remember, all words will connect toe-to-head.

HATCH _____(5) _____(4) _____(4)
_____(5) _____(4) _____(5)
_____(4) _____(6) _____(4)
_____(6) _____(4) _____(4)
_____(7)
_____(6)
_____(4)
_____(4)
_____(4)
_____(6)
_____(5)
_____(4)
_____(7)
_____(5)
_____(5)
_____(7)
_____(7)
_____(4)
_____(4)
_____(4)
_____(5)
_____(6)
_____(4)
_____(5)
_____(5)
_____(6)
_____(5)
_____(4)
_____(6)
_____(4)
_____(5)

```
H R M H D R I E S N I A R G
G A I N E D M Z K E V A E A
A H T J V I S G I A O Z P T
R R Q C A V K E P R I Z E S
D E S O H U I C O N Z S N N
R S P R S L E Y A G U H T W
M L W Z T G D U M B Q L R Z
D E S A R E N D G S G N I K
A G I R P S E I Z T R G Z C
M G H Q L P V V R O B A L E
P Q B A A L E I R R F L A N
R L U T B U O D Y M E A Q R
Y Q U R Z Z Z E Y Y G L E G
E Z A M Q H Q R E S C U E D
```

Solution is on page 383; list, page 399.

PHRASE PLAY

Welcome to Phrase Play. Each column below represents a portion of an old cliché or a familiar phrase. Column A gives the beginning, Column B, the middle, and Column C, the end of each phrase. Search for each entry in the diagram on the opposite page, then combine an entry from each column to make a common phrase. Our list of completed phrases is on page 399.

A	B	C
A CHIP	A DIM	ANALYSIS
A DIAMOND	A DULL	A PADDLE
A PRETTY	AND OUT	BANDWAGON
AS LUCK	A NEW	CANDLE TO
BRING	CAT OUT	HAVE IT
CANNOT	FINAL	KINDNESS
FOOD	FOR	LEAF
HIT THE	HOLD A	MOMENT
IN ONE EAR	HOME	MOON
IN THE	HUMAN	OATS
JUMP	IN A BLUE	OF FISH
LET THE	IN THE	OF THE BAG
NEVER	KETTLE	ROUGH
ONCE	NAIL ON	SHOULDER
RUB	ON THE	THE BACON
SOW YOUR	ON THE	THE HEAD
TAKE	THE WRONG	THE OTHER
THE MILK OF	WILD	THOUGHT
TURN OVER	WITHOUT	VIEW OF
UP THE CREEK	WOULD	WAY

```
N O O M Y W G T T U R N O V E R S
I F B R I A H N P K E L D D A P A
N A D L U O W T F I R T U O T A C
R E D L U O H S O N Y O F F I S H
T L V G N E Y L O D P O U N N L N
F I H E C H T W D N W I T G T U N
B T E R R T H L O E I H H J H C O
F A E V E H E O I S E M D C E K C
O E N A A E W V L S I S Y L A N A
K A P D L H R D C D B C H D G W B
L N M U W E O A E T A T I A N R E
I E U L B A N I I N U A T P I U H
M W J L A D G N N H M O T R R B T
E O K O L T E O O O F T H E B A G
H L M E N O T M N L M L E T T H E
T U T E T T E D E O I T S T I L K
F O M O N T H E E N D A V Y O W A
O S T A O T L E A C A A N D O U T
R G F I N A L E R E H T O E H T Y
```

Solution is on page 383; phrases, page 399.

If you've solved the other Tanglewords puzzles in this book, you should have no trouble entering the 39 words below into the diagram. We SALUTE you! Complete solving directions are on page 193.

ADRIFT

ALMOST

AMENABLE

BORED

CEDAR

CHIFFON

CLOD

DEBUTANTE

DECAL

DIMENSION

EERIE

EXPEDITION

FLEA

FREIGHT

GOURD

HAUL

HESITATED

ICING

INFANT

JULEP

LOCKER

MANATEE

MANSARD

NEGOTIATE

OBOE

OPERATED

PIANO

PIECEMEAL

POND

REDUNDANT

RICRAC

SALUTE

SERGEANT

SOCIAL

TAPIOCA

TEMPLET

TENET

UTENSIL

WEALTHIER

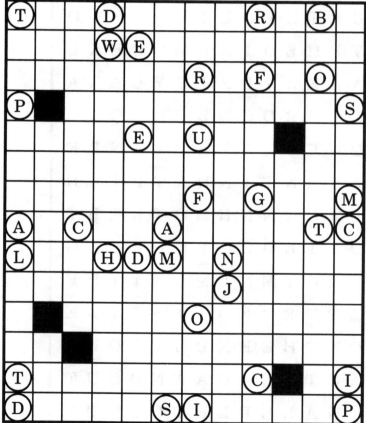

Solution is on page 383.

Each term below contains sets of numbers plus letters. With the help of the Roman numeral guide, change each number into letter combinations. For example, **A40E** becomes AXLE when 40 is changed into the Roman numeral XL. Then find AXLE in the diagram. Decipher each term below the same way.

M = 1000	D = 500	C = 100	L = 50	X = 10	V = 5	I = 1

A551B _____   SA55ER _____   S51TS _____

A51EN _____   SA55O _____   S54ER _____

A54E _____   S51D _____   SO55E _____

A11OM _____   S51GHT _____   VA55E _____

A11S _____   S51NG _____   WO55ES _____

A40E   AXLE

151NIC _____

151PS _____

DE54ER _____

DE55ED _____

501FFER _____

501G _____

501SSO55ES _____

504E _____

E51TE _____

E59IR _____

E55ER _____

E91SE _____

E11ST _____

FE51NE _____

F54VER _____

FO510 _____

GAS51T _____

HE59 _____

51E _____

51EN _____

51LY _____

54E51HOOD _____

54ER _____

54ERY _____

1009 _____

O54E _____

PO51TE _____

PRO59 _____

RE151NER _____

REVO55ER _____

SA51NE _____

SA54A _____

```
E  N  I  L  E  F  R  E  N  I  L  C  E  R
X  A  L  I  V  E  E  I  S  O  L  V  E  E
C  I  S  A  F  A  V  L  X  S  V  V  L  V
I  V  L  F  N  E  I  L  A  I  L  L  X  L
S  V  I  E  I  G  L  C  I  O  L  I  A  A
E  D  O  O  H  I  L  E  V  I  L  E  D  S
V  S  I  T  S  I  X  E  A  V  I  L  A  S
L  P  L  V  N  D  R  X  C  X  I  L  Y  G
O  I  X  I  E  E  I  E  L  B  I  R  A  P
S  L  C  I  V  O  R  G  V  N  E  S  O  R
S  C  I  I  M  E  V  N  E  V  L  L  I  O
I  E  L  V  E  R  R  I  I  I  I  I  L  L
D  E  V  L  E  D  L  L  T  T  T  L  O  I
D  E  W  O  L  V  E  S  E  R  E  Y  F  X
```

Solution is on page 383; list, page 399.

MATH FUN

Here's another puzzle that tests your math skills. To solve, first determine the answer to the first math problem, then take that answer to solve the second problem, and so on, until you have solved all 35. Then look for the answers in the puzzle diagram on the facing page. Your final answer should be SIXTY-ONE.

1. $49 \div 7 =$ _____

2. $+ 43 =$ _____

3. $\div 25 =$ _____

4. $+ 74 =$ _____

5. $- 57 =$ _____

6. $+ 31 =$ _____

7. $\div 25 =$ _____

8. $\times 8 =$ _____

9. $+ 74 =$ _____

10. $\div 18 =$ _____

11. $\times 16 =$ _____

12. $\div 20 =$ _____

13. $+ 33 =$ _____

14. $- 21 =$ _____

15. $+ 8 =$ _____

16. $\div 4 =$ _____

17. $+ 13 =$ _____

18. $+ 7 =$ _____

19. $- 17 =$ _____

20. $\times 11 =$ _____

21. $- 93 =$ _____

22. $+ 25 =$ _____

23. $- 26 =$ _____

24. $\times 3 =$ _____

25. $\times 4 =$ _____

26. $\div 20 =$ _____

27. $\times 4 =$ _____

28. $+ 8 =$ _____

29. $\times 3 =$ _____

30. $- 40 =$ _____

31. $\div 4 =$ _____

32. $\times 19 =$ _____

33. $- 93 =$ _____

34. $+ 7 =$ _____

35. $+ 52 =$ _____

```
N I N E T E E N E S T A N S
F I N E V E G I I H E R E E
A O N I X L G T I N A V V A
N R F E A H E R R A E N E E
I F I F T Y T W E N T Y S N
N R F Y W Y W N T W O O Y I
E E T M O T O Y T N E W T N
T W E N T Y S I X T Y R R Y
Y N E T T I A I R T U M I T
F A N X X S F X X O H H H E
I S I E V I F I F T Y R T N
V S N N V X S S A T E E M I
E O E E R A N I N E T E E N
R U O F Y T N E W T W E N T
```

Solution is on page 383; list, page 399.

"Homowo," the name of the month-long summer celebration that takes place annually in Ghana, means "hooting at hunger." The Ga people of Ghana feast on milled corn and fish in honor of their ancestors' legendary harvests, and chiefs sprinkle cornmeal and palm oil around houses while villagers drum, sing, and dance. For the origin of the festival, read below.

The Ga people of Ghana celebrate the Homowo festival for the entire month of August. Long ago they suffered from a severe famine. But when they had a bountiful harvest again they mocked and hooted at the hunger that had made them suffer.

```
F O R T H E O F A U G U S T
E R I T N E O G X C D A H H
D H T I G H A G O T H E Y A
N I M J K I L H U N G E R T
A A M O N T H O A A M R N A
F M A A C T R O Q R T E P B
S D O N D K H T N H V V Y O
U A J R A E E E E U E V U
F H P H F H W D M S H S S N
F Y X E T Y G Z U T G W A T
E E T T O X D F Q R N C B I
R H A U F P F H O M O W O F
E T A R B E L E C G L H I U
D L K J R B F E S T I V A L
```

Solution is on page 383.

When you want a break from the city, head on down to a country farm. There's no hustle or bustle, though you may be called upon to help with the daily CHORES. A farm visit can be a peaceful trip, and your days will be filled dealing with some of the things below.

ACRES
BALER
BARN
BUGS
CATTLE
CHICKENS
CHORES
CORN
CORRAL
CROPS
CULTIVATOR
DOG
EGGS
FARMER
FEED
FENCES
FOAL
FODDER
GARDEN
HAY
HEN
HORSE
HUSK
LAND
LOFT
MEADOW
MILK
MUD
PASTURE
PEN
PIG
PLOW
PUMP

RAKE
REAPER
ROAD
ROOSTER

SEED
SKIN
STOCK
STY

TRACTOR
TRAILER
TREES
TRUCK

WATER
WELL
WIRE
WREN

```
R Z C D M R S R N T O H P M
J E X I E U S E P I H C A Z
W E L L M E D M E K K C S Y
P K A I O R S R S R L S T R
U B H C A F O A L X T U U C
M P I G H R T F O D D E R H
P E N B N O T B E N E H E I
P D A L A R R O C N O E E C
R R C D A G O E Q R C K F K
N E A C O D O C S K A E C E
W O T D N W S E G R C U S N
R O T A V I T L U C R O P S
R O L E W R E N B T E T T O
W R E P A E R E G G S Y A S
```

Solution is on page 383.

I'LL FLY AWAY

Sharpen your pencil for TAKEOFF and enjoy your FLIGHT through the jumbo diagram on the opposite page. You'll find 55 terms relating to aviation. If you decide to bail out before completely solving the puzzle, be sure you're wearing that regulation life jacket called a MAE WEST—it FLOATS.

ALTITUDE	FLATS	PILOT
AVIONICS	FLIGHT	PLANE
BALLOON	FLIGHT DECK	PRANG
BANK	FLOATS	PYLON
BASKET	FLYPAST	RADOME
BLIMP	GLIDE	RIGID
BOMBER	GLIDER	RUDDER
BOMB RACK	GONDOLA	SLIP
CATWALK	GROUP	SOAR
CHASSIS	G-SUIT	SOARING
CLEAT	HANGAR	SPAN
DIHEDRAL	HELICOPTER	TAKEOFF
DIRIGIBLE	HYDROPLANE	TANDEM
DIVE	INFLATE	TAXI
DRONE	LIFT	TRIPLANE
FABRIC	LIFT-OFF	TURRET
FIDO	LOOP	VECTOR
FIGHTER	MAE WEST	
FLAP	NACELLE	

```
P S C I N O I V A F F I G H T E R
B A T A X D I V E F A L B R C G S
B A L A D A M E O C I B I I O S L
A I N F L A T E L D T P R G E U I
S G T K E F K A E B L O F I H I P
K L A W T A C R N A I H R D C T G
E O E J T E E M N D L G K J N N I
T S L R U D D E R P E T I A A E R
T P C A R S T I N S S M C R L M E
E A Q O R T H R L A I E P O I O T
D N N S E A G P P G L S O S N D P
U E A U T O I Y T L P P S O S A O
T F I L N L L E V M I O A W R C
I Z Y D P F F O T F I L D R H X I
T B O M B E R N A B L O I I D C L
L L A R D E H I D A B T F N D Y E
A K C A R B M O B F E R A G N A H
```

Solution is on page 384.

Here's another set of puzzles like the one on pages 204 and 205. Look there for solving directions. The terms in this puzzle begin with the letters "MA." There's MAPLE, as in the type of syrup you might pour over pancakes; MACHO, a description of Rambo, and MANY, MANY more!

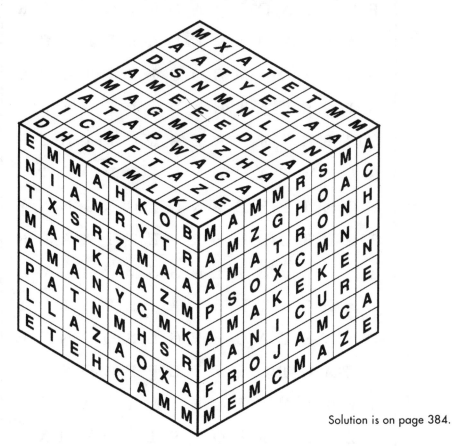

Solution is on page 384.

MACARONI	MAIN	MANE	MARTYR
MACAW	MAIZE	MANICURE	MASCARA
MACE	MAJOR	MANNER	MASH
MACHETE	MAKE	MANTLE	MAST
MACHINE	MALE	MANY	MAT
MACHO	MALLET	MAP	MATCH
MADAM	MALT	MAPLE	MATRON
MAGENTA	MAMBO	MAR	MAXIM
MAGMA	MAMMAL	MARBLE	MAYHEM
MAIDEN	MAMMOTH	MARE	MAZE
MAIL	MAN	MARK	

Instead of looking for Ma, Pa wants you to get started on the little doozy here. Search the cube-shaped diagram for PATH, PARALLEL and 44 other words that begin with the letters "PA."

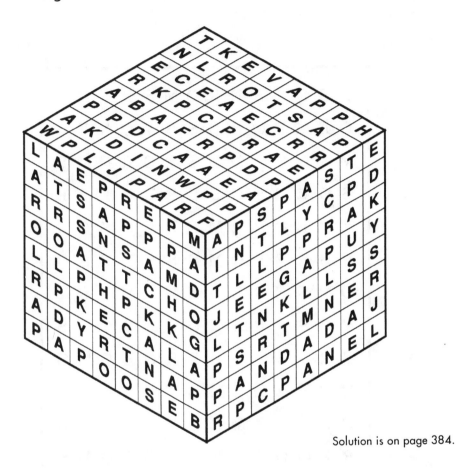

Solution is on page 384.

PACE	PALM	PAPYRUS	PASTE
PACK	PAMPER	PARADE	PASTEL
PACT	PANCAKE	PARALLEL	PASTOR
PAD	PANDA	PARASOL	PAT
PADDLE	PANEL	PARCEL	PATENT
PADRE	PANSY	PARENT	PATH
PAGE	PANTHER	PARFAIT	PATROL
PAGODA	PANTRY	PARK	PAUSE
PAIL	PAPA	PARLOR	PAVE
PAINT	PAPER	PART	PAW
PALACE	PAPOOSE	PASS	PAWL
PALE		PASTA	

Whether or not you're camping, with this puzzle you have SMORES. Graham crackers, chocolate and marshmallows are used to make the 31 SMORES hidden below. Can you find and eat them all?

```
R S S E S E R O M S R O M S
O E M E M S E S S M O R E S
M R O S R M M S E O R O M S
S O R M E O E S E R O M S E
E M E O R R M E R E O S O R
R S S E R O M S S S M M S O
O M S E R E O E M E M E S M
M O S E R S R O S E R O M S
S R S S M O R E S O E O M O
M E E R M E M E M E M O M R
O S R S S M R S M O R E S S
R E O O R O E M S E R O M S
E O M S M O R E S O E R M E
S M S S O S E R O M S M O S
```

Solution is on page 384.

This puzzle is solved like the one on page 218. There are 15 five-letter and 8 seven-letter combinations to be found in the diagram, 46 words in all.

YOUR WORD LIST

```
C L T W I F H E N L T O L P
Q U E D K A C N O A K A C E
T E S N O L A T E R D U Y W
B L N O I S F R E E Z E R T
G N I P E E B Y P N O I S E
W O S S C G N S W E G D K C
C E T E N O R T V G L A A F
H O H R I M A E L G V D R W
N P R T M N I E A E E H E D
Q P A R A S O L K T S N L R
U R L T T L R N E A T E S T
Y N O R I N A N E A I R E D
E M N P V P T R W F G V I G
Y B G O S E E H M R E E N R
```

Solution is on page 384; list, page 399.

Here's another Tail Tag puzzle. This time we give you no help in finding the 39 words of 4 letters or more used to complete this puzzle. The directions are on page 194, but here's a hint: You will complete this puzzle wherever you begin it.

_____	_____	_____
_____	_____	_____
_____	_____	_____
_____	_____	_____
		_____
		_____

```
S K L E G R T S A E L H Z E
C R Z N R H G E X U L T A L
H G I O I N Z T G B I C G D
I T F N M R H A H E H H R O
S S I K E D G C R A I N Z O
M K D C L A L U O P E N E D
R E Q A V L V D X W N R E F
L E E N K Q E E S H I R T O
L O L K R X W V Q L C G R O
M G F G U W R E H T E D E R
E O W T L Z I M J B L I M P
H H U L H R N Z U R R Z B M
T S I T N E D L J L W Q L X
J P L E H H C I T S A L E Z
```

Solution is on page 384; list, page 399.

Test YOUR solving skills with this Full House.

ALLOYS	NEON	POEM	ROYAL	SUMMER
CENTRAL	NEXT	PREACHER	RUNWAY	SURLY
COLA	NODE	QUICK	SELL	TALL
CONTRIBUTE	OBOE	RECITED	SKIPPER	TENDER
CORD	ONION	RELAY	SOMETIMES	TORRID
COURT	OVERT	RIDE	STALK	TRUSTEES
DANCE	PAMPER	ROMANTIC	SUES	YOUR
DENOTES				
DETRACT				
DRUB				
EXTRA				
GALAXY				
GORILLA				
HERE				
ICILY				
IDEA				
INCOME				
INDEED				
LADY				
LEAD				
LEAP				
LENT				
LIED				
LOCAL				
LOUD				
MAID				
MERRILY				
MORAL				

```
G A L A X Y L I R R E M S D
S O M E T I M E S U M M E R
Y N R D A Y C D E N O T E S
O I U I L D E I L W R L T E
L O O A L A C O L A A A S U
L N Y M E L N I C Y L R U S
A O K D N D A T T K L T R K
R E C I T E D R N N E X T I
T O I R E E R E H C A E R P
N B U R D D O V R E P M A P
E O Q O I N C O M E O P O E
C O N T R I B U T E N D E R
```

Solution is on page 384.

MOVIE FILL-INS ————————————

To solve, first fill in the missing words in the film titles listed below. Then search for those words in the diagram on the opposite page. Hint! The answers are in alphabetical order. If you can't think of the missing words, our list is on page 400. Good luck!

1. Pee Wee's Big _____
2. La _____
3. _____ Hills Cop
4. Mad Max _____ Thunderdome
5. The _____ Purple
6. Ferris Bueller's _____
7. St. Elmo's _____
8. _____ the 13th
9. Places in the _____
10. Harry and the _____
11. Hamburger _____
12. Star Trek IV: The Voyage _____
13. Full Metal _____
14. Jo Jo Dancer, Your _____ Is Calling
15. The _____ Daylights
16. _____ of the Universe
17. Brewster's _____
18. The Jewel of the _____
19. Superman IV: The Quest for _____
20. Pretty in _____
21. The Purple _____ of Cairo
22. Hannah and Her _____
23. Romancing the _____
24. The Secret of My _____
25. Desperately Seeking _____

```
K A G H E H E B E Y O N D E
B N N H C O W L E Z I N C X
E R I F Y M T J I V S A J P
E L V P A E R U T N E V D A
L A I N D H K O O P I R B D
M I L L I O N S L R A M L A
S A S I R E R I O O A T W Y
S S S O F E R S Q B C R V O
U Z N T D E E T E K C A J F
S T O N E U Z E O R B E L F
A E E L A R Q R A D U H E I
N H Q M O Z S S E C C U S J
```

Solution is on page 384; list, page 400.

You'll have a grand old time searching for the terms below that all start with "grand" or "great." Take the "grand" TOUR through this puzzle and search for the 28 terms. We've circled BASIN to start you off.

```
N R O T A P I C N A M E E S
S E K A L A C E D U K E L N
D P M W H I T E W A Y W A I
B N W A O D T S L T O U R A
A A A I D O O T K D U R C T
R X L B Z P L E E N R M E N
R T I L E A R (N I S A B) N U
I J Y R S A R A H R E B Y O
E N A S P O R D S I E R R M
R E K I H I F H J L L I R Y
R M D A M J A F A A U T A K
E S P M A L U N I P O A C O
E C I R L D I R O R C I R M
F A L L S F Z G Y N E N E S
```

Solution is on page 384.

BALLS OF FIRE
BANKS
   (Newfoundland)
BARRIER REEF
   (Australia)
BASIN
BEAR
BRITAIN
COULEE (Dam,
   Washington)
DAME
DANE
DUKE
EMANCIPATOR
FALLS (Montana)
FINALE
HORNED OWL
JURY
LAKES
LARCENY
MARSHAL
OPERA
PIANO
PRIX
RAPIDS (Michigan)
SALT LAKE
SLAM
SMOKY
   MOUNTAINS
TOUR
WHITE WAY
WIZARD

In this puzzle, we've hidden 32 movies with titles that start with the word "great." Take *The Great ADVENTURE* and see if you can find all of them. When you're done, the remaining letters, when read from left to right starting at the top of the diagram, will spell out the name of another "great" movie.

ADVENTURE (The)

BATTLE (The)

BRAIN (The)

CARUSO (The)

CHASE (The)

ESCAPE (The)

EXPECTATIONS

GABBO (The)

GAMBINI (The)

GATSBY (The)

GILDERSLEEVE (The)

GUNS

IMPOSTER (The)

JOHN L. (The)

LOVER (The)

MANHUNT (The)

MCGINTY (The)

MEADOW (The)

MIKE (The)

MOMENT (The)

NIAGARA (The)

O'MALLEY (The)

PRETENDER (The)

PROFILE (The)

RACE (The)

RUPERT (The)

SANTINI (The)

SINNER (The)

WALL (A)

WALLENDAS (The)

WALTZ (The)

ZIEGFELD (The)

```
W G S N O I T A T C E P X E
A A Y B S T A G C I B T S L
L B L J H N E G N H R C N T
T B O L O U R I E A A T U T
Z O V N E H T G I P I S G A
A L E B I N N E E R N T E B
D R R O A A D L E F G E I Z
V E U S M M G A A N D M Y S
E D P C U A E A S L E O T I
N N E W A L L I R A L M N N
T E R C I R N L D A I E I I
U T T F A N U O E K I N G B
R E O V E R W S E Y A T C M
E R N R R E T S O P M I M A
P P E V E E L S R E D L I G
```

Solution is on page 385.

In addition to finding all the terms below in the puzzle diagram, you'll also find them on "Z" map. That is, each of the terms is a geographical location anywhere in the world that contains the letter "Z."

ABRUZZI (Italy)
AMAZON (S. America)
ANZA (Jordan)
A'ZAZ (Syria)
AZUSA (California)
BAUTZEN (Germany)
BIZERTE (Tunisia)

BRAZIL
BRZEG (Poland)
BUZAU (Romania)
CADIZ (Spain)
CAZIS (Switzerland)
CORREZE (France)
CUZCO (Peru)

GAZA (Israel)
HARZ (Germany)
IZUMI (Japan)
KAZAKH
KAZAN (Russia)
KIRGIZ
KUNDUZ
  (Afghanistan)
LA PAZ (Bolivia)
LAZI (Philippines)
LINZ (Austria)
LUZ (Brazil)
MAINZ (Germany)
MAZATLAN
  (Mexico)
METZ (France)
MONZA (Italy)
MOZAMBIQUE
NAZE (Japan)
NIZWA (Oman)
PEREZ (Argentina)
RIZE (Turkey)
SEZZE (Italy)
SUEZ (Egypt)
SWITZERLAND
TA'IZZ (Yemen)
TANZANIA
TAZ (Russia)
TAZA (Morocco)
TEZPUR (India)
TUZ (Turkey)
VADUZ
  (Liechtenstein)
VENEZUELA
YEZD (Iran)

```
P D N A L R E Z T I W S Z E
L I A Z A T Z Z U B Q U I Z
I M N Z R A H U T D T A G A
Z U Y E Z D U H D E N Z R N
A Z Z A Z J A K G A M U I A
R I Z E Z T Z A E O V S K L
B O Z I E L U Z Z Z E A Y T
E G A Z A Z B A R C N Z N A
Z C P M N T M K B Z E I Z Z
E U A I A B A C A R Z E A A
R Z L S I Z A C E W U T L M
R C O Q A D O P A S E Z Z E
O O U N I A Z N O M L A Z I
C E M Z A I N A Z N A T F I
```

Solution is on page 385.

Solve the puzzle below and learn the history behind Veterans Day. When you've circled all the terms, the remaining letters will spell the name of a song befitting this holiday. Hint: Its title was also a Donald O'Connor film.

Following the truce signed on November eleventh, nineteen-eighteen, people observed Armistice Day to honor the armed forces who gave their lives during the first World War. But after the wars that came later, the name was changed to Veterans Day for all the servicemen of all wars.

```
G N S N A R E T E V O T W T T
N E P O H E E T S R I F E H T
I E E D N S J L T C A M E E N
R T O E O H E H E N N A Y N O
U E P N E M E C I V R E S A V
D N L G C I E O R M E O E M E
E I E I R T M C E O T N H E M
G N V S V H E D I Y F S T T B
N E A M R E T F A T U B L H E
A E G A R T S D L C S H L E R
H T O W O R L D W A R I A W O
C H H I A U N T A H T G M A F
S G W W H C R O N O H E O R Y
A I O B S E R V E D M E R S A
W E G N I W O L L O F A L L D
```

Solution is on page 385.

EXPRESSED EMOTIONS

Just about any emotion you might feel privately can be detected by the expression on your face! The list below contains 42 feelings and emotions that can be expressed facially. Can you find them all in the diagram on the opposite page?

AMAZEMENT	EAGERNESS	MEANNESS
ANGER	EMBARRASSMENT	MEEKNESS
ANGUISH	ENVY	PANIC
APATHY	FEAR	REGRET
BOREDOM	FRIENDLINESS	REMORSE
CALMNESS	GAIETY	RESTLESSNESS
CHEERFULNESS	GRIEF	SADNESS
CONCEIT	GUILT	SHYNESS
CONCENTRATION	HAPPINESS	SLYNESS
CONCERN	HATRED	SORROW
CONTENTMENT	HEARTACHE	SURPRISE
DISGUST	INTEREST	TENDERNESS
DISTRESS	JOY	TIMIDITY
DREAD	LOVE	WORRY

```
C L D A T X Y I L N Y D N A D M T B S T
Z A D R I L W V R X H L I D N E I S L E
R T L O E J I E N S T S A S N B E O S L
A N O M C A C U Y E A R S D G N E I R Y
Q E B D N N D T G Q P S E E R U R A C H
I M L R O E E B F E A R I E N P S O O A
S S N C C I S A D R N O G E R D N T N I
S S R I A C O S O E U A J U R T A T C F
E A N G U I S H S S E N S S E L T S E R
N R D P H R A S L E E V I N Z S S E N I
L R A E A O E Y E U G J T A Q E T R T E
U A S S E N N A E M U M G R R N Q E R N
F B Y S I E I I N B E Y R H E L Y T A D
R M M P S B U C M N P U I M A T Y N T L
E E P S H E A R T A C H E O I T R I I I
E A M E E K N E S S S Z F D Q U R S O N
H T N O J V O Y O A A R I E I E O E N E
C R E G R E T B H M D M U R V K W Y D S
L F T A E S R L A S I H M O W O R R O S
A D I S T R E S S T C L J B A C L A O J
```

Solution is on page 385.

This is the age of 900 numbers, but did you know that in 1982 there was a special telephone number set up so the public could listen to the crew of the space shuttle *Columbia*? The number was 900-410-6272.

2061	7813	9010
2064	7841	9041
2213	7943	9941
2248	7980	9980
2410		
2434		
2631		
2684		
2834		
2840		
5040		
5081		
5541		
5580		
5911		
5934		
6303		
6343		
6601		
6684		
6931		
6980		
7734		
7780		

```
4 3 7 7 5 0 0 1 3 1 6 0 2 5
6 4 8 5 8 4 8 3 0 0 1 6 0 0
9 3 4 4 4 3 9 8 8 1 0 4 0 8
0 1 0 8 3 0 6 9 5 1 4 2 4 1
1 8 4 3 4 8 7 3 9 8 4 8 8 3
0 2 0 7 1 3 2 4 3 3 0 1 6 3
2 3 7 7 8 4 1 8 4 9 9 8 0 2
4 8 0 1 8 4 4 5 3 0 1 4 3 5
0 8 4 3 3 1 0 3 5 2 8 4 0 1
9 5 9 1 1 6 9 1 0 8 3 4 0 1
8 9 0 1 4 6 2 2 0 1 0 1 8 3
3 1 4 8 3 3 8 2 3 1 0 1 0 4
0 4 6 1 4 4 4 9 8 3 4 4 3 9
4 6 0 2 8 3 6 3 1 8 7 2 1 7
```

Solution is on page 385.

What's a SCORP? It's a hollowing tool used for creating fine detail on bowls and chairs. You'll find this and another 34 woodworking tools hidden below.

ADZE

ANVIL

AUGER

BAND SAW

BRAD

BURR

CALIPER

CHISEL

CLAMP

DRILL

ENGRAVER

FERRULE

FILE

FRET SAW

FROE

GAUGE

GIMLET

GOUGE

HAMMER

INSHAVE

KNIFE

LATHE

LEVEL

MALLET

MANDREL

PLANE

PLUMB BOB

PUMICE

RASP

RULE

SCORP

SCRAPER

STROP

SWIVEL

VISE

```
D S C O R P Q E Z D A E A P
B E R R R U B L V U N V N R
M G L B G M L Y G F P A V V
Y U C A L I P E R O L H I D
J O U N R C R E R X V S L P
L G Q D X E T T E D E N Y T
E R A S P S S D V K N I F E
V R M A A V Q F A R G A R L
I N R W F F E R R U L E M M
W C H I S E L V G O L H B I
S L L X W P E B N R E T D G
L E N A L P V T E L L A M D
X B H A M M E R H P R L V R
V H A Q V P L U M B B O B E
```

Solution is on page 385.

An ice shelf is a thick mass of glacial ice which is attached to the land and extends seaward. The 1824 expeditions of Admiral Richard Byrd had set up base camp at Little America, located on the edge of the ROSS Ice Shelf. This is one of several ice shelves hidden below.

ABBOT	LARSEN
AMERY	RIISER-LARSEN
BACH	RONNE
BRUNT	ROSS
COOK	SHACKLETON
EKSTROM	SLAVA
FILCHNER	VENABLE
FIMBUL	VOYEYKOV
GETZ	WEST
JELBART	WORDIE

```
M K I O F G J V O M H R
O V L A R S E N S F I K
R K V R E N H C L I F R
T O C O A O E T S M A O
S L R B Y T S E N B Q N
K J L A M E R Y K U W N
E E E G R L Y O S L R E
L R E L A K O K S K I B
C T V R B C B A O D A J
Z V S A V A L S R V E C
W E S E C H R O R K A H
N J L H W S W T O B B A
```

Solution is on page 385.

There are a TOTAL of 63 terms in this puzzle, and they all have four or more letters. Words entirely within other words are not included. When you finish the puzzle, every letter will have been circled at least once.

ADES	BERTH	EDUCATION	HERE	JEST
AIRED	BRASS	EGOIST	HOBBY	LADDER
AMAZES	BUTTES	ELECT	HOST	LEASE
AMBER	CEDE	ENJOYS	HURT	LIMBER
AMPLE	CHEAT	ERRANDS	IMAGE	LIZARD
ARDENT	DEMON	ESTER	IMPORTED	LOCKETS
ASSET	DIPSY	GESTE	IMPULSE	MIMES
BEES	EBBED	HEART	JEER	MISTY

NEED
RELATIVES
RUTS
SCAM
SEAT
SEED
SENT
SHIN
SKIRT
SMILED
SPIES
SPRY
SQUASH
SQUINT
STREAM
SUCH
TAUPE
TESTIFY
TOTAL
TOWEL
TRINKET
WALKED
WELDS

```
I M A G E G O I S T A U P E
S M I L E D U C A T I O N N
D I P S Y F I T S E T S E J
N M T O T A L O C K E T S O
A E A C R Y H W A L K E D Y
R S E E B T D E M O N I H S
R L H D R R E L A T I V E S
E U C E E T E D Z R R A Q Q
D P B B R A S S E T T U B U
D M M B S E I P S K I R T A
A I R E D J E E R N H C U S
L I Z A R D E N T Y B B O H
```

Solution is on page 385.

This again is a Word Search in reverse. Circled letters are the initial letters of one or more words, and any letter may be part of more than one word. Fill in each word in a straight line without crossing any black squares; when you're done, every square will be filled. SAVIOR has been entered for you.

ACROBATIC
ADMONISH
BEACH
BOOMERANG
CLEANSE
COHERENCE
DEMEANOR
EASEL
EMPRESS
EXALT
FREEDOM
GATHERED
GENDARME
HILT
HUMORIST
IMMERSED
INFLAME
LEVEE
MEDIOCRE
NECKLACE
NODE
OVERBITE
OWNERSHIP
PECULIAR

PENSIVE
REDEEM
REPRESENT
~~SAVIOR~~

SCENE
STOW
TEACHER
TROCHE

UNITE
VARIETAL
V!XEN
WREATH

Solution is on page 385.

Singing is a universal pleasure: the only "instrument" required is the human voice. No wonder people of all cultures have appreciated the joy of singing for so many centuries. And no wonder that so many varieties of song have evolved, from the most humble TUNE to the grandest ORATORIO. Listed below are 32 types of songs.

AIR	AUBADE	CAROL
ALBA	BALLAD	CHANT
ANTHEM	CANTATA	CHANTEY
ARIA	CANTO	DIRGE
ARIETTA	CANZONET	DITTY
		DUET
		HYMN
		LAY
		LULLABY
		MOTET
		NOËL
		ORATORIO
		PAEAN
		PSALM
		RONDO
		ROUND
		RUNE
		SERENADE
		SERENATA
		THRENODY
		TUNE
		WASSAIL

```
H Y G U N A E A P L Y A W E
T L A E C D A L L A B T A S
N U O R A T O R I O Z T S F
A L N B N E D A N E R E S O
Y L U E T S A L P A R I A R
C A N Z O N E T E E G R I D
A B L A N O C N N P S A L I
N Y H M N U B A U B A R O T
T R T O L T T H R E N O D Y
A Y E T N A H C Y O H U N Z
T H U E I O S E O M L N O M
A C D T U D E P M Z N D R N
```

Solution is on page 386.

Did you know that the familiar verse below was originally part of an opera? John Howard Payne wrote "Home, Sweet Home" for the opera *Clari, the Maid of Milan*. The music, credited to Sir Henry Bishop, is said to be based on a Sicilian folk tune. Why not hum along as you circle the words and phrases hidden in the diagram.

'Mid
pleasures
and
palaces
though
we may
roam,
Be it
ever so
humble,
there's
no place
like
home!
A charm
from
the sky
seems
to hallow
us there,
Which,
seek
through
the world,
is ne'er
met with
elsewhere.
Home, home,
sweet, sweet,
home!
There's
no place
like
home!

```
M E T W I T H D I A S M E L N
Q A W R E L S E W H E R E B O
Z L T H O U G H Y A C H W A P
T Q O Y I A X A C H A R M Q L
E E H K B C M R B B L Y E J A
E M A S U E H D S W A H O M C
W O L E W O I O H R P S S S E
S H L H L M J T M I M Z R E C
T E O T O J S E R E H T E R A
E M W R I M H K L L D R V U L
E O F V E H E G T J E C E S P
W H C E R E W D U H J K T A O
S T S H S J N I T O E O I E N
M Q J Q C A K S R K R R K L I
E L B M U H U J I E E H E P N
B T H E W O R L D D L L T S V
```

Solution is on page 386.

Solve this puzzle by forming a chain of circled words in which the last letter of one word is the first letter of the next. The number in parentheses tells you the length of the word you're looking for. We have provided **CREDIT** to start you off.

CREDIT _____ (6)	_____ (4)	_____ (7)
T _____ (4)	_____ (5)	_____ (4)
_____ (4)	_____ (6)	_____ (4)
_____ (5)	_____ (6)	_____ (8)
		_____ (5)
		_____ (4)
		_____ (5)
		_____ (6)
		_____ (5)
		_____ (4)
		_____ (5)
		_____ (5)
		_____ (5)
		_____ (4)
		_____ (4)
		_____ (5)
		_____ (5)
		_____ (5)
		_____ (6)
		_____ (5)
		_____ (4)
		_____ (5)
		_____ (4)
		_____ (4)
		_____ (4)
		_____ (6)
		_____ (5)
		_____ (4)
		_____ (4)
		_____ (4)
		_____ (5)

```
C  Z  K  D  E  L  L  I  R  H  T  L  B  S
R  V  J  R  A  L  K  E  T  C  S  H  A  N
E  V  I  C  T  T  N  R  R  H  O  S  Z  I
D  E  Y  W  R  G  E  I  I  R  H  N  Z  A
I  R  N  N  I  V  H  D  P  W  O  R  L  R
T  A  S  K  O  L  Y  L  L  A  E  R  D  T
C  A  R  D  S  Q  A  Z  E  X  I  S  T  S
L  Y  L  R  S  T  N  Q  H  X  G  J  P  Y
A  S  Y  W  P  S  K  I  P  S  T  R  M  L
T  L  E  P  O  Z  S  I  N  K  L  U  O  S
P  N  A  Z  R  O  N  E  T  I  G  U  J  E
R  R  M  A  T  Y  E  W  R  N  V  L  L  V
W  A  R  T  S  R  Z  X  A  D  I  C  U  L
H  E  H  Q  S  O  L  I  D  S  O  L  V  E
```

Solution is on page 386; list, page 400.

Duck searching season has begun. Wade through this puzzle and find 30 types of feathered waterfowl. It should be "duck soup"!

AYLESBURY
BLACK
BUFFLEHEAD
CANVASBACK
CAYUGA
DIVING
DRAKE
EIDER
GADWALL
GOLDENEYE
GOOSANDER
GRAY
LABRADOR
MALLARD
MANDARIN
MERGANSER
MUSCOVY
PEKIN
PINTAIL
RINGNECK
ROUEN
SAWBILL
SCAUP
SCOTER
SHOVELER
TEAL
WHISTLER
WHITE
WILD
WOOD

```
M A N D A R I N P L Z J N V
T E T I H W P L K E I D E R
N E R E L T S I H W K R Y H
R R A G U Y A C N W E I E B
I O P L A F R Q M T O X N U
N D U R S N V U O T A O E F
G A A E V C S C B L Q I D F
N R C L N C S E L S N M L L
E B S E O P R I R W E A O E
C A N V A S B A C K I L G H
K L Y O M W N G A Y C L Y E
N K L H A R W R G H A A D A
G O O S A N D E R N B R L D
L L A W D A G N I V I D G B
```

Solution is on page 386.

Lydia Maria Child started America's first children's magazine, *Juvenile Miscellany*, in 1826. In addition she wrote one of the first books in America which advocated the abolition of slavery. The verse below, taken from the poem "Thanksgiving Day," is one of her more popular works.

Over

the river

and through

the wood,

To grandfather's

house

we'll go;

The horse

knows

the way

To carry

the sleigh,

Through

the white

and drifted

snow.

```
T H E R T E T O C A R R Y Y
T D O E L H G S W O E T H H
G A E R L L E E A V H R O G
R N S T L G K S I E Y U E U
O D A E F H O R L R S N E O
T T W T T I E S U E N O S R
T H O I O H R L G D I U R H
S R E H T A F D N A R G O T
H O W W C E H F D S S E H S
A U I E O T S W O N K A E E
H G T H R O G H T O A W H O
H H R T H E D Y A W E H T T
```

Solution is on page 386.

CHRISTMAS AROUND THE WORLD

Before going to bed on Christmas Eve, Spanish children put their SHOES near a window and wake to find them filled with small GIFTS. This practice is similar to that of Americans hanging stockings. Solve the puzzle and learn about some of the items used in Christmas celebrations around the world. We've provided an explanation for some of these listed items on page 400.

1. ASALTO (Puerto Rico)
2. BEFANA (Italy)
3. BELLS
4. BLACK PETER (Holland)
5. BULLFIGHT (Peru)
6. CALTA (Czechoslovakia)
7. CAPON (Italy)
8. CARDS
9. CARP (Austria)
10. CATS (Sweden)
11. CENA (Brazil)
12. CERT (Czechoslovakia)
13. CODFISH (Norway)
14. CRIB (Yugoslavia)
15. EELS (Italy)
16. EGGNOG

17. FIESTA (Ecuador)
18. FIRST-FOOTING (England)
19. GIFTS
20. GLÖGG (Sweden)
21. KALANDA (Greece)
22. KITES (Tobago)
23. KOLYÁDA (Russia)
24. KRIPPE (Germany)
25. KUBA (Czechoslovakia)
26. LANTERNS (China)
27. NISSE (Denmark)
28. ORCHIDS (Costa Rica)
29. PARADE (Philippines)
30. PAROL (Philippines)

31. PÈRE NOËL (France)
32. PIÑATA (Mexico)
33. POSADA (Guatemala)
34. PUTZ (Pennsylvania Dutch)
35. SANTA CLAUS
36. SHOES
37. STARS
38. STRAW FISH (Thailand)
39. SYLVESTER (Austria)
40. TAFFY PULL (Wales)
41. TREES
42. TURRÓN (Spain)
43. UKKO (Finland)
44. WAITS (England)

```
K C L R E T E P K C A L B L C T
H A T A F F Y P U L L T L L H C
L J L D P Z T U P S Q G R G L F
S A S A L T O S T I A W I E R I
U L R Y N L X F E T R F U G E R
A O C L J D I D S Z L K L G T S
L G G O L G A E Q L K J L N S T
C L C K D R I L U O K U X O E F
A E A N A F E B L B C I B G V O
T C R P N O I S P I N A T A L O
N P P T N I D S Z R O O T E Y T
A L O E O I S B H C P L R S S I
S N R S H O E S D R A C L R C N
L E E C A L J L E C C E A Z U G
P C R C L D H S N R E T N A L T
H O B S T R A W F I S H R B M C
```

Solution is on page 386; explanations, page 400.

LOOSE LETTERS ———————— 223

This puzzle can be solved by removing one letter from each term below to form a new word. Circle the new word in the diagram and write the removed letter on the space provided. When you have formed all 30 new words, a proverb will be revealed reading down the loose letters. We've done the first one to show you how.

BOA$TS   S
PAUPER   ___
BONDED   ___
RUDDER   ___
FEASTS   ___
TINNIER   ___
FRIGHT   ___
LARGER   ___
BAILED   ___
ESTATE   ___
SNACKS   ___
WADDED   ___
PURSER   ___
CHASTE   ___
HAZIER   ___
PRATTLE   ___
SHOVEL   ___
POURED   ___
STRINGS   ___
CREAMS   ___
TRUCKS   ___
FINALE   ___
GRIPPED   ___
SECANT   ___
MONTHS   ___
TRIPLET   ___
CARIES   ___
CINDER   ___
CENTER   ___
STEEPS   ___

```
R P S T I N G S M S N G R
E I C K S S T B R C M E A
T D G L C J O Z O A I R T
N N T H H A Z E R N S Z T
E H M O T H S Q I T E J L
D O Z S C U E T E N G D E
E V W Y H L C P A T T L Y
R E R U P J S K E T S A C
O L C I F A S T S N E W S
P Q R I D E P I R G M A M
L T N G D F D E L A B D A
R A C R I E S Z R U D E R
L A G E R Y R W H S K D C
```

Solution is on page 386; list, page 400.

"When ANGRY, count to ten before you speak; if very ANGRY, a hundred," Thomas Jefferson once advised those whose tempers flared. Because we know that you cannot always control your anger, we've provided 26 different ways to express it.

ADIRATO (Italian)

ANGRY (English)

BEIS (Yiddish)

BÖSE (German)

ENOJADO (Spanish)

ENYE HASIRA (Swahili)

FÂCHÉ (French)

FURIOZA (Esperanto)

GHADIB (Arabic)

HARAGOS (Hungarian)

IRADO (Portuguese)

IRATUS (Latin)

KOES (Hebrew)

KWAAD (Dutch)

MARAH (Indonesian)

ÖFKELI (Turkish)

OKOTTA (Japanese)

ROZGNIEWANY (Polish)

ROZZLOBENY (Czech)

SINT (Norwegian)

SRDIT (Serbo-Croatian)

SUPARAT (Romanian)

THIMOME'NOS (Greek)

VIHAINEN (Finnish)

VRED (Danish)

ZLÓY (Russian)

```
V G H K W A A D S R D I T R U L
B I O M N G H C S U R G Y Y O I
V E H T H O S A U G P N N C S W
S X Z A Q W S O G A R A H N B O
I J D T I O K M N D W S R F D F
E I K J K N B G F E D C X A G K
B F R O J F E T I R M N J H T E
V F T O V Z X N H V H O J M S L
C T N B Z S G H Y H N J M K U I
A X I N C Z S D R E R T Y I R D
Z A S D O K L F A C H E S A H X
O T A R I D A O M N B A T G H T
I J N B C Z S D B H J U S C V B
R F G J L U R A S E S Y G I O N
U F R O N M A R A H N B F S R S
F T Y H G T J I K N G Y E D S A
```

Solution is on page 386.

Here's another puzzle like the one on page 266. If you're a Tanglewords fan, you'll be happy to know there are even more on pages 291, 292 and 311.

AGED	LAUREL	OUTER	SMATTER
ANECDOTAL	LLAMA	PIROUETTE	TAME
ARIA	MOLECULAR	PLEAT	TERRAIN
BADGE	NECTAR	PRETENSE	TOLERABLE
BRIDGED	OCULAR	REDEEM	UPROAR
BRITTLE	OUNCE	REGIMEN	VILLAIN
COLLEGIATE			
COMIC			
CORRAL			
CRUTCH			
DOORMAT			
DUCAT			
EMOTIONAL			
EUCHRE			
FOIST			
FOREIGN			
GORGE			
GRADUATION			
HIDEOUS			
LACTIC			

Solution is on page 386.

Basketball player Hal Greer proves that you should be the best at *whatever* you do. He holds the record for the most personal lifetime fouls in the NBA—3,855 to be exact.

5	2	1	1	0	3	5	8	0	2	3		1020	4450
5	6	8	0	9	0	0	8	2	7	5		1086	4468
8	6	8	8	2	2	9	9	7	8	6		1120	4606
5	9	2	0	2	0	0	0	2	5	4		1125	4690
7	5	7	1	7	3	3	6	8	4	3		1220	4803
4	8	0	3	1	0	5	2	6	4	0		1250	4886
0	5	4	4	2	1	9	8	6	6	6		3368	7068
8	4	6	8	5	0	9	5	8	0	5		3578	7095
6	9	8	9	0	8	2	8	9	6	2		3580	7725
0	6	0	8	2	6	5	1	7	6	7		3599	7765
7	0	7	3	6	8	8	7	1	9	7		3707	7917
												3770	7980
												3798	7986

Solution is on page 387.

Lincoln was a very active Commander-in-Chief, visiting his armies and insisting that his generals keep him posted. This was sometimes a mixed blessing . . . .

One of Lincoln's generals in the Civil War tried to impress him by signing his letters, from "Headquarters in the Saddle." Lincoln said of him, "The trouble with Hooker is that he's got his headquarters where his hindquarters ought to be."

```
A G E N E R A L S C Y T U S
C H U Y E L E V D R S R X S
S I H C H T B I M P Z I R E
O S R E T R A U Q D A E H R
T O B E A S Q U O E T D X P
A B R S I D O U Q R M T B M
N S V N M N Q U A E T O R I
Y L T L E V O U G H T G R H
R H O O Z L Q U A W A S F F
E M F C X D D Z B R H E Z O
K I W N N B Q D I N T H E K
O C C I V I L W A R S E N G
O T H L T B L M G S I V R B
H I M B Y H T G N I N G I S
```

Solution is on page 387.

One aspect of Lincoln's personality that struck everyone who met him was his ability to find a joke or witty story for every occasion. Here's one.

When first shown the plans for the battleship *Monitor*, Lincoln made a comment that might have been thought a bit naughty in those days: "I feel like the girl who said, when she put on her stocking, 'There's something in that worth looking at.'"

```
F G N I K C O T S D E Y G H
I B F F L U R K A S T I B A
R N T X O O G W O H L V P I
S E A L T R H H G N T I J F
T H G I M E T U P E H S K E
Z W N N N N A H C S U E V E
K O I C I N T H E R E S R L
M B K O N H C L Y P L B H D
Z W O L T B B B R L R I V
K N O N H T W E I S Y A D O
G W L R A Z E G M X S E N E
Q O B B T N E M M O C D V S
T H G U O H T C H Y S A J M
O S T Q T B M W V G H M B L
```

Solution is on page 387.

MATH FUN

Here's another math puzzle. First complete each of the simple arithmetic problems in order, from left to right. Then write the answer in the space provided and search for that word in the diagram. We've done number 3 to show you what we mean. Warning: If you're looking for six, be careful not to circle part of sixty or sixteen! Answers may be repeated.

1. $26 + 13 + 52 =$ _____

2. $16 \times 5 \div 2 =$ _____

3. $99 \div 3 \div 3 =$ <u>ELEVEN</u>

4. $27 + 11 - 34 =$ _____

5. $4 \times 8 \div 16 =$ _____

6. $102 - 9 - 14 =$ _____

7. $5 \times 5 \times 2 =$ _____

8. $92 - 89 + 12 =$ _____

9. $8 \times 12 - 36 =$ _____

10. $14 + 38 + 28 =$ _____

11. $22 \times 6 \div 4 =$ _____

12. $42 + 18 - 60 =$ _____

13. $36 \div 4 \times 8 =$ _____

14. $61 - 18 - 40 =$ _____

15. $21 \times 7 \div 3 =$ _____

16. $14 \times 7 \div 14 =$ _____

17. $18 + 29 - 41 =$ _____

18. $30 \times 8 \div 16 =$ _____

19. $32 + 17 + 52 =$ _____

20. $330 \div 6 - 40 =$ _____

21. $82 - 11 - 51 =$ _____

22. $11 \times 36 \div 44 =$ _____

23. $53 - 44 + 17 =$ _____

24. $22 \times 18 \div 4 =$ _____

25. $8 \times 7 - 26 =$ _____

26. $72 \div 4 \div 2 =$ _____

27. $19 + 76 - 63 =$ _____

28. $101 - 19 - 76 =$ _____

29. $4 \times 9 + 27 =$ _____

30. $150 \div 5 \div 15 =$ _____

31. $3 \times 3 + 6 =$ _____

32. $180 \div 20 \times 10 =$ _____

33. $6 \times 24 \div 12 =$ _____

34. $42 - 18 + 65 =$ _____

35. $36 \times 6 \div 24 =$ _____

```
M O O S E V E N T Y T W O F
S N X I S Y T N E W T X I S
T E T V E N X N L B O F R O
N H V W V G I E E L T E I S
E U I E E N S N V E N W I F
E N A R N N I I E I T X O O
T D N I T N T N N T T F W F
F R N I Y Y R Y E Y Y T I I
I E W T N E T T T Y O E F
F D R G I E I H H T Y V N T
F O U R N O R G R I L T H E
F N R I E E R I H E R R T E
S E N T E R H E W T E T R N
S I X T Y T O T Z E Y B Y B
```

Solution is on page 387.

FIND THE GLOVES ——————————— 230

Now that temperatures are falling, you may have to take your heavy coat, scarf, hat and GLOVEs out of the closet—Did you say you can't find your GLOVEs? Well, if you've looked around the house and still can't find them, feel free to borrow a pair from the puzzle below. GLOVE is hidden there 41 times, so you'll have quite a few pairs to spare!

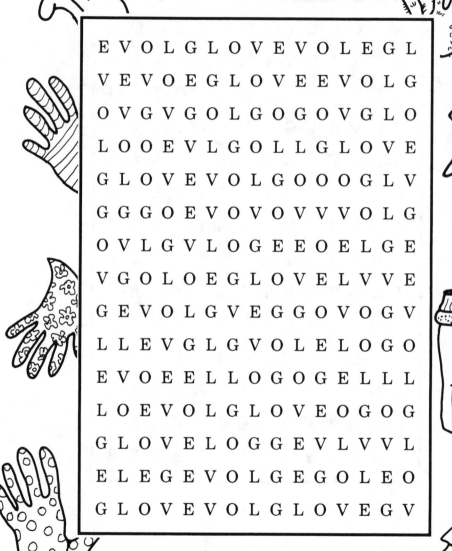

Solution is on page 387.

What statement about being ostentatious is hidden in the diagram? To find out, circle the 32 things that glitter, glisten, or glow. The uncircled letters will spell out the answer when read from left to right beginning at the top of the diagram.

AGATE

BUGLE BEADS

CANDLE

COALS

CROWN

CRYSTAL

DIAMOND

EMBERS

EMERALD

FIREFLY

FIREWORKS

FLASHLIGHT

GLASS

GLOWWORM

HALO

HEADLIGHT

ICICLE

JEWELS

LANTERN

LIGHT BULB

METALS

MICA

NEON SIGN

RAYS

RHINESTONE

RUBY

SEQUINS

SPARKLERS

SPARKS

SPOTLIGHT

STAR

TINSEL

```
T H G I L D A E H E P E O B P
M R O W W O L G E M E R A L D
L S E C W D I T H B A R L U Y
S O D O N H I T O E F B A B R
K A S A A S Y A R R S S U T A
R I C L E R L E M S P R N H S
O C O S O B F N E O N S I G N
W I R H I N E S T O N E T I I
E C N C E C R L A S E D S L U
R L S R S A I R G I K L L Y Q
I E E Y S G F A A U A R T A E
F L A S H L I G H T B L A L S
P O A T N L S R E L K R A P S
I L S A C I M M H J E W E L S
G E D L A N T E R N N W O R C
```

Solution is on page 387.

TRIVIA TOURNEY

Can you name the winner of the 1936 Miss Hungary pageant? And who was the first Olympic gymnast to score a perfect 10? If you guessed Zsa Zsa Gabor and Nadia Comaneci, you should have no trouble with the trivia questions below. The answers will be in alphabetical order down the list and are hidden in the diagram on the opposite page.

_____ 1. Soap Box Derby site

_____ 2. Beatles' record company

_____ 3. First Olympic women's marathon winner

_____ 4. First Heisman Trophy winner

_____ 5. British car trunk

_____ 6. Most populous country

_____ 7. TV commercial award

_____ 8. Sun's outer layer

_____ 9. Dr. Doolittle's ship

_____ 10. One followed by 100 zeroes

_____ 11. Finland's capital

_____ 12. "That'll Be the Day" singer

_____ 13. What remained in Pandora's box

_____ 14. Gene Kelly's cartoon partner

_____ 15. President Peace Corps founder

_____ 16. One nautical mile per hour

_____ 17. Abigail Van Buren's twin

_____ 18. MGM lion

_____ 19. Fifth US President

_____ 20. "Hunter" constellation

_____ 21. Sesame Street grouch

_____ 22. "Madam, I'm Adam," e.g.

_____ 23. "The City of Light"

_____ 24. "The Thinker" sculptor

_____ 25. July birthstone

_____ 26. Hebrew greeting

_____ 27. *Bridge on the River Kwai* country

_____ 28. Princeton football team

_____ 29. Ballerina's skirt

_____ 30. First sound barrier breaker

```
P A L A N I H C L B E R R W
L L Y I N N O R I O N E O N
E S D N A L I A H T G R A P
O O E C K T U T U A O O T R
R A N O R O C H E N S T O E
M O N R O E H Y E S C A M G
T I E R N Y O K J R A O H N
R C K F L O U N D E R B O A
U L O N O T A O S D R I P W
B E N O I T P T N N O R E R
Y D B G L S P I L A D C Y E
B E E O C O L M O L A H S B
A R I N O A E E G J R W A E
S I R A P T U T H O L L Y N
```

Solution is on page 387; answers, page 400.

There are many cities and towns in the US with the same names as places mentioned in the Bible. For instance, if you read Revelations, Chapter 1, verse 11 and Hosea, Chapter 9, verse 6, you'll see PHILADELPHIA and MEMPHIS, respectively. Travel through this puzzle and find the 35 "biblical" US towns.

ALEXANDRIA (VA)
ANTIOCH (CA)
ATHENS (GA)
BEREA (SC)
BETHANY (OK)
BETHEL (AK)
BETHESDA (MD)
BETHLEHEM (PA)
CARMEL (CA)
CORINTH (TX)
CRETE (NE)
DAMASCUS (MD)
DOTHAN (AL)
EDEN (GA)
EMMAUS (PA)
ENDOR (MD)
GOSHEN (IN)
HEBRON (ND)
JERICHO (NY)
JORDAN (MN)
LEBANON (MO)
LEHI (UT)
MEMPHIS (TN)
MOAB (UT)
NAZARETH (KY)
NEBO (NC)
PHILADELPHIA (PA)

PHILIPPI (WV)
ROME (IL)
SALEM (OR)
SARDIS (GA)

SIDON (MS)
SILOAM (KY)
SMYRNA (DE)
SYRACUSE (TN)

```
N E S U C A R Y S A R D I S
O H C I R E J O E T E R C A
N E O S U C S A M A D R Y M
A B R C A R M E L E H T E B
B R I D B E T H E S D A N B
E O N A M A Y S U A M M E T
L N T P L J N J S B G T B A
A I H P L E D A L I H P O N
Z I Y R H N X M H L D S Z T
S J N T Z D G A E T I O M I
M O A B N O J H N L O E N O
Y R H V S R E Y O D L D L C
R D T H Z M N A Z A R E T H
N A E D E N M O S T H I N A
A N B L I P P I L I H P A T
```

Solution is on page 387.

Using the "D" in the word LAND, the first word in our list, try to find the second puzzle word which begins where the first word ends. Each word thereafter will be formed in the same way. Sharpen your skills because there are more Tail Tags coming up!

LAND _____(4)	_____(7)	_____(4)
_____(5)	_____(5)	_____(6)
_____(6)	_____(4)	_____(4)
_____(4)	_____(5)	_____(6)
		_____(5)
		_____(5)
		_____(5)
		_____(6)
		_____(4)
		_____(5)
		_____(6)
		_____(4)
		_____(5)
		_____(4)
		_____(6)
		_____(5)
		_____(5)
		_____(4)
		_____(5)
		_____(7)
		_____(4)
		_____(4)
		_____(5)
		_____(6)
		_____(5)
		_____(7)
		_____(5)
		_____(4)
		_____(4)
		_____(5)
		_____(4)

```
R E B U S Q D E S I M M E R
E G N I K H K X W M N J L I
T R E L R O A E O R G Z W C
L Z O N P M Z R N L E V O H
I Y L D I M I T K E Y E L P
K N O M Z E U H W A L R L E
E X C U S E S R C D N V B A
I B L T E I G H T E I Y Y S
V J E H G L H G W R A M P A
O E Z H Q M T C N Q M B R N
M R T Q A R L N S A R A I T
G H A R Y A A H E N R V E R
M L K Y G W N R I G O M S Y
J G E G O S D R L E D O Y L
```

Solution is on page 387; list, page 401.

Perhaps only the first Christmas gifts of gold, frankincense and myrrh are more familiar than the gifts from the traditional English carol, "The Twelve Days of Christmas," which are printed below. But, of course, it's not the gift, but the thought that counts!

Twelve	maids	birds,
drummers	a-milking,	Three
drumming,	Seven	French
Eleven	swans	hens,
pipers	a-swimming,	Two
piping	Six	turtle
Ten	geese	doves,
lords	a-laying,	and a
a-leaping,	Five	partridge
Nine	gold	in a
ladies	rings,	pear
dancing,	Four	tree.
Eight	calling	

```
E P I E E R T A F T A U S D B A E
H E U P S T S N H I Q S D J O L A
R L K G O E M R E N S D R O L E C
F E G S V S E W E E X B I E L A S
S V O E N E Z G W M S K B T P P K
I E N A V A D J L A M O R B R I A
G N I M M I W S A I I U L T E N P
J M X G R I E S N D T C R Z T G A
F E D T H U L A Y S I X F D M L N
I O R U Q T R K N K O R S E A N A
R A U T U I G S I A E T B Y N D R
P H M R W N V N G I P I P N I O
S S M Y I E V E C E G N R A P D N
E G I C R P L H E J G N I L L A C
V E N F Z E O V S V T K N O O B M
O A G S L A D I E S I O G Y I W O
D L E S E R E W R D S F S C L S T
```

Solution is on page 388.

The comedian Groucho Marx (1895-1977) once said, "I wouldn't want to belong to any club that would accept me as a member." Here's how club membership was once determined.

The word "blackball," meaning to exclude someone, comes from an old voting method used by clubs. Members voted on a new person by dropping balls into a box— with a white ball for a "yes" vote and a black ball for a "no" vote. If the person was voted against with a black ball, he was barred from the group.

```
T D D N A E T O V I F T H E
B L M E T H O D W A D E U B
A O B N E S R E B M E M S L
R N L W E K N O V E T O B A
R A O Y H A X G F R O R U C
E R A V N O T N I L V F L K
D Y P O O L B I B R L I C B
U E R E S T S N I A G A Y A
L W M O R F E A H O L D B L
C A A K E S M E V R R L G L
X W B S P S O M E O N E H P
E H W L V R C N P F T S N E
O I T O A W B P I L N I A M
T T T I I C I B A L L S N W
M E T T W N K K C A L B A G
D T H E G R O U P B D E S U
```

Solution is on page 388.

TANGLEWORDS ———————— 237

Surprise! Here's another Tanglewords puzzle. We know you are **CAPABLE** of hitting your **TARGET** by solving this puzzle and all the others featured throughout this issue. See page 266 for solving directions.

ALARM	CAPABLE	FEINT	HORN
ALTERNATOR	CAPITALIST	FRACAS	INFUSE
BACTERIAL	DETRIMENT	GILT	INTRICATE
BLOT	ELLIPTICAL	GROMMET	LEASED
BRIMMED	ENLIGHTEN	HILLSIDE	MAIZE
			MEASURED
			MELTING
			OUTER
			PERMEABLE
			PORE
			PUREE
			RANGE
			REIN
			RETRACTED
			SECURE
			STING
			SUBMERGED
			TALLOW
			TARGET
			TEXT
			TREADMILL
			UNHEARD
			WOLF

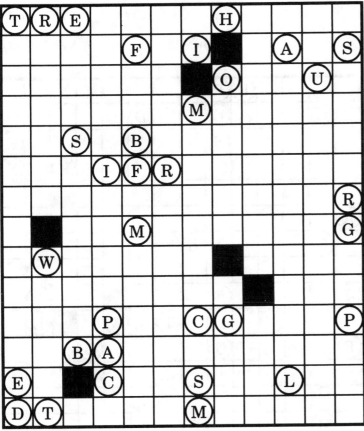

Solution is on page 388.

This isn't an ORDINARY Tanglewords. After you've solved the puzzle, five additional words will have been formed in the diagram that all relate to Christmas. Can you find them?

ABOARD

ADMIRE

BLURB

BOTHER

BOUND

CEASE

CRUET

DAUGHTER

DEFRAUD

DELETE

EMBRYO

FINISHING

FLUID

FOUR

GUEST

HAUNTED

HOMESTEAD

INERTIA

INTERCOM

JUNIPER

KAZOO

KNOT

LEVEE

LIGAMENT

MURMUR

NEWER

NUCLEAR

OFTEN

OPTIC

ORDINARY

REDUNDANT

REVERTED

RIPPLED

SCHOOLBOY

SURMISE

SWEETEN

TIGHTEN

TRITE

UPHILL

UTMOST

WEIGH

WHINING

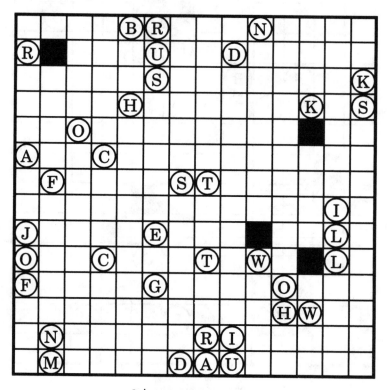

Solution is on page 388.

It's turkey time again and in honor of this special holiday, we've included a puzzle with 53 4-letter words made from the letters found in "Thanksgiving Day." (There are no plurals or proper nouns.) Can you trot through this puzzle and find them all?

T	H	A	N	K	S	G	I	V	I	N	G	D	A	Y

YOUR WORD LIST

```
G  N  I  S  T  D  S  H  N  I  H  S  A
N  I  H  D  A  T  I  D  Y  I  S  N  K
I  A  I  I  Y  N  A  V  N  A  K  H  I
K  V  N  A  D  S  D  T  A  H  I  S  N
V  N  N  S  T  I  K  S  V  G  D  A  A
K  K  I  N  N  G  S  K  Y  I  N  D  H
N  I  H  T  K  H  A  K  S  K  G  A  T
A  V  N  A  A  G  T  H  N  Y  N  I  T
H  A  N  D  S  T  A  Q  S  G  D  A  N
S  G  G  T  I  I  D  N  G  A  I  N  T
T  N  S  A  T  N  S  A  G  A  G  I  H
A  I  G  N  N  S  V  T  N  Y  K  V  I
G  D  N  V  A  S  T  A  Y  K  N  I  S
```

Solution is on page 388; list, page 401.

Beauty contests today mean elegant gowns, bathing suits and lots of photographs and TV coverage. But in the beginning the contests—and the contestants—were much more modest.

The first modern beauty contest was held in Spa, Belgium, in eighteen seventy-six. In those more modest days, the contestants wore crinoline dresses, and were kept from the view of anyone but the judges by being driven to the contest in a closed carriage.

```
D E S O L C T V B D A Y S B
C O N T E S T Y T N E V E S
O R X O E P B L I V I L G E
N D I D Y E Y T H E G L A G
T R O N I N S T W I H C I D
E M X N O R A O U C T U R U
S B G K I L F M U A E K R J
T S J F X X I E D L E H A Q
A K E Z R N I N H R N B C D
N H E S S O T S E T N O C T
T E M P S Y M W S V T U X O
S R A O T E D T O Q I U Q T
M O D E R N R C H Y U R B H
I W A S A E Z D T E L B D E
```

Solution is on page 388.

While a shower is invigorating, taking a bath is relaxing. It's a perfect way to pamper yourself and unwind after a long day. Listed below are items that are used for this purpose.

BATHTUB

BEADS

BOATS

BRUSH

BUBBLES

CLOTH

CONDITIONER

CREAM

MAT

MINERAL SALTS

MUD PACK

OILS

PERFUME

PILLOW

POWDER

PUMICE

RAZOR

ROBE

RUBBER DUCKIE

SHAMPOO

SHIPS

SOAP

SPONGE

STEAM

SUDS

SWABS

TOWEL

TOYS

VAPOR

WATER

```
S P I H S H T O L C R W Q T
T J S M S P L P V X E Z M Q
A M R E D W O P L A N X A S
O S I G L H A N S Y O T T D
B K D N D B H B G O I L S U
M J B A E R B F S E T J J S
R U B B E R D U C K I E A B
O L D T U B A W B P D F B R
Z E A P M T O L E R N J G U
A W A U A L H R S R O B Z S
R O K M L C F T J A C P T H
S T R I B U K M A V L E A Q
X Z P C M B K L J B A T R V
B M A E R C O O P M A H S D
```

Solution is on page 388.

THE AZTEC CALENDAR

From the 12th century, when they came to central Mexico, until the Spanish Conquest of 1519, the civilization of the Aztec Indians flourished. The Aztecs were exceptional engineers, architects and astronomers. Both archaeologists and astronomers have been impressed with the Aztec system of time keeping, with its calendar of thirteen months of twenty days each in a 52-year cycle. Both the names of the 20 days of their calendar month and the names of the 20 religious symbols associated with them are found in the diagram. Numbers will not be found in the diagram.

Days	Names	Symbols
1	CIPACTLI	CROCODILE
2	EHECATL	WIND
3	CALLI	HOUSE
4	CUETZPALLIN	LIZARD
5	COATL	SNAKE
6	MIQUIZTLI	DEATH
7	MAZATL	DEER
8	TOCHTLI	RABBIT
9	ATL	WATER
10	ITZCUINTLI	DOG
11	OZOMATLI	MONKEY
12	MALINALLI	DRY HERB
13	ACATL	CANE
14	OCELOTL	JAGUAR
15	CUAUHTLI	EAGLE
16	COZCACUAUHTIL	VULTURE
17	OLIN	EARTHQUAKE
18	TECPATL	OBSIDIAN KNIFE
19	QUIAHUITL	RAIN
20	XOCHITL	FLOWER

```
M A Z A T L N E N K A C D E L C Q
O O T E X O C H I T L R W E R T U
C L Q D R T O C A L A I N C R R I
X U N C H U A T R Z T I O I N E A
H I E D I L T N I U C Z T I L W H
W R F T L N L L O E C L I G K O U
T U I I Z J A G U A R L A U E L I
E H N O I P E Q C V W E C N Q F T
C L K H E K A U Q H T R A E J I L
P U N L O W A L E A B C T A A X M
A J A Q T U M A L I N A L L I T C
T Q I U H O S I I I L J L F H I B
L H D T H H L E D M N T T T P B J
E L I W L T J E O G O D A A C B C
K L S R H I L N C J X E C M F A D
A I B C E L K I O O D T E U O R C
N N O B R E H Y R D L K H F V Z V
S T N L Y J D O C I C R E T A W O
```

Solution is on page 388.

When looking for the words associated with Christmas in the puzzle below, you'll find that each word will bend at an angle and no two words will cross. For example WISE MEN is outlined to show you how. There are 25 terms hidden below. Can you find them all?

BIRTHDAY
CANDY
CAROLERS
CELEBRATION
CHRISTMAS TREE
COMPANY
FAMILY
FEAST
FRANKINCENSE
FRIENDS
GIFTS
GLITTER
GOLD
HOLLY
HYMNS
MAGI
MANGER SCENE
MYRRH
PRESENTS
SANTA CLAUS
SLEIGH RIDE
SNOW
TOYS
TRADITION
WISE MEN

```
G I E L S H E H T R I B E C
H T S A A R S D S T N E E S
R A M E A R N A D L S L C N
I G B F Y M E Y O E E A H M
D I O M P O C G R B N D Y Y
E Y T A M C N P R A T I O N
S E N Y A T I K N A R F O W
S Y O L S O S S R E L O O O
U Y H L T M D I F I G R S N
A L R O R A I A R T A A G S
L I A C E N T N R H S C L D
C M A F E G I E E T C A I N
A T N A S E O M E R E T T E
E N E C S R N E S I W F R I
```

Solution is on page 388.

298

Scan the grid in all directions for 62 familiar five-letter words, arranged in pairs. Each word in a pair crosses its partner through the center letter, forming either a "+" or an "x" shape. One pair has been circled to start you off.

YOUR WORD LIST

```
H J L I R H L E T E V Y C E
U O A E F O B C P P N R A D
D E V A W Z A R M O R R U B
L A I E D E N S E G L O O T
S N R D R N J P T Y R S S B
T T P I A N O E L P M A I E
G S A M E C I L S S E H S U
Y L L I H K N R B Y L A W P
F B E A N P T E L L E I C O
A O R O T W S U I T E N T H
Y D R A H E A W N L A A O R
N T O C Y T T I K D A M O N
H L R B E H I J E N E E E J
G I Q U E H N S U Y B R I D
```

Solution is on page 389; list, page 401.

BIOGRAPHY: DUNCAN PHYFE

This puzzle is about a Scottish immigrant whose craft contributed to America's artistic history. To learn about Duncan Phyfe (1768-1854) and his occupation, read the information given below. Then circle the terms hidden in the diagram on the opposite page.

A cabinet-
maker and
furniture
designer,
Duncan
Phyfe won
fame
for the
artistic
beauty
of his
furniture.
Phyfe
used
reeding
and carved
leaves,
cornucopias
and wheat
ears

in his
ornamentation.
Born in
Scotland,
he first
settled
in Albany,
New York
and then
moved
to New York
City.
He became
the leading
American
furniture
maker
of his
time.

```
A H T G N I D A E L E H T B I O T I
K R O Y W E N A W A R B E T K F C A
B F N E P M E F C N D A O O U H F N
D D E V R A C D N A U Y H R A I W D
E N W C R F R A R T B T N N S R W
L V Y S O V C E Y L R I Y A U I L H
T I O E C I E P T N T C N M C D N E
T P R H R D A S H U A U S E D N S A
E E K E I U R L R Y D B M N T E U T
S M M N Z I T E I F F A L T V L S D
C A G D F V I I M A K E R A N D C E
N C I E E K S N N E H A E T N Y O L
K E H E L S T E R R I L M I U I T C
A B H H S A I P O C U N R O C E L S
C E R T T S C G R F H F H N V G A I
O H I R D D M L N I C K U I E E N H
R M N O R N N O W E F Y H P S H D F
E L C F F E A V F U R N I T U R E O
```

Solution is on page 389.

LESS is not more in this puzzle, which is made up of the 67 words listed below. Solve it as you did the one on page 265.

ADJUSTS
AIRY
ARCH
AREA
BETS
BLACK
BODY
BOOR
CANOE
CHATTERS
CHOW
CIVIC
COBRA
CROONER
DATE
DELL
DUTY
EXCURSIONS
FEES
FLAKE
FOXY
GOURD
HONOR
HOOD
HOOT
HOWL
ILLS
JUICE
JUROR
KIDNAP
LASH

LEARN
LESS
LORE
LUXURY
MAJOR
MORSEL
NOEL
NOODLE
ORBIT

ORTS
PLANT
PUBLIC
QUAYS
RACKET
RARE
RITES
ROLL
SCAN

SHALE
SHARK
SNAIL
SODA
SORTS
SPINACH
SPIRIT
SPREADERS
SQUIGGLES

STORKS
THAT
THRUSH
TOED
WASH
WHEEL
WISE
YARN
YODEL

```
L W O H C A N I P S H A R K
D U T Y O D E L L C I V I C
F O X Y R O E L A H S D W A
E X C U R S I O N S N A I L
E C O B R A R R T A H T S B
S G I O A Y M E P W H E E L
K T M U D A B N D O H K T E
R O R U J R O O N A A C I O
O O A O U N O O D L E A R N
T H R U S H R R F Y Y R I A
S R E T T A H C I L B U P C
Q U A Y S Q U I G G L E S S
```

Solution is on page 389.

You can't visit Disneyland without hearing the song "It's a Small World" at least once. In fact, it is estimated that the song is sung there approximately 270,375 times a year!

0734	0943	2434
0788	0966	2486
0813	2233	2641
0848	2284	2686
		5033
		5084
		5521
		5566
		7631
		7643
		7736
		7786
		7836
		7841
		7931
		7986
		9146
		9188
		9234
		9284
		9343
		9368
		9433
		9443

```
3 4 9 0 9 1 0 6 8 1 3 3 0 5
1 3 4 4 7 6 8 8 3 4 6 3 8 1
3 4 4 3 8 3 2 7 4 4 8 6 2 1
9 3 6 6 6 1 4 6 4 8 3 1 7 2
7 3 8 8 1 4 3 4 4 4 1 8 4 5
4 7 8 4 6 3 4 3 3 6 4 3 1 5
7 9 1 8 8 2 7 9 9 1 9 2 3 4
2 6 8 4 8 7 1 3 1 3 6 8 3 0
6 4 3 3 3 2 7 4 4 6 4 8 7 4
4 1 8 6 8 9 7 8 6 3 6 8 4 6
7 8 6 6 3 4 6 1 3 1 8 5 6 3
6 6 2 8 4 6 1 4 4 6 8 4 5 3
3 3 1 2 9 3 4 6 1 4 9 2 8 4
1 9 5 0 8 4 2 8 0 8 1 3 6 9
```

Solution is on page 389.

The struggle between good and evil has long been a classic literary theme. But before American westerns put white hats on the "good guys" and black ones on the "bad guys," it wasn't always so easy to spot the villains. Listed below are some villains from the works of William Shakespeare. In parentheses is the title of the play in which each character appears.

ANTIOCHUS (*Pericles, Prince of Tyre*)

ANTONIO (*The Tempest*)

BRUTUS (*Julius Caesar*)

CASSIUS (*Julius Caesar*)

CLAUDIUS (*Hamlet*)

DON JOHN (*Much Ado About Nothing*)

FREDERICK (*As You Like It*)

GONERIL (*King Lear*)

GUILDENSTERN (*Hamlet*)

IAGO (*Othello*)

LADY MACBETH (*Macbeth*)

LUCIUS (*Timon of Athens*)

LUCULLUS (*Timon of Athens*)

MACBETH (*Macbeth*)

PROTEUS (*Two Gentlemen of Verona*)

REGAN (*King Lear*)

ROSENCRANTZ (*Hamlet*)

SCROOP (*Henry IV Part One*)

SHYLOCK (*The Merchant of Venice*)

TYBALT (*Romeo and Juliet*)

```
N E W U Q N L R S O A L E D L
R A D Y Z I C L A U D I U S A
Y O G T R X S Y S U I C U L D
N E R E T B A C N E H S K M Y
G H N F R E D E R I C K S E M
I O O U T O A T E O D B H A A
G N T J C H S P T O O R D S C
H U W Z N A R E S A V P T R B
S S U H C O I T N A O Y I E E
H O N S T E D T E C B F H O T
Y W Y E D S O V D A R T G N H
L F U R N N U G L N B A I D A
O S O C I Y F T I G I O N L C
C N R O N L U C U L L U S T O
K H T E B C A M G A I N F M Z
```

Solution is on page 389.

Danger and risk are inherent in all of man's ventures, but all of the words below help to lessen worry and increase safety. How many of these protective items and people can you find in the diagram?

```
Q A L L E R B M U Q J N T C S Q
B Z N K A C W O U R T R D Q E J
Q R O L Z Q T S Q T A H D R A H
S A R S S L E Q L F R E L Q T D
U I P E Q U L U F J C O Q L B R
N N A N T Z N I T I C Z F M E A
G C Z T L S C T L K S K H R L U
L O M R Q L I O A Q J E Q A T G
A A G Y I M P N Q N L Z K L M Y
S T N G W Q D E A M L S J A Q D
S N H Q L K C T E B Q O S E R O
E T O Q E E Q T L R R K T R S B
S L L Y R O S I V Q N F Z I T Q
D L E I H S D N I W O Q Q F O J
L R U B B E R G L O V E S Q O N
H H Z R C E D A R T S U L A B Q
```

Solution is on page 389.

APRON
BALUSTRADE
BANISTER
BODY GUARD
BOOTS
BRAKES
FIRE ALARM
FORT
GOGGLES
HARD HAT
HELMET
LOCK AND KEY
MASK
MITT
MOSQUITO
   NETTING
POLICE
RAINCOAT
ROOF
RUBBER GLOVES
SEAT BELT
SENTRY
SUNGLASSES
SUNTAN LOTION
TRAFFIC LIGHT
UMBRELLA
VISOR
WINDSHIELD

RADIO CHARACTERS

Although the characters on radio shows could only be heard and not seen, the cast of a show could almost make the action "visible" to the listener. Of course, this required a good rapport between the stars and supporting actors of the particular series. Listed below are the names of supporting characters from some of the most famous radio shows of the past. The names of the shows are in parentheses and will not be found in the diagram.

BEULAH ("Fibber McGee and Molly")

BIG-EARS BENNY ("The Thin Man")

CHARLIE THE CREEP ("The Thin Man")

CLANCY ("Mr. Keen")

DIGGER O'DELL ("The Life of Riley")

DOC GAMBLE ("Fibber McGee and Molly")

EMMY LOU ("Ozzie and Harriet Nelson")

FOGGY WILLIAMS ("Fibber McGee and Molly")

GLORIE ("Ozzie and Harriet Nelson")

ISH KABIBBLE ("Kay Kyser")

JANE ("My Friend Irma")

JUGHEAD ("Archie Andrews")

KINGFISH ("Amos and Andy")

KNOBBY ("Joe Palooka")

LIGHTNIN' ("Amos and Andy")

MAYOR LA TRIVIA ("Fibber McGee and Molly")

OLD TIMER ("Fibber McGee and Molly")

PASQUALE ("Life with Luigi")

PEAVEY ("The Great Gildersleeve")

PEDRO ("Judy Canova Show")

ROCHESTER ("Jack Benny Show")

ROSA ("Life With Luigi")

SAPPHIRE ("Amos and Andy")

SENATOR CLAGHORN ("Fred Allen Show")

SHORTY THE BARBER ("Amos and Andy")

STONEWALL THE LAWYER ("Amos and Andy")

TEENY ("Fibber McGee and Molly")

THORNY ("Ozzie and Harriet Nelson")

TONTO ("The Lone Ranger")

UNCLE BAXTER ("The Life of Riley")

WIMPY ("Popeye the Sailor")

ZOOKIE ("Mel Blanc Show")

```
T E E N Y Q L K D A E H G U J Q P R
M Q S M A I L L I W Y G G O F R E E
W S R R A Q Q N I N T H G I L O E Y
S Q U O L Y M M E J G Q G D Q C R W
T E K P L Q O C Q I L F O D R H C A
J A N E P D E R N N K C I Q M E E L
U L Q A B T T L L Y G O E S Q S H E
N W B V T Q E I B A B I O W H T T H
C Y Q E P O U L M B T B Q Z Y E E T
L Z C Y M H R B A E I R O L G R I L
E T O N T O L C Z U R B I N Q Z L L
B R Q R A E Y P L L Q Q A V K H R A
A O I O D L S B Q A H S A K I Q A W
X S Z H Q E C H K H G E A Q H A H E
T A Z T P H P Q W I P H H P L S C N
E Q W I M P Y H X L F Q O K Q H I O
R H R E B R A B E H T Y T R O H S T
Z B I G E A R S B E N N Y Q N B L S
M A C L E L L E D O R E G G I D K B
```

Solution is on page 389.

"MIXED" FRUITS AND VEGGIES ────────────

If you enjoy mixed fruits or mixed vegetables, we've got a concoction for you! Below are the scrambled names of 30 fruits and vegetables. Unscramble them and you'll have an alphabetized list of the words hidden in the diagram on the opposite page. The unscrambled list of foods can be found on page 401.

1. PLAPE _____

2. OCTIRAP _____

3. KETCHORAI _____

4. UGSSPAARA _____

5. DOOVAAC _____

6. AANBAN _____

7. TEBE _____

8. COILBORC _____

9. SELSBRUS RUTOPSS _____

10. ORCART _____

11. CLEYRE _____

12. RHYCER _____

13. NRCO _____

14. MECCUBUR _____

15. TAED _____

16. ATPEGGLN _____

17. PERGA _____

18. CEUTLET _____

19. MLIA NABE _____

20. NOONI _____

21. GORNEA _____

22. HAPCE _____

23. SPAE _____

24. SHAIRD _____

25. CASHNIP _____

26. YSAWBRETRR _____

27. AMOTTO _____

28. PRINTU _____

29. MANOWRETEL _____

30. CHINZUIC _____

```
A B Z A C U C U M B E R P A Y G
M A U H S I D A R X A Z K R S M
A M C I C E N O L E M R E T A W
N O C C C A C T F O O L U I E O
A X H I R C N A B B E O R C H Y
N O I N O A E M S C R I C H T O
A B N L L I F O A P R I C O T R
B P I P P H Y T S P I E N K R A
S U G A R A P S A E L N P E L N
A G H T O R L T H P T C A M B G
E Q U A R E N R P K V A U C R E
P M E B S R A A V O C A D O H S
A I C S B H E W A T P I N R U T
R W U B A W B B L Q X O N M Z O
G R T R H C A E P P J G D O H R
B O T E L I M R F G R U J D L R
B E E T K S I R F T A B A N A A
S K L A N H L Y E T Y R R E H C
```

Solution is on page 389; list, page 401.

The verse below, taken from the poem "A Psalm of Life," was written by Henry Wadsworth Longfellow (1807-1882). It appeared in his first volume of poems titled, "Voices of the Night."

Lives of	sublime,
great	And,
men	departing,
all	leave
remind us	behind us
We can	Footprints
make	on the
our	sands
lives	of time.

```
S D R E M I N D U S
Y U E R G R E A T U
L V B P E H T N O D
E I L L A S I D F N
A M V B I R J Y A I
V A I E P M T C S H
E K L T S D E I D E
W E O R F W E N N B
P O U X C O I U A G
F O S E V I L A S D
```

Solution is on page 389.

Here's an OPPORTUNITY to solve another Tanglewords. See page 266 for solving directions.

ABLATE
ALBUM
ARROGANT
BENEATH
CUTE
CYPRESS

DATE
DIMPLE
DIPLOMATIC
DISCREET
ECHO
EMULATE

FRET
GARLAND
GUESSER
GUEST
HANGAR
HIBACHI

KEENEST
LAPEL
LIABLE
MACRAME
MARBLE
NOISY
OPPORTUNITY
OUTPUT
PAUPER
PLATELET
PRACTICAL
RHOMBOID
RHUBARB
ROACH
SEMINAR
SLATE
TENTATIVE
ULTERIOR
UPDATE
VACATION
VERSIFY

Solution is on page 390.

311

Here's another Tail Tag to tackle. See page 269 for solving directions. HIGH, the first word, is entered on the dash to start you off.

HIGH	(4)	_____	(4)	_____	(6)
_____	(6)	_____	(4)	_____	(5)
_____	(5)	_____	(4)	_____	(4)
_____	(6)	_____	(7)	_____	(5)
_____	(7)	_____	(4)	_____	(4)
_____	(5)				
_____	(5)				
_____	(4)				
_____	(7)				
_____	(5)				
_____	(5)				
_____	(4)				
_____	(4)				
_____	(5)				
_____	(4)				
_____	(6)				
_____	(4)				
_____	(6)				
_____	(6)				
_____	(6)				
_____	(5)				
_____	(6)				
_____	(4)				
_____	(4)				
_____	(5)				
_____	(4)				
_____	(5)				
_____	(5)				
_____	(5)				

```
K S I H W L Y R E P A T D F
E N H G H E S I R S C O U R
L T W G N W R N Q E T B L A
P R I N C E Y D L Q M I D Z
V E Y N X C Y E N I M A X E
R V P Y T H U S Q N N H T E
N I A D R O Z P L E E W L R
U D Z P I N S U A O K N A E
G G E Y L G F R G W O H H H
G L I Z Z A S N E X T S M W
E Z N H O S T E L K A Z E O
T A G G E D O E Q T N N A N
N I W H Q Z R X S Q I I S W
H N R Y B L Y A R D H C T H
```

Solution is on page 390; list, page 401.

Whether you eat out at a fine restaurant or a local diner, you're sure to find all or most of the items listed below as part of your surroundings. For now, see if you can find them in the diagram.

A LA CARTE
APPETIZER
ASH TRAY
BEVERAGE
BOOTH

BUFFET
CANDLES
CASH REGISTER
CHEF
COFFEE

COOK
COUNTER
DESSERT
DOGGIE BAG
DOORMAN
ENTREE
GRILL
HOSTESS
MAITRE D'
MATCHES
MENU
MINTS
MUSIC
NAPKINS
PEPPER
SALAD
SALT
SERVICE
SOUP
STEAM TABLE
STOOL
TAB
TABLE
TIP
TOOTHPICKS
TRAY
VALET
WAITER
WAITRESS
WATER

```
B E V E R A G E D O G G I E B A G
Q R D O O R M A N N D E R T I A M
S E K V S E L D N A C O U N T E R
S P C C N J E Q A P P E T I Z E R
E P G U T S A R J K I M Q W H A E
R E T R S V T D T I I J C H C L T
T P A E I A S J S N W H D O T A S
I Y R P B L S A T S E M P S O C I
A T A L I E L S L F T T Z T O A G
W M E S R T S O M A M B A E T R E
J A J V H T O O B U D U K S H T R
L T I R E T A W U U S L S S P E H
C C Q T S R R W I P F I C I I T S
E H O T E B B A E E F F O C C C A
D E J O S R J L Y Z Q B E R K I C
F S Q W K E L B A T M A E T S U Z
```

Solution is on page 390.

APPETIZERS — 256

Now that you've located the numerous restaurant items on the previous page, search your mind to see if you can come up with the 30 appetizers we've hidden in the diagram below. Our list is on page 401.

YOUR WORD LIST

I	N	I	H	C	C	U	Z	D	E	I	R	F	W	P	A
H	U	S	S	T	O	R	R	A	C	E	K	I	M	S	B
W	C	R	E	G	G	R	O	L	L	S	K	I	C	C	J
I	T	C	P	H	J	U	S	Q	D	E	R	N	A	A	U
R	S	K	A	L	S	E	Q	A	R	H	A	V	E	L	I
S	O	M	N	O	L	I	V	E	S	E	I	A	G	L	C
A	T	C	A	K	B	T	D	S	T	A	N	E	A	I	E
R	S	U	C	L	Y	I	S	A	R	Z	S	M	S	O	M
D	A	I	N	V	C	U	P	R	R	E	T	I	U	N	M
I	P	D	L	L	Y	R	E	L	E	C	K	L	A	S	O
N	I	O	I	S	T	F	D	H	I	T	R	C	S	O	S
E	T	N	B	P	O	W	C	O	Z	N	S	P	A	T	N
S	N	O	L	L	I	U	O	B	S	H	E	Y	A	R	O
D	A	W	V	S	P	I	P	C	V	T	A	Z	O	P	C
S	M	O	O	R	H	S	U	M	H	E	R	R	I	N	G

Solution is on page 390; list, page 401.

Here's a puzzle to get you in the spirit of the holiday season. Unscramble the letters below to form words associated with Santa. If you need some help, the word list is on page 401.

GASB
RABED
SLEBL
ZILBNET
TOBOS
SOBW
DAYNC
HEFLUREC
RINHECLD
HYMINCE
SHAMRSTIC
OCTEM
DIPUC
CADREN
HERSAD
LOSLD
REDNON
SELVE
CALERIFEP
TIFSG
PAHYP
ALODIHY
PEOH
LOYLJ
SILT
ILAM
REYMR
SMR. SLUCA
TROHN LOPE
CRENAPR

DRE ITUS
NIDERERE
OFOR
OLDPHUR
GLIHES
OWNS

SKITGSONC
SYOT
RETE
INXEV
WRITEN
REDNOW

```
R H G I E L S U A L C S R M R
E Y N T F R E W O N D E R Q E
C O R E I S G N I K C O T S E
N S O R R U L Y O N S L L O D
A R E O E D S A A T T L B T N
R M O V P M L D F B E E E G I
P F Y L L O J I E B A M R S E
Y O P U A E G L H R O G A W R
E M P B C N O O D C W M S O U
N R A L E P E H T S T O O B D
M E H I H L E X S S Y S N I O
I N Z T L C P R I Y O D P S L
H N R Z R L O R L V O U N V P
C O G E R E H S A D C T R A H
N D Y N O C E L U F R E E H C
```

Solution is on page 390; list, page 401.

"YES, VIRGINIA ..."

The following letter appeared in the *New York Sun* on September 11, 1897. An excerpt from the reply follows the letter below.

Dear

Editor:

I am 8

years

old.

Some

of my

friends

say

there

is no

Santa

Claus.

Papa

says

"If you

see it in

the sun

it's so."

Please

tell

me the

truth;

is there a

Santa

Claus?

Signed:

Virginia

O'Hanlon.

Yes,

Virginia,

there

is a

Santa

Claus.

He exists

as certainly

as love

and

generosity

and

devotion

exist,

and you

know

that

they

abound

and give

to your

life its

highest

beauty

and joy.

```
E R E H T D E N G I S 8 N T A B
M X S U A L C L A U S E Y A P E
O 8 I F Y O U S T I E F I L A A
S Y A S M 8 S E N S R A E Y P U
E S N T T M D A A C L A U S E T
E A D H R A N D S 8 S A T I H Y
I N Y E A N E L L E T S A A T L
T T O S E D I T O R I M T I E N
I A U U D J R I V X 8 H S S M I
N E I N N O F R E I E O E A S A
O R M N A Y U E O E R E H T A T
L E Y 8 I O H F O E Y G G M N R
N H A T Y G M K N O W E I E T E
A T S O O Y R E T R U T H N A C
H S T A N D G I V E H T 8 T I S
O I S N O I T O V E D N U O B A
```

Solution is on page 390.

JACKPOT BINGO

The words in the Jackpot Bingo card are your word list. Find as many words as you can in the diagram, crossing them off the Jackpot card as you go. When you have found all the words you can, use the uncircled letters to form the single 5-letter word, which, when crossed off the Bingo card, will give you Jackpot Bingo, which is seven words in a row, across, down or diagonally. Hint: There will be 11 uncircled letters from which to form the Jackpot word. CLEAR has been looped to start you off.

J	A	C	K	P	O	T
PAPER	THINE	LATER	CHEER	EAGER	ALIAS	REACH
PARTY	THINK	LEARN	CHICK	EARLY	ALIVE	REBEL
PEACH	TORCH	LEMON	CHILD	EBONY	ALLOY	REPAY
PEARL	TOXIN	LINER	CLEAR	EIDER	ALONE	REPLY
PIECE	TRACE	LOOSE	COUNT	ELUDE	ALTAR	RESIN
PRICE	TRAIL	LOSER	CRANE	EPOCH	ARENA	RIFLE
PRINT	TROOP	LOTTO	CREEP	ERASE	ARGUE	RINSE

Solution is on page 390.

318

```
R P A N E R A P R I C E
E E R E B E L E A H O L
S R P I O I H A I E V U
O A E L N O L C H I L D
L S E E Y T K H A D I E
F E R E A T T (C L E A R)
G S C R P O H O I R R M
T N R A E L I P A R T Y
R I I C R A N E S O O L
O R E S K T E I R L X R
O I S R E E H C L L I A
P A P E R R H A L O N E
```

Jackpot word: __ __ __ __ __

The early Dutch settlers spelled "St. Nicholas" as "*Sinterklass*," which later became anglicized to the name "Santa Claus." The origin of the Santa Claus story is given below.

The Santa
Claus
myth

is based
on St.
Nicholas,

the bishop
of Myra
and
the patron
saint of
children,
who was
born
in the
Turkish
town of
Lycia
in the
fourth
century.
He was
famous
for
his
generosity
and
kindness to
children,
and
his
legend
was brought
to America
by the
Dutch.

```
S M T H G U O R B S A W F E
A U R O R E H T N I N R O B
L T O Y W E N S C D I N U F
O R N M W N I E N I S S R O
H T M A A H O E R S B T T T
C F S O S F G F E O A S H N
I T O A M E R I C A S V H I
N T E R L R H D Y E E I C A
O W H O W A S T N M D O T S
N E T E N I N D Y A N O U Y
I T U D B A N T H S D F D R
N E R D L I H C T U N M E U
T H K W K C S H O A A Y L T
H T I E S Y C H I L D R E N
E Y S I W L O R O C L A D E
G B H B N O R T A P E H T C
```

Solution is on page 390.

CHRISTMAS INSPIRATIONS ——————— 261

It is interesting to note that two of our most popular Christmas melodies were actually written on Christmas. What inspired the composers and the names of these two hymns are noted below.

Charles Wesley, author of "Hark, the Herald Angels Sing," said that he was inspired to write the hymn after hearing church bells one Christmas morning. And Lewis H. Dedner, composer of "O Little Town of Bethlehem," claimed that its melody came to him in a dream on Christmas Eve.

```
Y F M N O M A E R D A E C T
D O H S I W E L E D E R A H
O N R T Y M E M C E H H M C
L W D I A S I N H D T R E R
E O T L S A C H O N K I T U
M T T T L M A F T E R M O H
S E A C A T G N I R A E H C
T S H W O S E L R A H C O H
I G T E L I D Y S A D M L R
H N E E L R T E E A P N S I
E I G V A H N L R O W L A S
R N D N E C T S S I L E G T
A R W H I T D E B E P L H M
L O Y E I S R W B E A S O A
D M S L T O W R I T E C N S
N V O S F O R O H T U A H I
```

Solution is on page 390.

Here's another Tail Tag puzzle. This time we give you no help in finding the 39 words of 4 letters or more used to complete this puzzle. The directions are on page 269, but here's a hint: You will complete this puzzle wherever you begin it.

_____   _____   _____
_____   _____   _____
_____   _____   _____
_____   _____   _____
_____   _____   _____

```
L Y D R W Y E L L R C P K S
R D I O D W L I M M R S S T
Q M M E R L M R V O H I S U
S M P Q O P R O U G H L T P
C T L Y L A E D J O L L B O
H J E J R L W B M I H S U R
E X S A N D O Z T E K C O R
I Z R M I V B H V P R O M E
S B L V Q M N V O N Z O Q W
T E A K U L Q H V L S W D E
T O R N L U S Q T S T E R N
U B C A Q N G G J H Z W A Q
A Y H C G C Z M G A Q Z M B
T L I K L H O L D E L B A V
```

Solution is on page 391; list, page 402.

Solve this puzzle like the one on page 274. Remember, you are circling the new words in the grid. None of the original words can be found. The proverb can be read down the page.

HOSTING   ____

METEOR   ____

COOPING   ____

MARCHER   ____

GRANDEUR   ____

WINCED   ____

HAILED   ____

EXPERT   ____

FAUCET   ____

BREADTH   ____

DINNER   ____

DIETER   ____

PRINCE   ____

FINGER   ____

WHOLLY   ____

BRAIDS   ____

GRAVEL   ____

SIMPLER   ____

CROWED   ____

CHORDS   ____

POINTS   ____

SKEWER   ____

CAREER   ____

FAILED   ____

DRAWER   ____

NOOSES   ____

GOLDEN   ____

```
G R Y L L O H T A E R B
D E F L E B O F I L E D
R P L N R C S W A V V G
E M G A E S I W A C N R
N I D S T N N R O I E J
I S N N E D G R P W D T
F N I D D Q D O A E L R
H P N G Y S C R L W O E
R O W E D Z C I E Z Z W
C A R E R H A X Z T Q E
T R E X E X J N O S E S
M N G R A N D E R B L M
```

Solution is on page 391; list, page 402.

It's the holiday season, and probably the last time you'll see Aunt Jennie, Grandpapa John and your host of other relatives and friends together until this same time next year. Why not take a picture to mark this special occasion? Now that you've got the notion, find the CAMERA, hidden once in the diagram below, and start shooting!

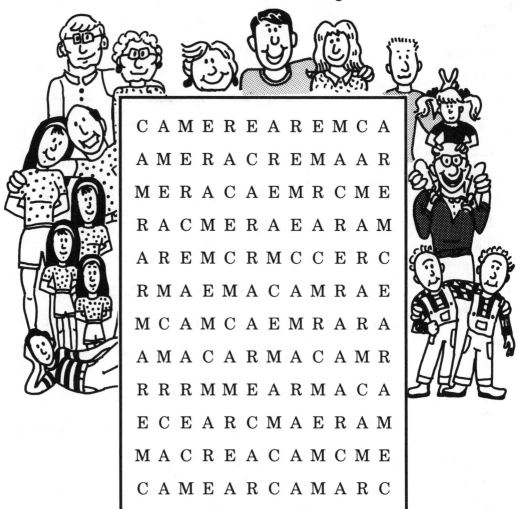

```
C A M E R E A R E M C A
A M E R A C R E M A A R
M E R A C A E M R C M E
R A C M E R A E A R A M
A R E M C R M C C E R C
R M A E M A C A M R A E
M C A M C A E M R A R A
A M A C A R M A C A M R
R R R M M E A R M A C A
E C E A R C M A E R A M
M A C R E A C A M C M E
C A M E A R C A M A R C
```

Solution is on page 391.

Here's the final Tanglewords of this book. See page 266 for solving directions.

ACCREDITED

ASPECT

BOOTED

BROADEN

CHIN

CHORUS

CITADEL

DELINEATE

DIVISION

DONATE

EAVESDROP

EYED

FLESH

FOLIAGE

HALVE

HOTEL

INCITE

INTERLOPER

IRIS

KNIT

LEAGUE

MENAGERIE

MOOSE

NOSED

OVERRAN

PHRENETIC

PROMISOR

RECEIVE

ROOSTER

SAFEGUARD

SATIRE

SERAPE

TALLY

TIMBRE

VAGABOND

VENT

VINTAGE

WORSE

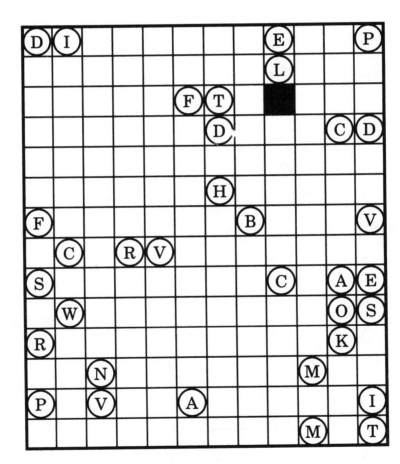

Solution is on page 391.

MATH FUN

Here's another puzzle that tests your math skills. To solve, first determine the answer to the first math problem, then take that answer to solve the second problem, and so on, until you have solved all 35. Then look for the answers in the puzzle diagram on the facing page. Your final answer should be THREE. A similar puzzle is on page 280.

1. $62 + 35 =$ _____
2. $ - 17 =$ _____
3. $ \div 2 =$ _____
4. $ \div 10 =$ _____
5. $ + 13 =$ _____
6. $ + 34 =$ _____
7. $ - 44 =$ _____
8. $ + 53 =$ _____
9. $ \div 20 =$ _____
10. $ \times 5 =$ _____
11. $ \div 3 =$ _____
12. $ \times 12 =$ _____
13. $ - 2 =$ _____
14. $ - 54 =$ _____
15. $ \times 4 =$ _____
16. $ \div 2 =$ _____
17. $ + 62 =$ _____
18. $ \div 14 =$ _____

19. $ + 27 =$ _____
20. $ \div 4 =$ _____
21. $ + 37 =$ _____
22. $ \div 9 =$ _____
23. $ \times 18 =$ _____
24. $ \div 10 =$ _____
25. $ + 29 =$ _____
26. $ - 25 =$ _____
27. $ + 37 =$ _____
28. $ \div 10 =$ _____
29. $ + 61 =$ _____
30. $ \div 6 =$ _____
31. $ - 9 =$ _____
32. $ \times 3 =$ _____
33. $ + 53 =$ _____
34. $ - 50 =$ _____
35. $ \div 3 =$ _____

```
I N E V E S E R O V E R E R
N F O V R N E W E A R V O U
N N I W I U T V L N I N I O
S F I F T Y O N E F I Y L F
E I G O T R O F V N T Y I I
E O X R O Y Y N E E T F I F
R V I T M X E T N R T E N T
H H I Y Y I Y I O Y O B E Y
T R O F A S N F G Y R Y E N
T H G I E Y T R I H T O T I
E H R V R T M H M H T X R N
A N E E T X I S G T H G I E
M N I R E I I I G I R N H S
S M Y N X S E S E V E N T Y
```

Solution is on page 391; list, page 402.

IRREGULAR PLURALS

More than one "car" may be "cars," but more than one SHEEP are still SHEEP! SHEEP is included in the list below of irregular plurals, which are words whose plurals differ from the regular plural formation of adding "s" or "es" to the singular. The singular for each word is listed in parentheses next to it.

AXES (axis)

BACTERIA (bacterium)

BASES (basis)

BEAUX (beau)

CRISES (crisis)

CUMULI (cumulus)

DATA (datum)

DEER (deer)

DICE (die)

ELLIPSES (ellipsis)

ELVES (elf)

FEET (foot)

GEESE (goose)

HALVES (half)

KNIVES (knife)

LARVAE (larva)

LEAVES (leaf)

LIVES (life)

LOAVES (loaf)

MEDIA (medium)

MEMORANDA (memorandum)

MEN (man)

MICE (mouse)

MOOSE (moose)

NEBULAE (nebula)

OASES (oasis)

OXEN (ox)

SELVES (self)

SERIES (series)

SHEAVES (sheaf)

SHEEP (sheep)

SHELVES (shelf)

SPECIES (species)

STRATA (stratum)

SWINE (swine)

TABLEAUX (tableau)

TEETH (tooth)

THESES (thesis)

THIEVES (thief)

TROUSSEAUX (trousseau)

TROUT (trout)

WIVES (wife)

WOLVES (wolf)

WOMEN (woman)

```
E R L H T R O U S S E A U X C U M U L I
F P T X M X U A E B A N L E M F I E Q A
S A H R D V U S S L V A A G I I R D N I
E A I E E I A A O I R L L Q O B C D S R
V T E O C B F T H V U C R I S E S E E E
A R V O X A E S A B T D I T W S E R S T
O X E I V E I E E J A I Q I E Z V J P C
L S S S F R N N V T O C V K E O L N I A
L H P S M E D I A Q R E N S S R A W L B
I E C E P C Q W X O S O E D O G H L L S
K L A L C E D S E V L E U J E V N I E S
I V R V I J C O S R G Q S T N O P V T T
N E I E E S E I R E S P E E H S I E A R
S S R S O S S H E A V E S S H N E S F A
T A B L E A U X O S U L A I K T A L B T
Z I C L O S B I P E S O O M H Q J I T A
A D N A R O M E M B L O X W O M E N S O
```

Solution is on page 391.

"Tell me that you want the kind of things that money just can't buy" is a line from the Beatles 1964 hit "Can't Buy Me LOVE." Have you run out of money before buying gifts for several people left on your list? Don't fret. Take a cue from the Beatles, and consider giving some of the items below—special gifts that money just can't buy.

```
R T C E P S E R E N I T Y N
R T V L S S E N D N I K R O
Z O D N I M F O E C A E P I
L K N L T D A J M N C V K T
M L A O R L I R Q N Z N R O
X E H A H L T K O Y J U Q V
Z T G M N R H C C D S R T E
T E N R C S J R P T R J L D
R K I N D H E A R T P A O T
O K P Q O M D L R L R R Y E
F P L P E C N E I T A P A C
M E E T S E E Q J M I Z L A
O P H N M H K L R T S J T L
C Q R S C C O U R T E S Y O
E S Y R B H A P P I N E S S
```

Solution is on page 391.

ARDOR
CHEER
COMFORT
CONCERN
COURTESY
DEVOTION
ESTEEM
FAITH
HAPPINESS
HELPING HAND
HONOR
HOPE
KIND HEART
KINDNESS
LOVE
LOYALTY
MERCY
PATIENCE
PEACE OF MIND
PRAISE
REGARD
RESPECT
SERENITY
SMILES
SOLACE
TRUST
ZEAL

Would you believe that Mr. Ed, television's talking horse, has a Social Security number? Of course! It's 054-22-5457.

0017	6643
0067	6653
0134	6813
0162	6839
2235	8201
2244	8261
2374	8401
2385	8491
2415	9355
2437	9357
4526	9534
4570	9570
4625	9717
4685	9771
4730	9941
4798	9971

```
1 1 9 4 8 3 5 7 7 8 2 2 3 5
7 3 7 5 1 1 3 5 4 3 2 7 7 1
0 9 3 3 7 4 6 1 7 3 7 6 1 7
8 0 7 6 2 5 8 1 3 5 1 3 1 9
3 5 6 3 2 5 1 7 2 7 7 0 3 5
1 7 3 7 1 5 3 9 7 7 3 5 1 3
6 6 5 3 5 4 4 9 1 5 5 8 6 4
8 1 5 5 7 7 3 0 3 1 8 1 7
6 2 5 3 2 0 0 1 7 7 3 4 3 7
6 3 0 7 7 6 3 3 5 9 5 7 2 5
4 1 3 1 5 7 4 7 4 5 0 7 5 3
3 8 4 0 1 5 4 1 8 3 1 7 5 9
7 5 7 7 3 5 2 3 5 3 5 3 5 1
1 4 9 9 1 3 2 7 2 6 1 0 5 9
```

Solution is on page 391.

SEASHELLS BY THE SEASHORE

A trip to the beach is never complete without a search for some beautiful seashells to take home with you. Listed below are the names of some seashells you might find if you were to visit Florida's sunny coastline.

ABALONE	FIG	PYRAM
ANGEL WING	FROG	QUAHOG
ARK	HAIRY	RISSO
AUGER	HELMET	ROCK
BONNET	HOOF	SCALLOP
CAECUM	HORN	SIMNIA
CARRIER	HORSE CONCH	SLIPPER
CERITH	JANTHINA	SUNDIAL
CHITON	JEWEL BOX	TELLIN
CLAM	LIMA	TRITON
COCKLE	LIMPET	TRITON'S TRUMPET
CONCH	MARGINELLA	
CONE	MITER	TRIVIA
COQUINA	MOON	TULIP
CORAL	MUREX	TUN
COWRIE	MUSSEL	TURRID
CUP-AND-SAUCER	NUTMEG	TUSK
CYPHOMA	OLIVE	VASE
DIPLODON	OYSTER	VENUS
DOVE	PAPER NAUTILUS	VOLUTE
DRILL	PEN	WENTLETRAP
DRUPE	PERIWINKLE	WHELK

```
E N T S N G D R I L L N T E P M I L E H
M B O N N O T I H C R A W H L A T H A L
U N E O V R D X C O N C H T I R E C I K
R K I E M F O O H N A U E C O Y N N N M
E N O L A B A R L E O P L C Y P H O M A
Y U Q A L M E P A P M A K S R M O C I L
A T S E I E C O Q U I N A G O U B E S C
F M W L S V T U R R I D M N T S U S O Y
T E M L E H I T S D V S R I S S O R E P
J G N K L E S R E G N A O W Y E A O L H
P A P E R N A U T I L U S L R L J H K O
A U N C O N C R N L H C A E C U M S N F
R G V T Q X I L E D A E I G H T U L I P
T E I L H T S N E L I R U N I S R G W U
G R E V O I I T L O R A K A T R E T I M
T O S N O G N O K A Y T L S O E X U R A
N U H Y R L P A C H O S E T U L O V E I
Y N E A T H I N O W E N T L E T R A P N
C E M S U N E V C O W R I E T E N N O B
S V C O N Q U R E P P I L S R L E W E J
```

Solution is on page 391.

High schools and colleges both have four years of learning. The word "freshman" represents someone new to the experience, while a junior is young and subordinate, and a senior is older and above others in rank. The origin of the word "sophomore," however, is noted below.

The word "sophomore," meaning a second-year student, comes from the Greek words of "sophos" and "moros," meaning "wise" and "foolish." The idea of a person being a wise fool after only a short period of study is also shown in our use of the word "sophomoric" for someone who is immature but opinionated.

```
B A N W O H S S T U D E N T
R U S T Y S E N O E M O S H
A F T E R I H O T R F O S E
E A A P C L B A F O O E D G
H R G M S O N E O S M M T R
C Y L N O O N L T O T H L E
I W C I I F P D C R E U G E
R S H N G E T H E W O R D K
O O I O N I B F O O I H E Y
M P E R I O D R O M N O S P
O H F U N S D K M E O A D A
H O S L A S I A S A S R N L
P S T M E W T I R N R U E D
O N O Y M U W G O I E O S A
S R W O R D S O F N P N I N
F O A E D I E H T G A I W D
```

Solution is on page 392.

We've hidden below the names of 40 long distance runners who have won Olympic gold medals. Can you keep up the pace and track them all down?

BARTHEL (Joseph, 1952)

BIKILA (Abebe, 1960-64)

BIWOTT (Amos, 1968)

BORDIN (Gelindo, 1988)

BRAGINA (Lyudmila, 1972)

BRASHER (Chris, 1956)

COE (Sebastian, 1980-84)

COVA (Alberto, 1984)

DELANEY (Ron, 1956)

DORIO (Gabriella, 1984)

ELLIOTT (Herb, 1960)

FLACK (Edwin, 1896)

HILL (Albert, 1920)

HODGE (Percy, 1920)

ISO-HOLLO (Volmari, 1932-36)

IVAN (Paula, 1988)

KEINO (Kipchoge, 1968)

KORIR (Julius, 1984)

KUTS (Vladimir, 1956)

LARVA (Harry, 1928)

LOPES (Carlos, 1984)

MILLS (Billy, 1964)

MIMOUN (Alain, 1956)

NGUGI (John, 1988)

NURMI (Paavo, 1920-24-28)

PULCA (Maricica, 1984)

RITOLA (Willie, 1924-28)

RONO (Peter, 1988)

SAMOLENKO (Tatyana, 1988)

SCHUL (Bob, 1964)

SHORTER (Frank, 1972)

SNELL (Peter, 1964)

SON (Kijung, 1936)

TEMU (Naftali, 1968)

VASALA (Pekka, 1972)

VIREN (Lasse, 1972-76)

WALKER (John, 1976)

WOLDE (Mamo, 1968)

YIFTER (Miruts, 1980)

ZABALA (Juan, 1932)

```
H I L L E N S A C L U P M B
O N I D R O B N Z O N N I A
D U R A N Q T U K T V W L R
G Y I F T E R O E R O A L T
E E R R O R R M A T S U S H
L N O E L N U I T A R C H E
L A K E I N O M V S E P O L
I L N C O V K R T B K B R K
O E E G A L A U Q R L I T R
T D L L U L B N T A A K E I
T L O M A G F C A S W I R T
O O M B O N I S O H O L L O
L W A N I G A R B E R A L L
B Z S C H U L O I R O D E A
```

Solution is on page 392.

As you APPROACH this puzzle containing bowling terms, you should look for terms hidden at every ANGLE, leaving none to SPARE.

ADDRESS (starting position)
ANCHOR (last bowler)
ANGLE (imaginary line)
APPROACH
    (predelivery steps)
BED POSTS
    (a 7-10 pin split)
BLIND (score given for
    absent player)
BRIDGE (distance
    between fingers)
CHANNEL (gutter)
CLEAN (clearing all
    pins)
CONVERT (to pick
    up a spare)
COUNT
    (pins picked up)
DEUCE (200-point
    game)
FRAME (game
    division)
HEAD PIN (the 1 pin)
HOOK (curve ball)
LANE (bowling
    area)
LEAVE (pins left
    standing)
LIFT (a release
    technique)
NOSE DIVE (to hit
    the 1 pin head
    on)
OPEN FRAME
    (spareless or
    strikeless)
PIN BOY
    (pin setter)
PINCHING (tight
    ball grip)
POST (sliding foot
    movement)
RACK (normal pin
    set-up)
RUNWAY
    (approach area)
SPAN (distance
    between thumb
    and fingers)
SPARE (hitting 10
    pins in two turns)
STRIKE (hitting 10
    pins in one turn)
TARGET (spot
    aimed for on
    lane)
WALL SHOT (strike
    caused by pins
    bouncing off wall)

```
T E G R A T S O P D D R B E
D S A L L U P O R A R S E S
J V S E A A A H O A U N D H
E E A E T G N I H C N I P R
C V S T R I K E C B W C O O
E E I L P D C E N E A D S A
N N H D E U D M A P Y P T N
K C A R E Y P A P S H O S G
A E N D O S T R E V N O C L
H G T B E N O F D T S L O E
H D N C H A N N E L I B R K
C I U E C E I E E F R A M E
P R O H R L F P T G P D R I
M B C A B C T O H S L L A W
```

Solution is on page 392.

Whether it be in a MEMO, a LYRIC or a NOVEL, written words help us communicate with the world. Below are 64 written ITEMs. Take pen or pencil in hand and locate them all.

ACT
ALLEGORY
BALLAD
BOOK
BRIEF
BULLETIN
CANTO
CHAPTER
CITATION
COMEDY
COMPOSITION
COPY
DIARY
DIGEST
DISSERTATION
DRAFT
DRAMA
EDITORIAL
EPIC
ESSAY
FABLE
FARCE
ITEM
LAY
LETTER
LIBRETTO
LIMERICK
LYRIC
MEMO
MESSAGE
MOTTO
NARRATIVE
NOTE
NOVEL
ODE
OPUS
PAPER
PASSAGE
PIECE
PLAY

POEM
POTBOILER
REPORT
REVIEW
RHYME
SAGA

SATIRE
SCENE
SENTENCE
SERIAL
SESTINA
SKETCH

SKIT
SPEECH
STANZA
STAVE
TALE
TEXT

THESIS
TOME
TRACT
TREATISE
VERSE
VOLUME

```
V E R S E V I T A R R A N S T T
E C N E T N E S O E N O M T C X
M E O P P T R E A T I S E A A E
O W T A S O E D O T T O M N R T
T S E N T L R I A E E E O Z T D
I P D I A R Y T E L L P R A N P
T E A T V Y R O G E L L A B O V
E E N S E E C R A F U A A T I O
M C B E S H R I S R B Y B Y T L
Y H R S C A Y A S S E O P N A U
H D I T L S G L E R I T A S T M
R D E L B A F E M L L C P H I E
S K F M S D I G E S T Y E A C P
S U B O O K D R A F T S R E H I
C O P Y K C I R E M I L I I D C
L E V O N O I T I S O P M O C O
```

Solution is on page 392.

To solve, rearrange the words below into first names commonly given to boys and girls. After you've formed the names, find them in the diagram. As an example we've rearranged CLEAN to form LANCE, which is hidden in the diagram. For extra help in solving, the list is arranged so that the answers are in alphabetical order.

REDAN _____
INANE _____
BYTES _____
CUBER _____
CABLE _____
CORAL _____
CLEAR _____
DUCAL _____
CIGAR _____
LYRIC _____
LARDY _____
BREAD _____
LADLE _____
NAIAD _____
GRADE _____
WINED _____
TOILE _____
LIVES _____
THANE _____
FARED _____
CAGER _____
GREAT _____
CLEAN   LANCE
AURAL _____
ALONE _____
WILES _____
DOLLY _____
DAILY _____
MANLY _____
AMBLE _____
GAMED _____
GAMER _____

ALARM _____
SMILE _____
CANNY _____
LADEN _____
MANOR _____
VOILE _____

PALER _____
OSIER _____
MEALS _____
HAIRS _____
ISSUE _____
LAZED _____

```
N E L D A D E R F P L E K T
M O W P R L E B A M C E O L
E A R B E D W I N N E I R E
L E K M E A N G A R L W D W
V T N L A R R L R E P D U I
I H L C N Y B L U E Y W A S
S A I D Y L G E A O T E L U
E N L U I E V I L O R A C S
L L D R D Z E L D A E E R I
M E Y I A N O E L I C G O E
A C S M A M R C N L U R S D
D A T P A N B N E C R A I G
G R E R D N A N C Y B M E A
E G B A M I L E S H A R I R
```

Solution is on page 392; names, page 402.

Who do you call if you find yourself trapped inside of a steam room? If there's a phone nearby, just dial 555-2368 to reach Jaime Sommers at her home in the series "The Bionic Woman." She just might be able to help.

0089	1227	2468	3558
0373	1558	2972	3579
0808	1992	3123	4041
1133	2050	3333	4086
			4247
			4707
			5003
			5131
			5522
			5674
			5970
			6440
			6536
			6979
			7089
			7370
			7564
			7946
			8180
			8789
			8850
			9002
			9660
			9905

```
3 2 1 2 5 8 3 3 5 2 0 1 0 1
0 1 7 9 3 5 2 4 9 7 8 3 1 0
3 5 7 3 4 1 9 4 7 6 5 8 2 3
3 5 0 0 3 1 0 9 6 5 0 6 3 8
3 8 7 2 8 3 0 8 0 8 8 0 4 3
0 7 9 5 6 3 9 7 1 9 1 2 8 6
1 9 4 5 9 3 0 8 3 3 4 2 3 7
1 7 0 6 8 3 5 7 1 7 0 5 8 8
2 9 8 0 7 0 4 5 3 4 6 5 2 4
9 0 6 3 4 0 1 9 8 0 8 9 6 0
7 2 5 6 4 9 7 0 4 0 4 1 3 0
9 1 8 5 0 2 9 0 3 8 1 4 6 0
6 7 1 5 2 4 6 2 7 9 2 5 6 4
0 5 6 1 9 1 8 4 5 4 8 3 7 3
```

Solution is on page 392.

Again, solve this puzzle by forming a chain of circled words in which the last letter of one word is the first letter of the next. The number in parentheses tells you the length of the word you're looking for. We have provided QUICK to start you off.

QUICK_____(5)   _____(5)   _____(5)

K_____(4)   _____(4)   _____(4)

_____(7)   _____(5)   _____(4)

_____(4)   _____(5)   _____(6)

_____(6)

_____(5)

_____(6)

_____(4)

_____(4)

_____(5)

_____(4)

_____(4)

_____(7)

_____(5)

_____(4)

_____(5)

_____(5)

_____(4)

_____(7)

_____(7)

_____(5)

_____(4)

_____(5)

_____(4)

_____(5)

_____(5)

_____(4)

_____(4)

_____(6)

_____(5)

_____(6)

```
J M H Z S O L O Q S K L O Y
R I N G S R B M M U Y Z H F
E Q N Q T E W O X E I B G E
T O L Z A V H R L D L C L P
S S A R G L A C Z S R E K U
A J D Z J I I H T X H E T T
O S I Z E S L I W E E D A S
T Y X Y R E S R U N K N I M
B F D I E S E L Z J R X R Z
L L E Y L N P R I T N Y R H
U Z K D N G S H A V E L E G
C Q R Z L A H Y X V E X M U
K A A I Q R M O D L E S I O
Y Z B B L D E Z A D D T R T
```

Solution is on page 392; list, page 402.

Like the other jackpots, solve this puzzle by inserting a letter from below into each of the circles in the diagram. This letter should be one that will let you form as many 5-letter words as possible. If you have entered the correct letters into the circles, you should be able to find 51 words in total. We've inserted the letter "P" to start you off.

B D F H K L M P R T V

YOUR WORD LIST

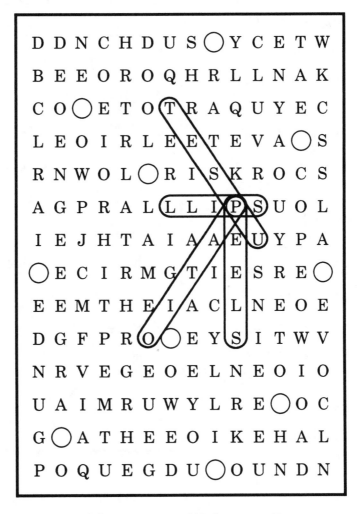

```
D D N C H D U S O Y C E T W
B E E O R O Q H R L L N A K
C O O E T O T R A Q U Y E C
L E O I R L E E T E V A O S
R N W O L O R I S K R O C S
A G P R A L L L I P S U O L
I E J H T A I A A E U Y P A
O E C I R M G T I E S R E O
E E M T H E I A C L N E O E
D G F P R O O E Y S I T W V
N R V E G E O E L N E O I O
U A I M R U W Y L R E O O C
G O A T H E E O I K E H A L
P O Q U E G D U O O U N D N
```

Solution is on page 392; list, page 402.

Each term below has a number following it in parentheses, which refers to the numbered dashes below the diagram. Each word forms a box, reading clockwise or counterclockwise. (HOMESPUN has already been boxed to start you off.) As you find each term in the diagram, enter the unused letter that's in the middle of each box on the correspondingly numbered dash below the diagram ("E" has already been entered). When you have finished, the letters on the dashes will spell out a phrase that applies to this puzzle.

ALUMINUM (5)

BIANNUAL (2)

COMMENCE (6)

DISAGREE (13)

EXPLICIT (20)

FORENSIC (4)

GARDENIA (16)

~~HOMESPUN~~ (9)

IDOLATOR (3)

JUVENILE (21)

KNAPSACK (7)

MIGRAINE (17)

OPERETTA (8)

PEDIGREE (10)

QUANDARY (18)

ROULETTE (12)

SEQUENCE (1)

TELECAST (14)

TENDENCY (15)

UMBRELLA (19)

VERMOUTH (11)

```
A I N E B T E L E J U R E P
G A G M D T T E L E V E N O
E R G I F S A C I N E T T A
I H S I C P R K D I R O E G
J K N R F A N K O U O U L L
I T E R O A R D L A T R A D
C B X M N G E E H O M Y L N
I L P O N A I N N E E Q U A
U E D I N O B P U P S F E Q
T E F S U A L L S R E C N E
V R G A L U O E E P W E O M
R E V M C M B R R E N C O M
M S H U N I X G I D H Y Y Z
O U T B A R D U L N E T N A
```

Solution is on page 392.

— — — —   — — — — E̲ — —
1 2 3 4   5 6 7 8 9 10 11

— —   — — —   — — — — —
12 13 14 15 16 17 18 19 20 21

342

We have titled this puzzle "LO and B-hold" because each of the words in the list begins with the letter B and contains the letters LO.

```
R E T T O L B B B L O N D
E E S N O O L L A B O R
S E P U L O T A O L B O
R B L O O D O N B T K L
E L G M O L O G L W C E
M O S S O L B O O O O H
O W O L L I B L N L L C
O E O I O L E O O B L A
L R U L O B O B O T U B
B O O W L T O L L A B L
B G N O L E B L O C K O
Y E N O L A B A I L O R
```

Solution is on page 393.

BACHELOR
BAILOR
BALLOON
BALLOT
BALONEY
BELLOW
BELONG
BELOW
BILLOW
BIOLOGY
BLOAT
BLOB
BLOCK
BLOND
BLOOD

BLOOM
BLOOMERS
BLOOPER
BLOSSOM
BLOT
BLOTCH
BLOTTER
BLOUSE
BLOW
BLOWER
BLOWN
BOLOGNA
BOUILLON
BULLOCK

Here is a group of words that go back and forth. The letter order in each one spells out one word frontwards and another word backwards—and *both* words are in the diagram. See if you can find all 22 pairs of these back and forth words.

ADOS

BIN

BUD

BUTS

DEMIT
(dismiss)

DESSERTS

DUB

GOT

GUNS

'AIR

LOOP

MOOR

NIB

PANS

PAT

PEELS

POOL

RAT

RAW

REBUT

RIAL (currency)

ROOM

SLEEP

SNAP

SNUG

SODA

SPAY

SPIRT
(British ''spurt'')

SPOT

STRESSED

STUB

SWAT

TAP

TAR

TAWS (marbles)

TIMED

TOG (cloak)

TOPS

TRIPS

TUBER

WAR

WAY

YAPS

YAW

```
M P E T P D D S G O T E S
L O R I A L E B P Q W L V
A O O S N W S M N A E A O
I L N R S L S S I E Y N R
R A S T S J E Y P T O P S
P T T N O D R S U I N I B
G L U T U G T U B E R Y A
R G B B D R S S P A Y T D
T A W S E T A P R A D U O
I N T S R R L A W B B O S
M W S T O I W O I G U N S
E E A T O P S N O R T A P
D R E Y M S L E E P S D E
```

Solution is on page 393.

The mathematical value of "pi" (π) is a never-ending fractional number, which has been determined to over a million decimal places. The terms in this puzzle are pi (3.14159) and the next 145 of these decimal places, listed in groups of five. You'll find them hidden diagonally, horizontally or vertically on all three sides of the cube-shaped diagram. One term may be entirely hidden on one face of the cube or it may bend onto a second, or a third. Pi's 51st–55th decimal digits, 58209, has been circled as a starter.

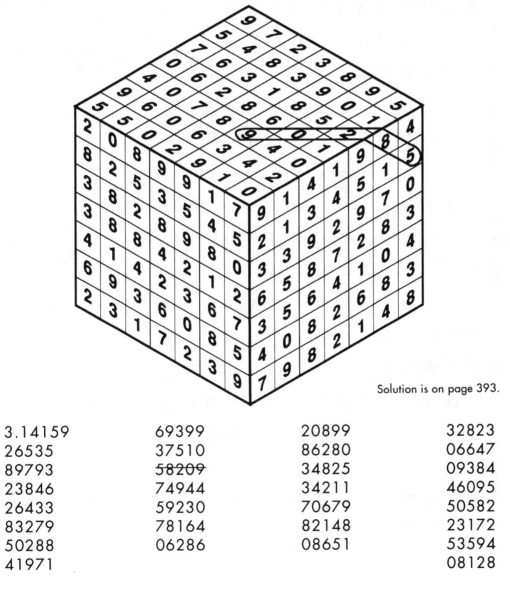

Solution is on page 393.

3.14159	69399	20899	32823
26535	37510	86280	06647
89793	58209	34825	09384
23846	74944	34211	46095
26433	59230	70679	50582
83279	78164	82148	23172
50288	06286	08651	53594
41971			08128

The English physician Edward Jenner (1749-1823) developed and promoted the idea of inoculating people against smallpox, and the origin of the word "vaccine" reflects his early work. When you have circled all the terms, the uncircled letters will spell out a comment about doctors.

```
A S U A G A I N S T D R T V
E G N I S U F O G E E H O A
Z H N E T A H T T I E S A C
I F T D V W O I N I T A L C
N C O H T E D C D O A R W I
U A S R T E R E N N E J E N
M S I M R I A D D H O L C E
M K H C A N W H E O P O W S
I S C O I L E S V O W P M E
O W I O T S L P E D W A R D
T O H E D S Y P L C L N S L
V R W I H E I H O L G D E T
A D A I R Y N W P X O T M O
C M O R F S P O E E T H O G
C C O W P O X I D D H E C E
A O U T X C O N C E P T O F
```

The physician Edward Jenner noticed that dairy maids who got cowpox never got smallpox, and he developed the idea of using cowpox shots to immunize people against smallpox. He is credited with the concept of vaccines, and the word comes from "vacca," which is Latin for "cow."

Solution is on page 393.

SIX-LETTER WORD SEARCH — 284

We've hidden 29 common 6-letter words in the diagram below. Can you find them all? Note: No plurals or proper nouns are included.

YOUR WORD LIST

W	N	P	H	R	A	S	E	L	O	S	K
N	Y	M	I	J	B	T	S	N	E	T	H
D	R	E	S	I	S	T	R	V	R	A	E
W	A	E	S	A	E	R	C	O	U	P	S
E	S	E	T	A	N	E	S	M	S	L	C
A	O	I	C	A	T	S	U	P	S	E	O
S	R	P	L	C	A	E	W	H	A	I	R
E	K	E	H	C	Y	D	M	E	F	L	T
L	I	S	T	U	I	N	S	E	R	T	R
B	N	T	H	S	S	T	R	E	E	E	X
U	D	E	A	E	A	H	M	B	S	K	W
Y	A	R	T	S	A	M	E	O	I	S	Y
S	M	O	K	J	I	E	L	D	D	A	S
T	W	E	H	S	A	C	T	Z	E	B	H

Solution is on page 393; list, page 402.

Using the letters from each word below, form two 5-letter words, then search for the 5-letter words in the diagram. For example, we used the letters in the word "compromise" to form the words CRIMP and MOOSE, and circled them both in the diagram. If you solve it correctly, you will find 42 five-letter words.

1. ALPHABETIC

2. ALTOGETHER

3. APPRECIATE

4. AUCTIONEER

5. BIG-HEARTED

6. BRIDGEHEAD

7. CAPTIVATED

8. CARTOONIST

9. CELLOPHANE

10. CHANDELIER

11. COMPROMISE
CRIMP   MOOSE

12. DISHARMONY

13. GALVANIZED

14. INDELICACY

15. NEWSWORTHY

16. OVERACTIVE

17. PEREMPTORY

18. STEWARDESS

19. SUSTENANCE

20. TIRESOMELY

21. UNATTACHED

```
R O N I M W T C V T N A C S
C O G L A Z E K H R E K N D
B L P S D V W M B A V E R T
A L T E E S O O M P I E C E
D E B M R I U I L A S N Y T
G H R P S J N A C S T S N O
E P A T T I C D C E W U I T
B L I Y R E E L T T A E C H
N E D H W V B A R H E D G E
S G R E A T R K A N R D M I
B N L P R I C R I M P E D R
T O O C S B W J N W R E W T
F Z E W N A C E P N A V I D
S H A D Y H O T E L R H E T
```

Solution is on page 393; list, page 403.

Scan the grid in all directions for 56 familiar five-letter words, arranged in pairs. Each word in a pair crosses its partner through the center letter, forming either a "+" or an "x" shape. One pair has been circled to start you off.

YOUR WORD LIST

```
E L H N T E A C D H E I P W
B G C A J I L E T O S H E K
P A N I C O B R A R O S E I
E G U A A O U R D T O R V Y
Y A H T R I M O O R G U B S
K O T V E E I E P W O N T Y
S I R E D E X A T E C I W T
C T A N R O A I R O N T R Q
G L E Z I A M A E T S E U P
B P T E E D E A E N A C T
S U E I D N M N D I L S S S
E U G R A C E G A T S E I K
I H E L V R I R P L R A G L
T Y B I E F T V T C G P T Y
```

Solution is on page 393; list, page 403.

Search this diagram for the 24 items below that a *señorita* (a Spanish girl) might typically have in her *cuarto* (bedroom). Then, to learn the English equivalents of these Spanish terms, solve the puzzle on the opposite page.

```
A E S C R I T O R I O N X Y
R E L O J M L R T M A C E Z
B A E M R A R O V I O S R A
M I D E M E C S R R T C E D
O L K P O A V E T A S O F A
F A A N D X L I N G H J O H
L R G O T E N T S U K I R O
A M R W P A E D F T M N J M
L A B A S E O C A M A E D L
L R P A T N I T B K P S T A
I I S I L L O N R S M N W V
S O R D A U C C E P I L L O
K E A M U L P E R F U M E L
```

Solution is on page 393.

A.	ALFOMBRA
B.	ALMOHADA
C.	ARMARIO
D.	CAMA
E.	CEPILLO
F.	COJÍN
G.	CORTINAS
H.	CUADROS
I.	ESCRITORIO
J.	ESPEJO
K.	ESTANTE
L.	LÁMPARA
M.	MUÑECA
N.	PAPELERÍA
O.	PEINE
P.	PERFUME
Q.	PLUMA
R.	RELOJ
S.	REVISTAS
T.	SILLA
U.	SILLÓN
V.	SOFÁ
W.	TINTA
X.	TOCADOR

This is the companion puzzle to the one on the preceding page. Here you will be searching for the same items found in the room of a *señorita*, but this time you will find them as they would be described by an English-speaking girl. After you've found all 24 terms, see if you can match each Spanish term to its correct English translation. For example, the English word SOFA looks the same in Spanish—*sofá*. See page 403 for matchup answers.

1. ARMCHAIR
2. BED
3. CARPET
4. CLOCK
5. COMB
6. CURTAINS
7. CUSHION
8. DESK
9. DOLL
10. DRESSING TABLE
11. HAIRBRUSH
12. INK
13. LAMP
14. MAGAZINES
15. MIRROR
16. PEN
17. PERFUME
18. PICTURES
19. PILLOW
20. SHELF
21. SOFA
22. STATIONERY
23. STRAIGHT CHAIR
24. WARDROBE

```
S N I A T R U C W O L L I P
Z E D H N Y G I O B E D J E
R P B A K C L V T M L P R R
E S J I A C L S N H B I X F
P W A R D R O B E V A Y K U
I C P B Z F D L G H T W T M
C E L R A Q U D C I G O P E
T U X U S T A T I O N E R Y
U G S S K Y H B A E I J N G
R D S H M G L O L F S C S Z
E S E N I Z A G A M S H B U
S N Q A R O L B M D E R X I
H B R I R E N O P L R B E N
Z T L L O W M U F L D E S K
S T R A R M C H A I R B R U
```

Solution is on page 393; matchups, page 403.

Can you guess the odds on Velvet's racehorse, Piebald, in the Grand National Steeplechase in the 1944 movie *National Velvet?* They were 100 to 1 against "The Pie," but he came in first place. Elizabeth Taylor played Velvet in the film, and King Charles, the grandson of Man O'War, played her winning horse, which the studio later gave Miss Taylor on her 14th birthday.

0000	7981	8486	9128
0350	8208	8708	9739
0404	8311	9000	9978
0731			
1530			
1651			
1707			
1918			
2041			
2287			
2462			
3035			
3339			
3774			
3863			
4522			
4704			
4763			
5005			
5040			
5251			
6096			
6177			
6527			
6688			
7158			
7676			

```
2 0 0 3 1 0 9 5 3 6 3 8 1 7
8 7 2 8 3 8 5 4 3 8 4 2 7 1
6 5 0 3 7 3 8 4 5 4 8 1 9 1
7 0 3 9 7 3 9 1 2 8 6 6 5 9
6 7 9 1 4 3 7 5 8 2 3 5 6 7
7 2 5 6 4 3 7 0 4 0 9 1 3 0
7 3 2 4 3 3 8 0 3 9 5 4 1 9
5 7 6 8 6 2 0 5 2 5 1 7 4 9
8 5 6 8 7 0 8 1 5 3 1 7 0 7
0 3 8 1 4 6 0 9 1 8 5 0 2 9
6 3 4 0 1 6 9 0 9 8 0 8 9 0
4 3 5 6 5 2 4 7 0 4 9 2 6 0
3 5 2 0 1 0 1 3 2 1 2 5 8 3
9 7 2 6 4 2 5 1 7 6 4 6 5 2
```

Solution is on page 394.

This puzzle is solved in two parts. The first part requires that you guess the words needed to complete the chart below. Beginning with each letter in the chart, there is an appropriate world capital, card game, dog breed, movie and composer. Using the same words you used to complete the chart, go to the second part by finding them all in the diagram. If you can't find the word that you're looking for, you may have to guess another word that fits the chart. We've entered BACH in the chart and circled it in the diagram for you. The completed chart is on page 403.

	B	C	P	R	S	M
Capitals						
Card games						
Dog breeds						
Movies						
Composers	BACH					

```
O  M  P  T  R  E  V  E  I  R  T  E  R  T
P  O  O  D  L  E  P  U  T  S  R  L  R  E
F  N  E  B  R  S  N  G  P  T  O  U  S  R
F  T  S  G  Y  T  R  A  Z  O  M  O  N  I
I  E  S  C  D  E  N  R  M  M  T  E  L  A
T  C  H  O  P  I  N  P  Y  R  B  S  C  T
S  O  C  L  E  T  R  A  V  E  E  N  S  I
A  O  A  L  B  A  M  B  I  P  A  P  O  L
M  L  B  I  R  T  W  O  L  L  G  K  U  O
O  S  L  E  S  S  U  R  B  E  L  R  S  S
W  R  K  C  B  A  T  A  O  L  E  V  A  R
O  O  I  A  H  N  S  W  O  C  S  O  M  O
P  D  C  A  M  A  R  N  I  E  K  C  A  M
L  I  N  I  C  C  U  P  S  O  R  Y  R  E
```

Solution is on page 394; chart, page 403.

Need something to cool you off these hot summer days? How about a little ice? All the words hidden below contain the letters "ice." In case you didn't NOTICE yet, the puzzle on the opposite page also deals with "ice."

ADVICE	CHOICE	DICE	INVOICE
BENEFICENT	CORNICE	ENTICE	JUICE
CAPRICE	DE-ICE	EPICENTER	JUSTICE
CHALICE	DEVICE	ICELAND	LATTICE
			LICENSE
			LICORICE
			MALICE
			MICE
			NICE
			NOTICE
			OFFICE
			POLICE
			PRACTICE
			PRICE
			RICE
			SACRIFICE
			SERVICE
			SLICE
			SPICE
			SPLICE
			SUFFICE
			TWICE
			VENICE
			VICE
			VOICE

```
E C I T T A L E C I N E V J
E C I I R D N O T I C E U U
N C I N E N E N T I C E J I
E C I V D A B E R I T E U C
B E I O C L B P N N L E S E
R C E I V E A E E I C S T S
E I C C N C C C I L L I N
T V I E I I I O P O L I C E
N R W C F F R S E R I C E C
E E T F E I F F I C I E B I
C S U N C R D O D E I C E L
I S E E E C I N R O C O E A
P B E P R A C T I C E I H H
E C I L P S E E C I L A M C
```

Solution is on page 394.

For a brief return to the Ice AGE, solve the chilling puzzle below. It's located in any icy LAND, so be wary of an approaching ice STORM as you search for 39 terms which form new words or phrases when preceded by the word "ice."

AGE
BAG
BERG
BLINK
BOAT
BOX
BREAKER
CAP
CHEST
CREAM
CREAM CONE
CUBE
DANCING
FALL
FIELD
FLOE
FOOT
HOCKEY
HOUSE
LAND
LAND MOSS
LAND SPAR
MAKER
MAN
MILK
NEEDLE
PACK

PICK
PLANTS
POINT
RINK

SHEET
SHELF
SHOW
SKATE

SKATER
STORM
TRAY
WATER

```
S S O M D N A L E Y R K T
J K K D N A L Y G S C U C
A Y A B L W N A M A U A N
M R O T S E H C P A B O X
T A B W E Y I W I L E T H
T P A C P W M F C N R R J
H S X O O A X A K E G A C
I D I H K T F N K R Y Y M
N N S N E E I S A E R B C
T A I H R R T K K K R T I
E L D E E N O C M A E R C
B R J O A L O O A E T Y J
O M I L K H F L H R L E E
G X P F A L L S U B T T R
```

Solution is on page 394.

Often thought of as the home of towering buildings, New York City has many parks within its five boroughs. Some of the more popular parks are listed below, and the location of each is in parentheses.

ASTORIA (Queens)
BARRETT (Staten Island)
BATTERY (Manhattan)
BENSONHURST (Brooklyn)

BRONX (Bronx)
BROOKVILLE (Queens)
CARL SCHURZ (Manhattan)
CASTLE HILL (Bronx)

CENTRAL (Manhattan)
CLAREMONT (Bronx)
CLOVE LAKES (Staten Island)
CROCHERON (Queens)
CROTONA (Bronx)
CUNNINGHAM (Queens)
EAST RIVER (Brooklyn)
FLUSHING MEADOW (Queens)
FOREST (Queens)
FRANCIS LEWIS (Queens)
FT. GREENE (Brooklyn)
FT. TRYON (Manhattan)
HARRIS (Bronx)
HIGHLAND (Brooklyn)
JACOB RIIS (Queens)
KISSENA (Queens)
LA TOURETTE (Staten Island)
LINCOLN (Brooklyn)
MARINE (Brooklyn)
PROSPECT (Brooklyn)
SUNSET (Brooklyn)
TOMPKINS (Brooklyn)

```
J P W O D A E M G N I H S U L F S
A A R C F A C A T P R U B M K A C
C C L O V E L A K E S M A R I N E
O H R L S C A R R S S H P R O A L
B A K B A P R S E L G N F R S N C
R R B A R R E T T N S R U T E O X
I R Y E L O M C I O A C X S N T E
I I R R A H O N T N R C H R E O T
S S E O A S N K C A R I D U E R T
N K T I C U T I V O N N A H R C E
I L T O C H S R C I A E T N G Z R
K C A S T L E H I L L X S O T B U
P R B R E B E R H V B L N S F J O
M W K W T R X G O N E O E N I C T
O T I K O N I K O N Y R R E N K A
T S N N I H E T I K O B T B W F L
N L O C N I L C N F T T R Y O N F
```

Solution is on page 394.

Northeast across the Atlantic from New York City is London, England. London's largest parks are known as the "royal parks," or parks which once formed part of royal estates but are now open to the public. Central London has five royal parks: ST. JAMES'S Park, HYDE Park, GREEN Park, KENSINGTON Gardens, and REGENT'S Park, all of which are hidden in the puzzle. Search for these and other London parks.

ALEXANDRA
BATTERSEA
BELSIZE
BROCKWELL
BUSHY
EALING
GLADSTONE
GOLDERS HILL
GREEN
GREENWICH
    (site of the
    Greenwich
    Observatory)
HACKNEY
    (Marshes)
HAMPTON
    (Court,
    residence of
    Henry VIII)
HYDE
KEMPTON
KENSINGTON
KEW GARDENS
MITCHAM
POSTMEN'S
PUTNEY HEATH
QUEEN'S
REGENT'S
RICHMOND
RUSKIN
ST. JAMES'S
ST. QUINTIN
VICTORIA
WIMBLEDON

```
D O H G L A R D N A X E L A P S
A I R O T C I V O L C I T E R O
I D Y L E T N O T P M E K S I M
L C H D S T N E G E R Y E T C I
L O Y E N Q E W N S L Q W K H M
E H G R E E N W I C H X G T M A
W I S S B Y O S S M L B A E O H
K D N H L A E S N R B E R I N C
C B R I V E T N E E H L D O D T
O V E L T J I T K Y M L E N T I
R I O L A N Q C E C G T N D H M
B R C M S W I N H R A L S X O G
S U E Q C I T U E L S H I O G N
T S S N Y U Z E Q U E E N S P I
S K C H P N N E U T B B A I K L
C I Q U Y T E N O T S D A L G A
E N O T P M A H N E O Q S O N E
```

Solution is on page 394.

When you look for the terms in this puzzle, you'll find that each bends at an angle. POPLAR is outlined to show you how. There are 25 additional types of wood hidden below, and none of the terms overlap. Can you find them all?

```
D L A W O L D S U T P Y L
E E K O L L R E C U R A D
L I R A L I A Q P P C O I
P A M W A W L O S U O F R
E W O M D C P S E W D E R
Y O L W N A U O Y R O K U
D T E A A M N D T H S C Q
O Q U L S W O L O T A I R
O I A N O M S A L U O H I
U Y O O A A N B D C G C F
Q N D H H E I B N E Y L S
E A O K C I P E I N N P A
S G B I R H C E L S S E R
```

Solution is on page 394.

ALDER
ASH
BALSA
BEECH
BIRCH
COTTONWOOD
CYPRESS
DOUGLAS FIR
ELM
EUCALYPTUS
FIR
HICKORY
LINDEN
MAHOGANY
MAPLE
OAK
PINE
POPLAR
REDWOOD
SANDALWOOD
SEQUOIA
SPRUCE
SUMAC
WALNUT
WILLOW
YEW

SPOONERISMS ——————————————— 296

A spoonerism is a phrase in which the initial sounds of two words are reversed. An example is "tragic mix" for "magic tricks". Notice that it is the initial *sounds* that are switched; the spelling doesn't matter as long as the sound is the same. Listed below you will find spoonerisms for some well-known phrases; the corrected phrases are hidden in the diagram. The list is in alphabetical order according to the spelling of the *correct* phrase. Those phrases are on page 403.

```
D E O D N H O J T F A P Y F
O C O A S T G U A R D A L O
N A P A I T Q L Y R C R A F
M M R D F J A T M E I T U E
F A N M A I L E S J H Y G D
I H L M F T J N U G H H H N
R I H S O R E N I W F A I A
E G S B A N K L O A N T N H
D H U O M M D A I E M L G D
R T R H A E S R E N A S G A
I I D I R E B E T M E A A L
L D L H O A W A E L T E S G
L E O H L O E D K E Q A E L
E L G L H Y U B M E V E L G
T E O N E C P A N O Z T E P
R I E Y K E N O B Y N N U F
```

Solution is on page 394; phrases, page 403.

1. Lank bone _____
2. Hair bug _____
3. Ghost card _____
4. Late dine _____
5. Bear fall _____
6. Man fail _____
7. Car fry _____
8. Dire frill _____
9. Bunny phone _____
10. Mass gain _____
11. Had gland _____
12. Rolled gush _____
13. Tie hide _____
14. Don Joe _____
15. Monk jail _____
16. Dame luck _____
17. Gaffing lass _____
18. Tame nag _____
19. Hearty pat _____
20. Led right _____

359

Keep your eye on the ball as you scan the grid for 17 PITCHes that were hurled and 17 CATCHes retrieved at Little League batting practice.

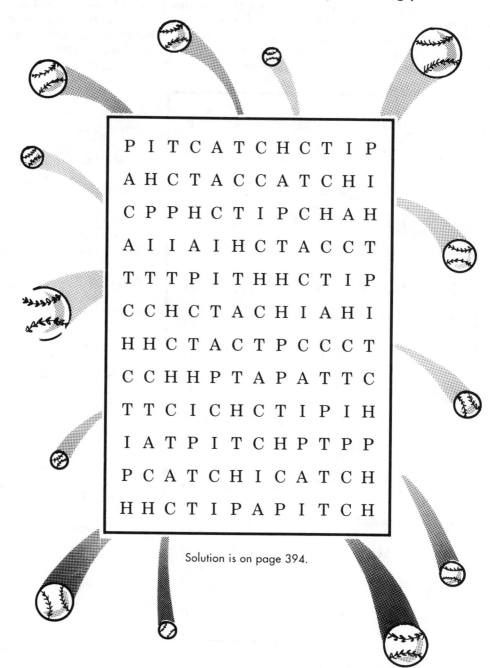

```
P I T C A T C H C T I P
A H C T A C C A T C H I
C P P H C T I P C H A H
A I I A I H C T A C C T
T T T P I T H H C T I P
C C H C T A C H I A H I
H H C T A C T P C C C T
C C H H P T A P A T T C
T T C I C H C T I P I H
I A T P I T C H P T P P
P C A T C H I C A T C H
H H C T I P A P I T C H
```

Solution is on page 394.

ANSWERS

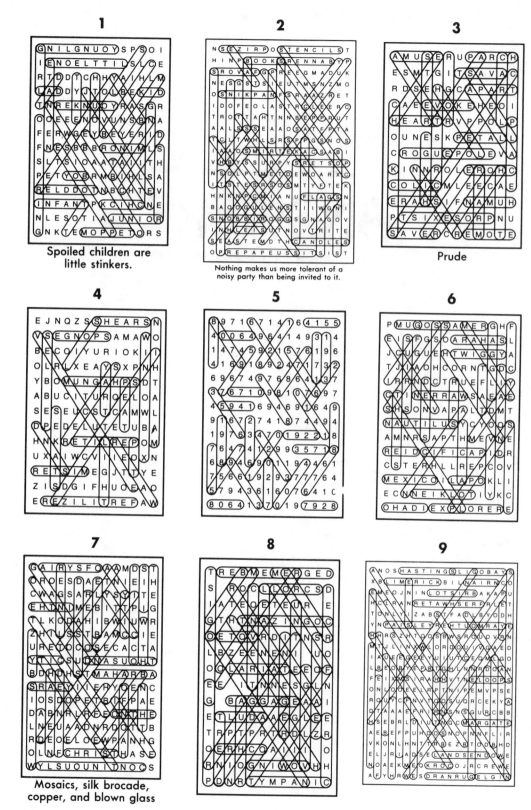

1

Spoiled children are
little stinkers.

2

Nothing makes us more tolerant of a
noisy party than being invited to it.

3

Prude

4

5

6

7

Mosaics, silk brocade,
copper, and blown glass

8

9

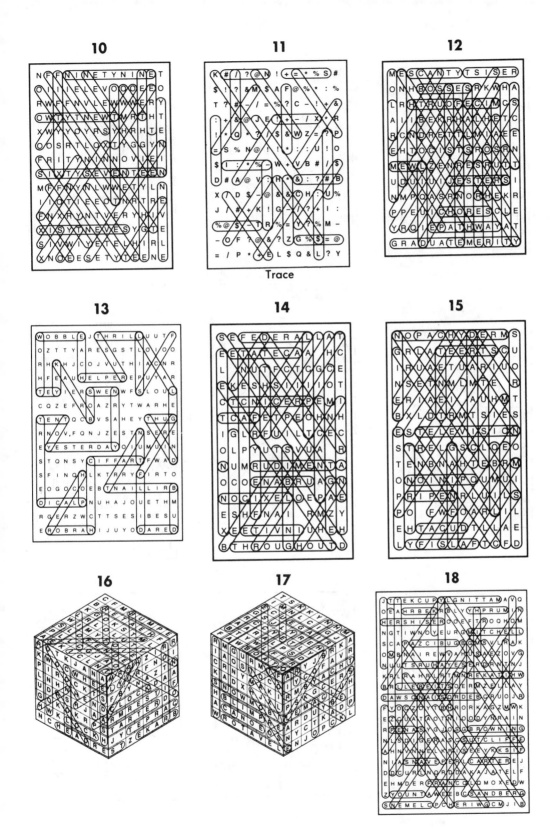

363

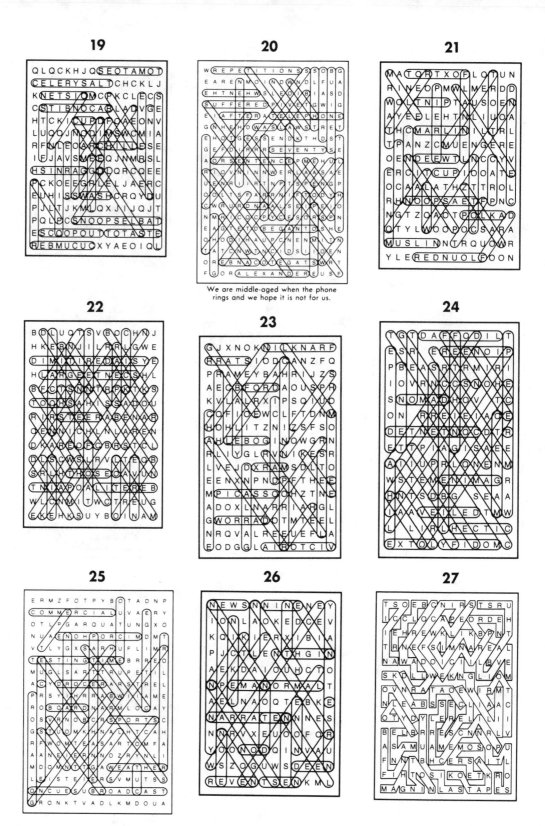

We are middle-aged when the phone
rings and we hope it is not for us.

364

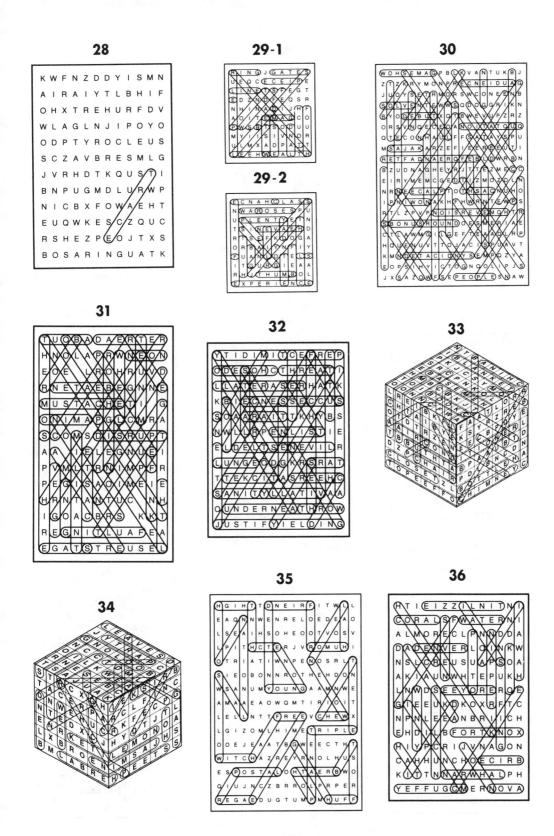

365

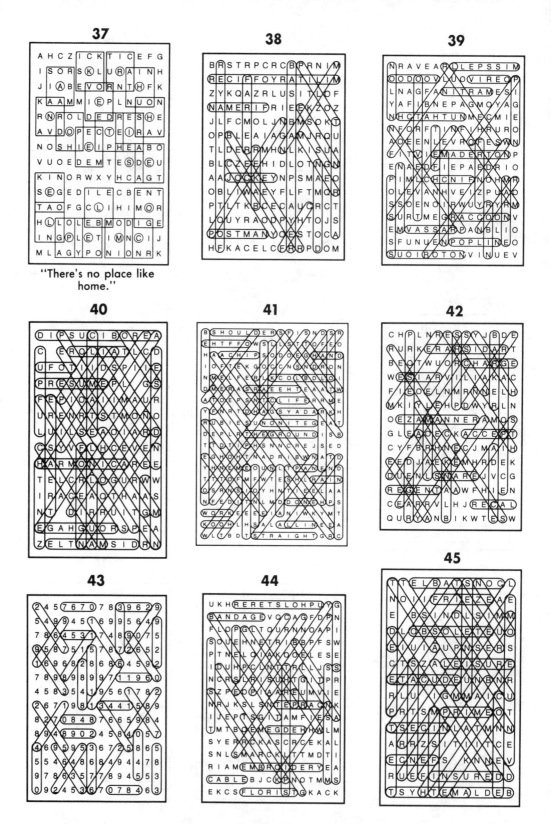

37

"There's no place like home."

38

39

40

41

42

43

44

45

46

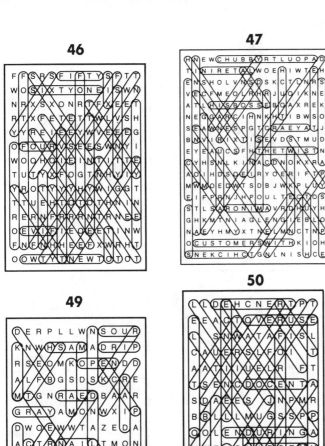

47

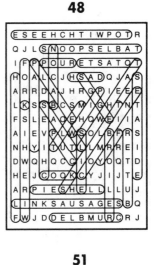

48

49

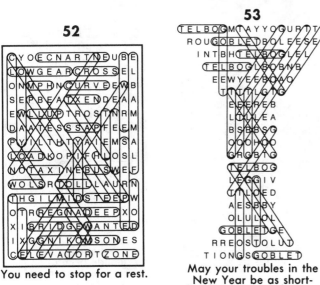

50

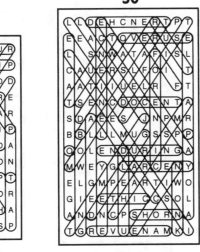

51

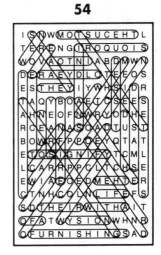

The Defense Department's
Pentagon Building

52

You need to stop for a rest.

53

May your troubles in the
New Year be as short-
lived as your resolutions.

54

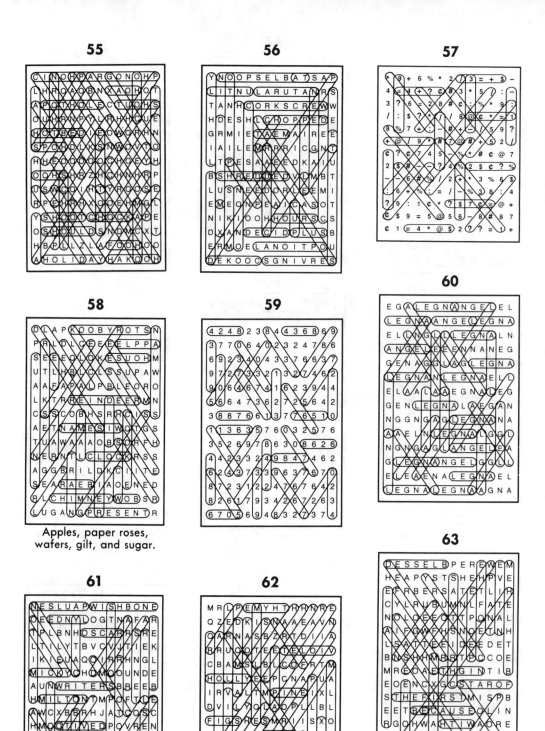

55

56

57

58

59

60

Apples, paper roses,
wafers, gilt, and sugar.

61

62

63

Perhaps the best
Yuletide decoration is
being wreathed in smiles.

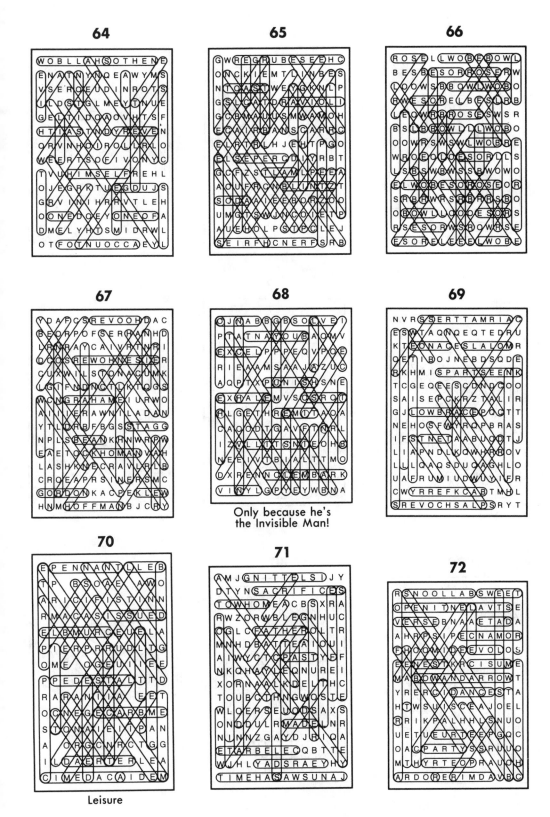

64

65

66

67

68

Only because he's
the Invisible Man!

69

70

Leisure

71

72

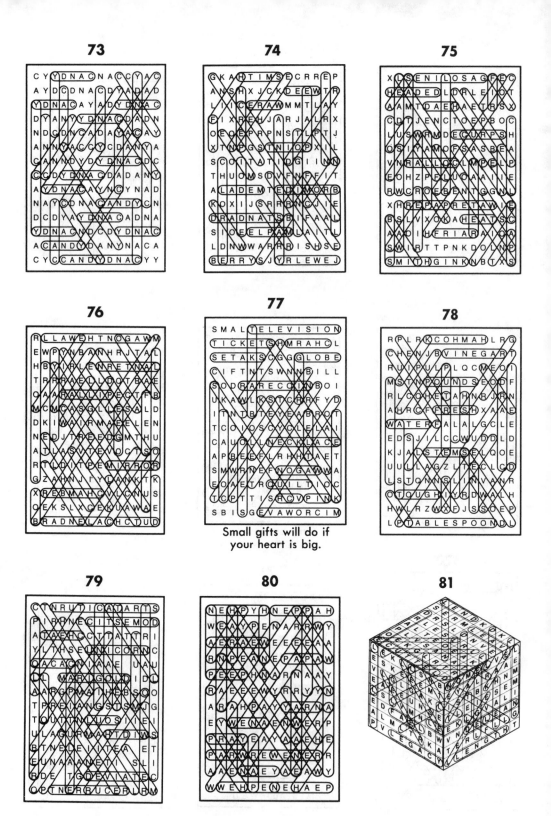

73

74

75

76

77

Small gifts will do if
your heart is big.

78

79

80

81

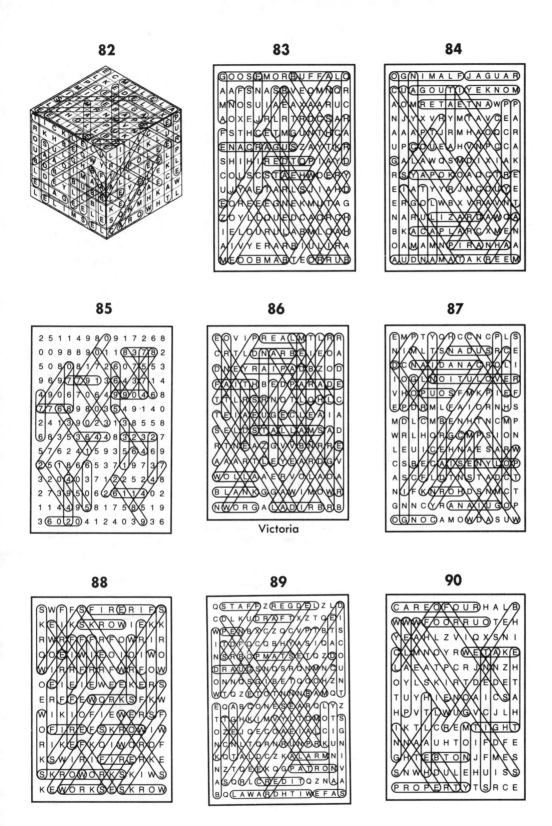

82

83

84

85

86

Victoria

87

88

89

90

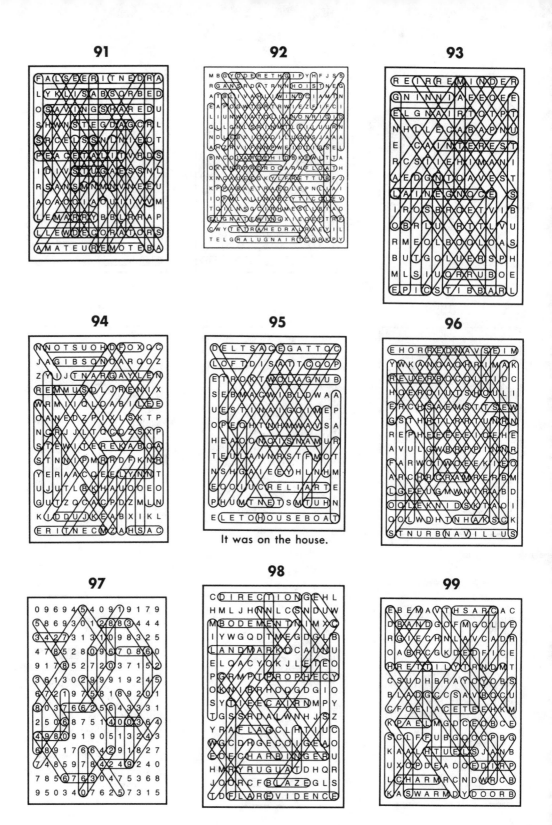

91

92

93

94

95

It was on the house.

96

97

98

99

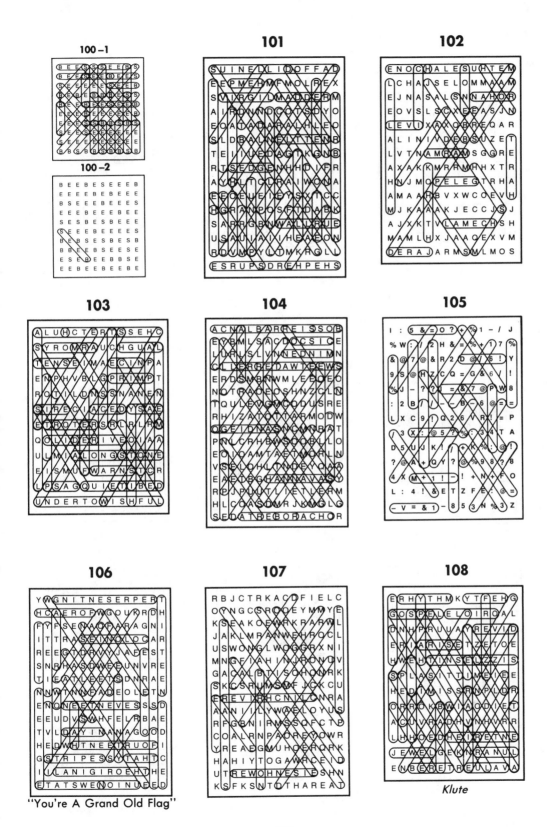

"You're A Grand Old Flag"

Klute

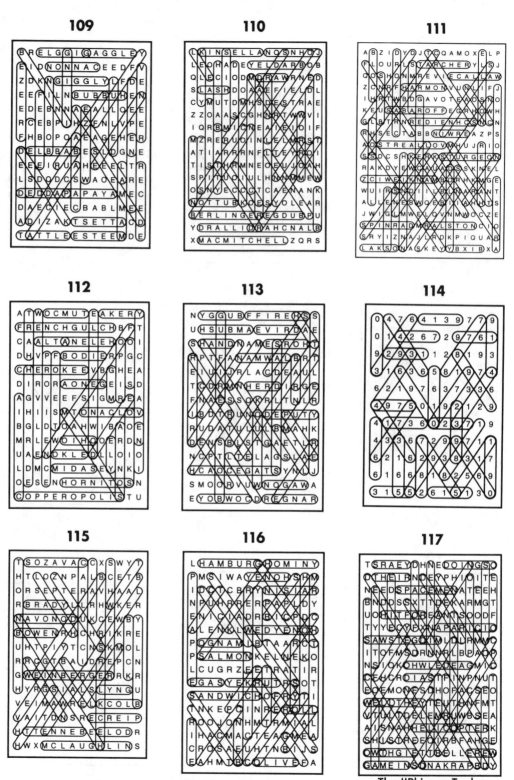

109   **110**   **111**

112   **113**   **114**

115   **116**   **117**

The "Phineas Taylor
Barnum" of baseball.

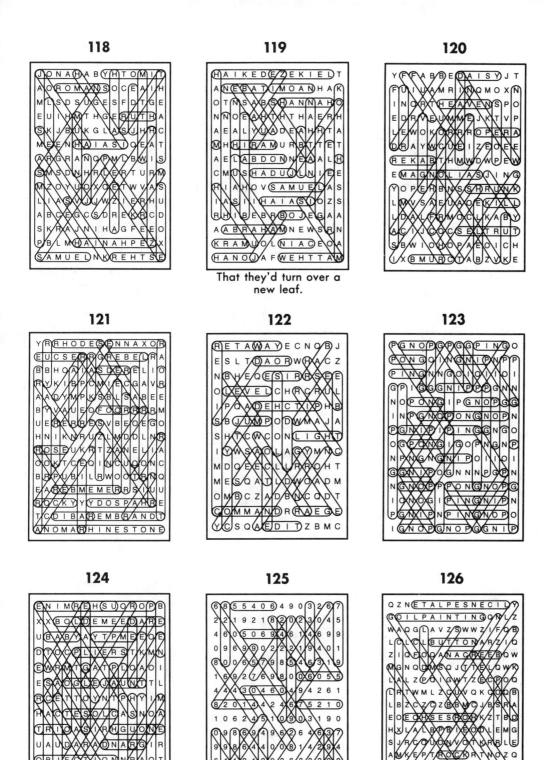

118

119

That they'd turn over a new leaf.

120

121

122

123

124

125

126

375

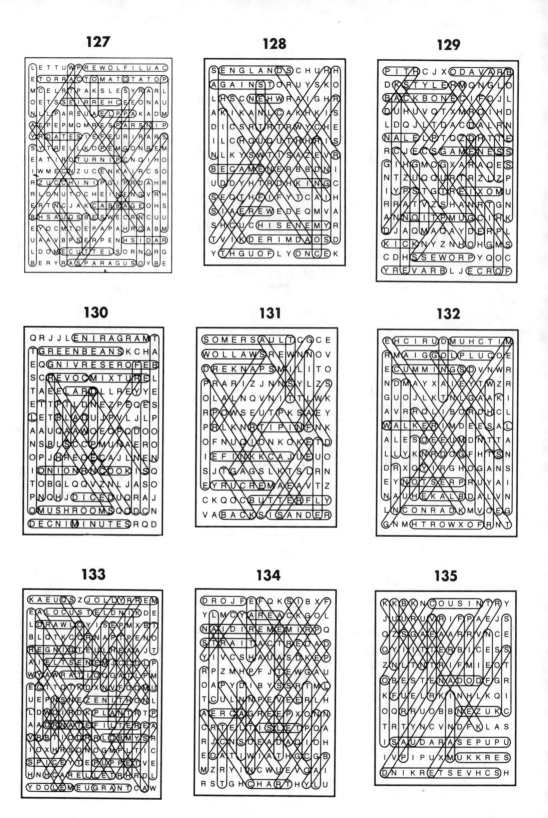

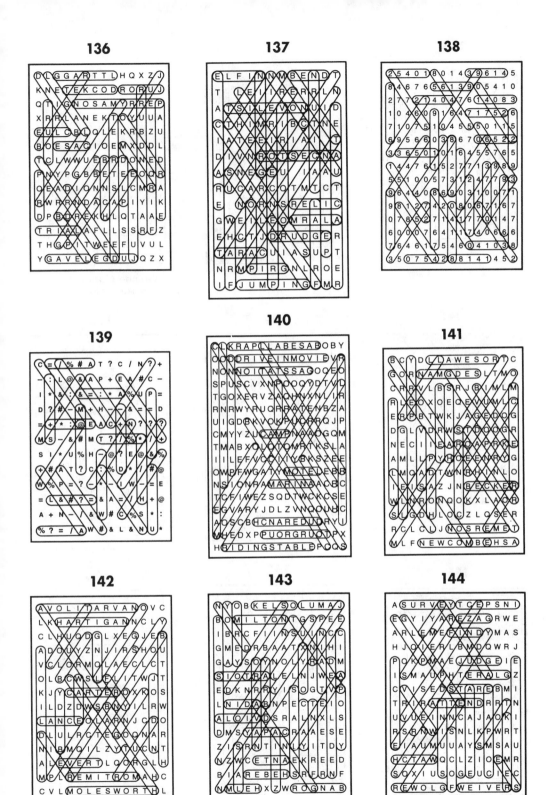

377

145

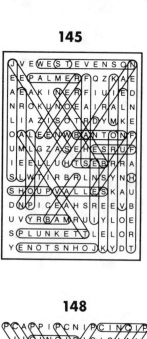

146

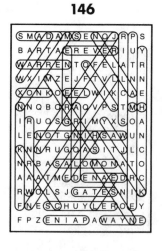

147

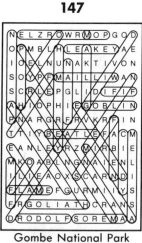

Gombe National Park
in Tanzania, Africa

148

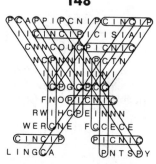

A picnic is an outing for
when we're feeling antsy.

149

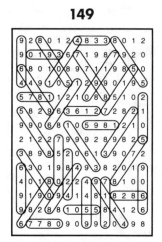

150

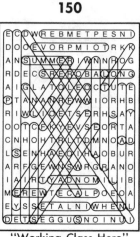

"Working Class Hero"

151

152

Ten pennies will buy no
more than one dime.

153

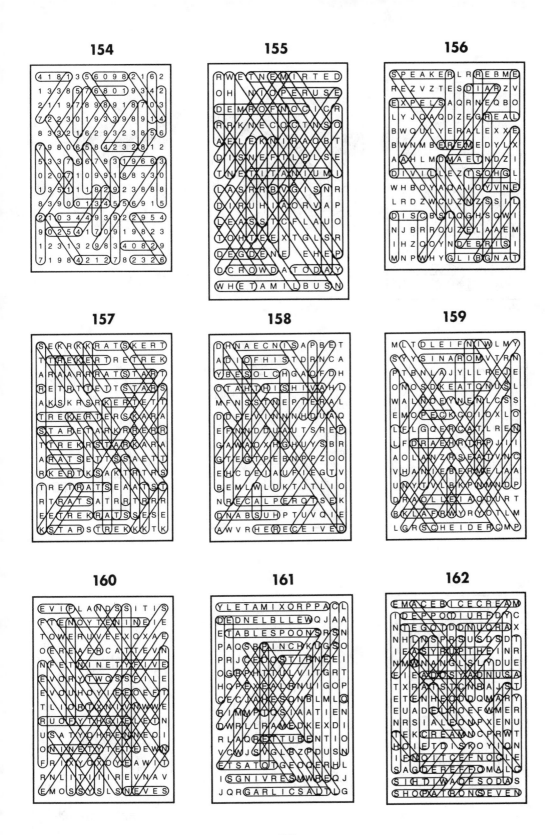

379

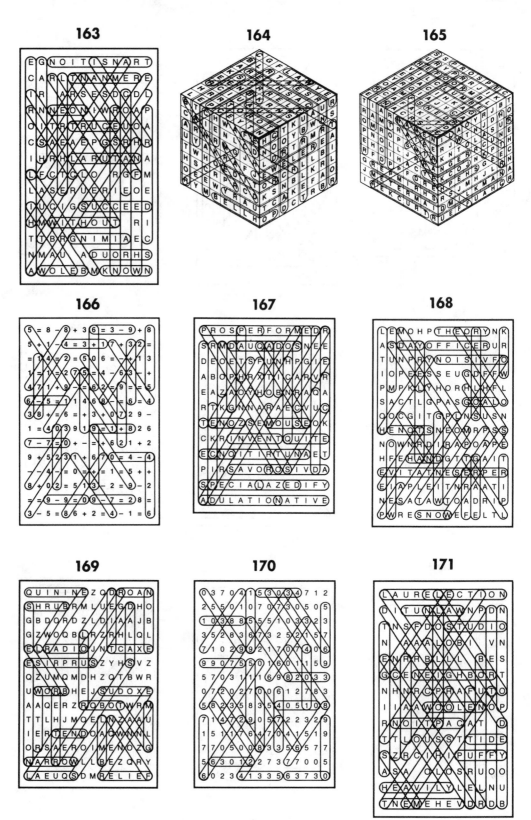

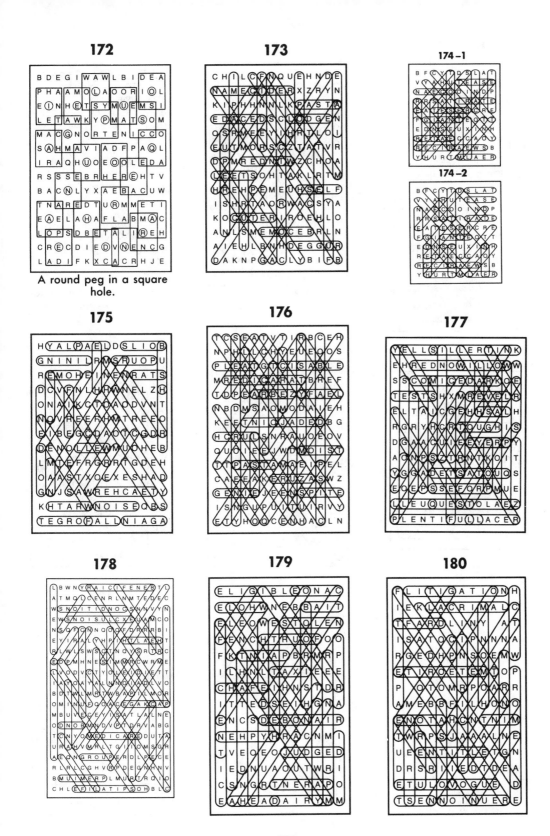

172

A round peg in a square hole.

173

174–1

174–2

175

176

177

178

179

180

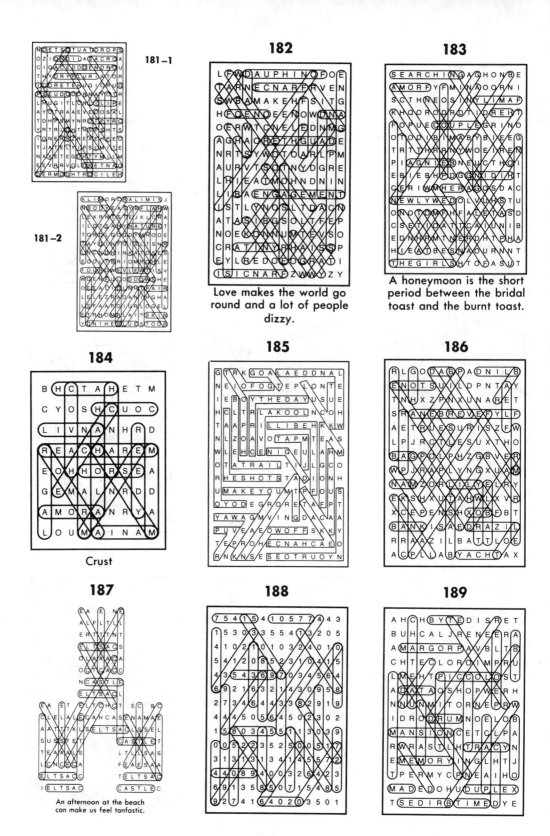

182

Love makes the world go round and a lot of people dizzy.

183

A honeymoon is the short period between the bridal toast and the burnt toast.

184

Crust

185

186

187

An afternoon at the beach can make us feel tanfastic.

188

189

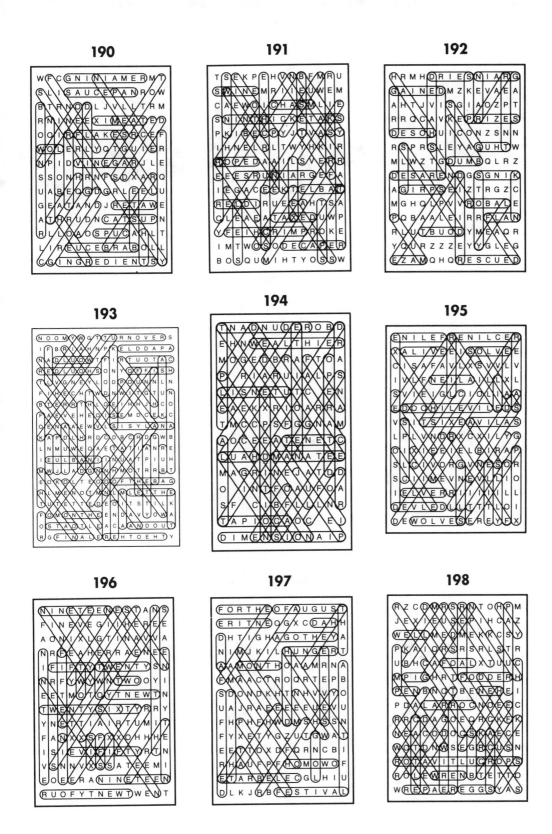

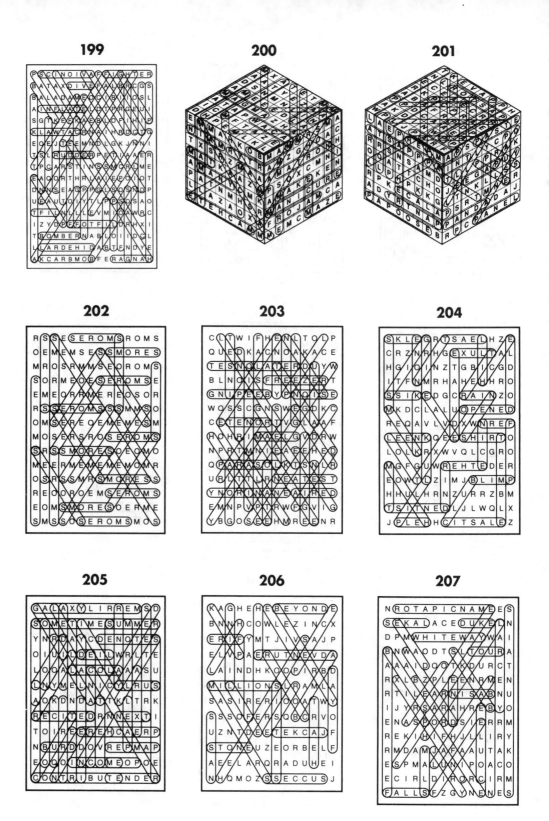

199 **200** **201**

202 **203** **204**

205 **206** **207**

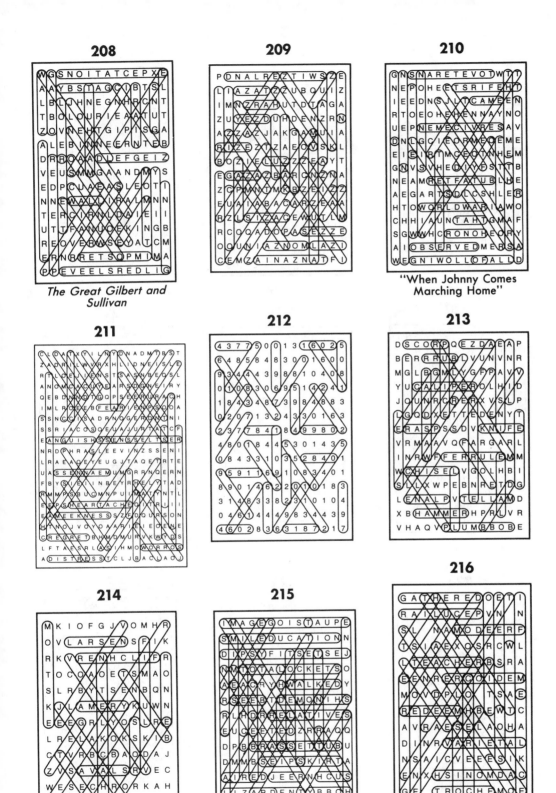

208

The Great Gilbert and Sullivan

209

210

"When Johnny Comes Marching Home"

211

212

213

214

215

216

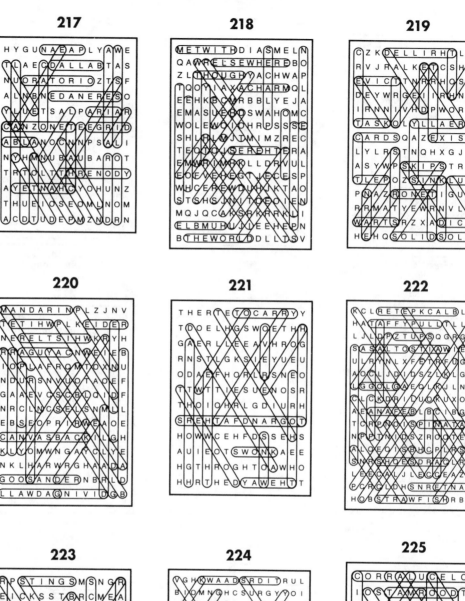
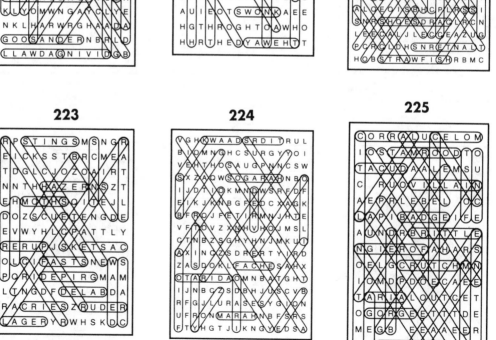

226

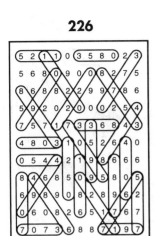

227

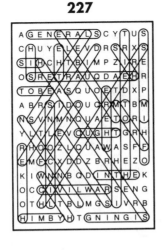

228

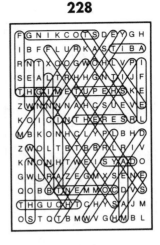

229

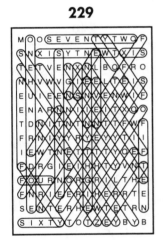

230

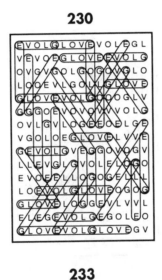

231

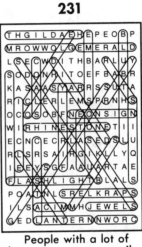

People with a lot of
brass are not necessarily
at all polished.

232

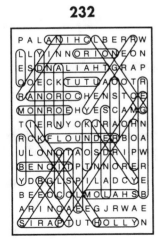

233

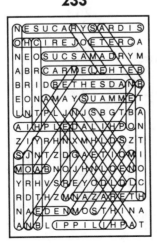

234

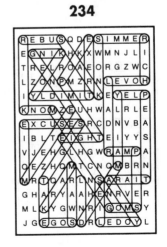

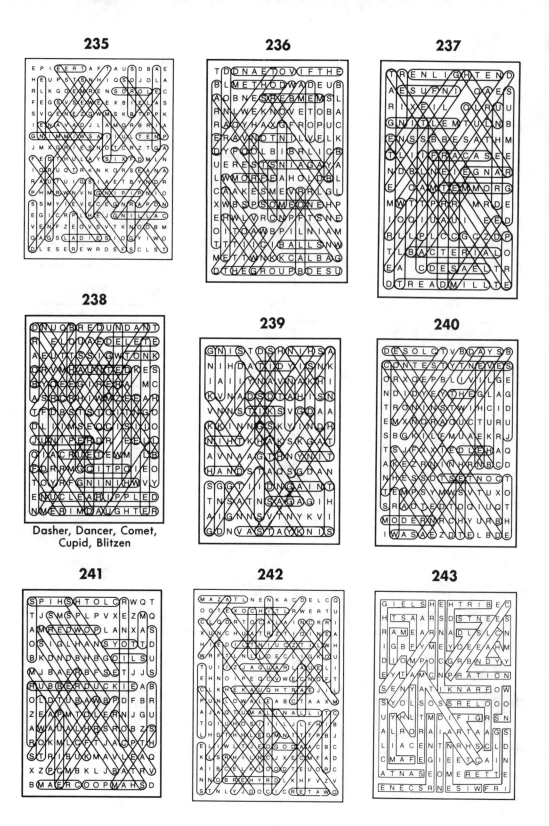

238
Dasher, Dancer, Comet,
Cupid, Blitzen

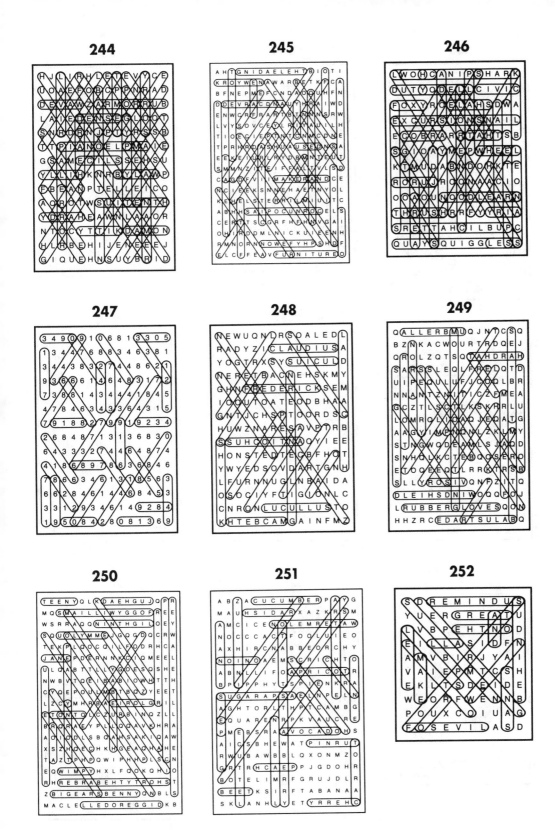

389

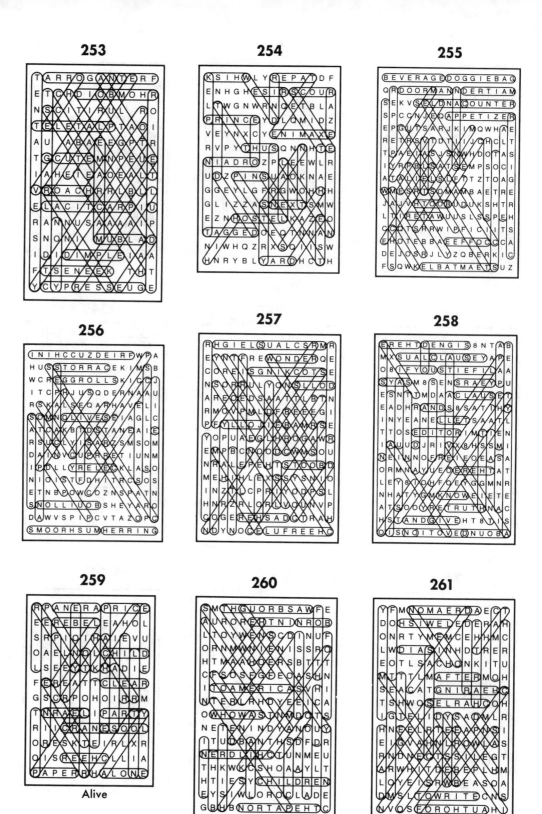

253

254

255

256

257

258

259

Alive

260

261

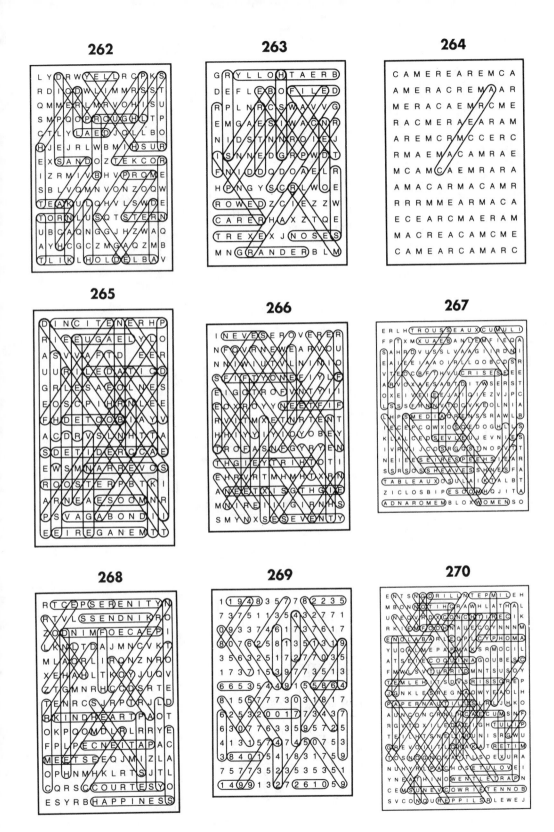

262

263

264

265

266

267

268

269

270

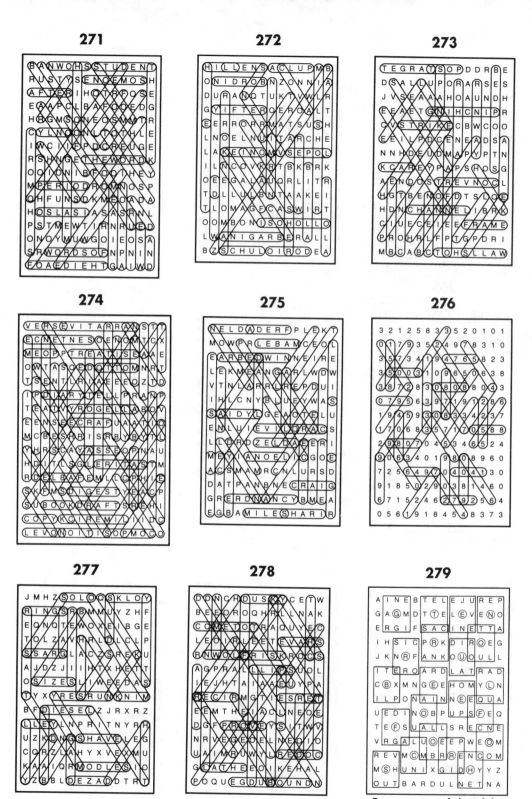

271

272

273

274

275

276

277

278

279

Four corners of the globe

392

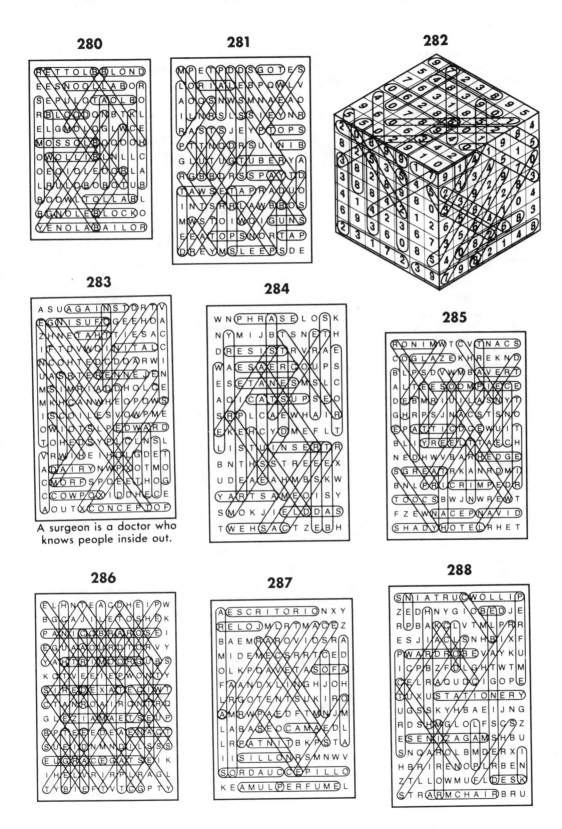

283

A surgeon is a doctor who knows people inside out.

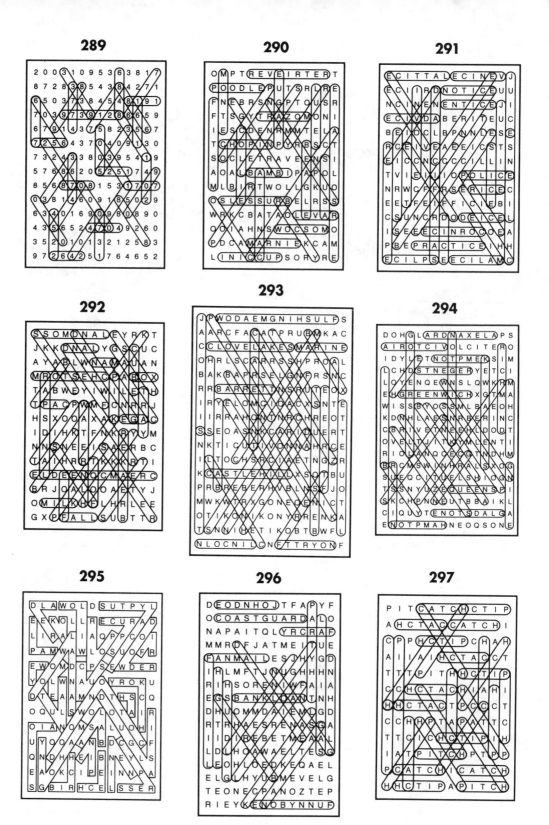

6 TRIVIA TOURNEY 1. archy 2. aspirin 3. calf 4. chess 5. Churchill (Winston) 6. Denis 7. diamond 8. Explorer 9. Fuji 10. gaggle 11. gossamer 12. GUM 13. Houston 14. Idaho 15. Maggie 16. Mexico 17. My Day 18. Nautilus 19. opal 20. Pacific 21. Poppins (Mary) 22. Reid 23. Sahara 24. Service 25. Sirius 26. SPAR 27. Strauss (Johann) 28. Taft (William Howard) 29. Thames 30. Tolkien (J.R.R.) 31. Twiggy 32. Venice 33. Vicky 34. warren

10 MATH FUN 1. Three 2. Twenty-two 3. Fifty 4. Eight 5. Sixty-seven 6. Two 7. Ninety 8. Three 9. Fifty-six 10. Seven 11. Twenty-two 12. Seventeen 13. Six 14. Two 15. Fifty-one 16. Eighty-eight 17. Ninety 18. Forty 19. Twenty-two 20. Two 21. Eleven 22. Fifty 23. Eighteen 24. Seventeen 25. Five 26. Seventy-six 27. Sixty-six 28. Three 29. Eighteen 30. Eleven 31. Ninety-nine 32. Two

13 TAIL TAG Focus, spill, local, legend, diet, thug, gruff, fluid, dared, dumb, brilliant, train, nut, traffic, clench, harbor, reach, hop, placid, dessert, tent, toy, yesterday, yearn, news, sob, break, key, yet, throw, wobble, each, helper, rust, thrill.

21 SCAVENGER HUNT

	C	F	M	T	W	P
Dances	cancan	fox trot	minuet	tango	waltz	polka
Presidents	Cleveland	Ford	Monroe	Tyler	Washington	Pierce
Fish	carp	flounder	marlin	trout	walleye	perch
Measuring units	cup	foot	mile	teaspoon	watt	pint
Fabrics	cotton	flannel	muslin	tweed	wool	poplin

22 + AND x SEARCH Acorn + shoot, actor x bathe, baton x otter, beret + nerve, birth + large, borne x shred, brisk x reign, broom x close, burro x mural, camel + timid, chest x their, click + daisy, deign x faint, drink x while, flask x slain, float + those, liter + lotto, ocean + steer, paint + slice, panel x sonar, react x slant, scent + spear, siren + tired, small x stack, sneer x stein.

26 "N" DEFINITIONS 1. Nail 2. Name 3. Nanny 4. Napkin 5. Narrate 6. Narrow 7. Nation 8. Navy 9. Near 10. Neat 11. Neck 12. Need 13. Needle 14. Nervous 15. Nest 16. Net 17. Never 18. News 19. Next 20. Nice 21. Nickel 22. Night 23. Nine 24. Nod 25. Noise 26. None 27. Noon 28. Normal 29. North 30. Nose 31. Note 32. Noted 33. Notice 34. Novel 35. Nudge 36. Number 37. Nurse

29 SQUARE PAIRS

1	2	1	2	1	2	1	2	1	2
bed	roses	gift	gab	month	Sundays	rule	thumb	touch	class
bill	sale	land	plenty	pane	glass	side	beef	waste	time
fourth	July	line	fire	piece	pie	speed	light	wealth	experience
game	chance	lump	coal	point	honor	staff	life	wheel	fortune
gates	heaven	manner	speaking	ring	truth	time	day	winds	war

35 TAIL TAG CHALLENGER Frost, tub, breath, hop, planet, triple, extent, tonic, chew, women, novel, lash, humor, roof, friend, destiny, young, gone, etch, hint, thigh, hello, open, national, lass, swallow, witch, half, free, embrace, eager, rip, postal, leg, graph, huff.

36 TRIVIA TOURNEY 1. Alaska 2. Avon 3. Brice (Fanny) 4. coral 5. Cronkite (Walter) 6. Delphi 7. Denver 8. Eeyore 9. England 10. fencing 11. Fort Knox 12. hat 13. Hawaii 14. Homer 15. India 16. John 17. Koko 18. Mancini 19. McGuffey 20. narwhal 21. New York 22. Nipper 23. nucleus 24. Pluto 25. seven 26. Sinai 27. surfing 28. Tin Lizzie 29. water 30. Wendy

38 THEY WEAR HEADGEAR Astronaut, baker, baseball player, beekeeper, chef, cowboy, doorman, farmer, fireman, football player, jockey, military officer, milkman, miner, nurse, pilot, policeman, postman.

39 SCAVENGER HUNT

	P	V	F	N	R	M
Sew what?	poplin	velvet	felt	nylon	rayon	muslin
Hitchcock	Psycho	Vertigo	Frenzy	Notorious	Rear Window	Marnie
Double letters	possess	voodoo	football	needless	raccoon	misspell
Universities	Princeton	Vassar	Fordham	Notre Dame	Rutgers	Michigan
Birds	pigeon	vireo	finch	nuthatch	robin	martin

41 PHRASE PLAY A chip off the old block, A flash in the pan, All in a day's work, A method to one's madness, At a loss for words, Bark up the wrong tree, Easier said than done, Get in on the ground floor, Hook, line, and sinker, Lend a helping hand, Lock, stock, and barrel, More than meets the eye, Not yet dry behind the ears, Paint the town red, Rain cats and dogs, Read the fine print, Straight from the shoulder, The time of one's life, Throw caution to the wind.

42 JACKPOT 5 letters Amaze, arena, argue, blank, enemy, entry, hardy, lacer, loser, moral, niche, nymph, piece, prose, raged, raise, seize, share, shore, snare, spare. **6 letters** Accent, accept, advice, barker, change, charge, cinema, defame, errand, gallop, manner, mister, radish, regent, scheme, shrimp, solace.

46 MATH FUN 1. Twenty-eight 2. Forty-four 3. Sixteen 4. Eight 5. Fifty-six 6. Forty-two 7. Fourteen 8. Fifty 9. Thirty-five 10. Twenty-four 11. Forty-eight 12. Twelve 13. Two 14. Four 15. Forty 16. Sixty-one 17. Three 18. Thirty 19. Ninety 20. Eighteen 21. Three 22. Thirty-nine 23. Six 24. Nine 25. Seventy 26. Fifty 27. Twenty-two 28. Twenty 29. Sixty 30. Five 31. Thirty 32. Twenty-one 33. Seven 34. Five

WORD LISTS

49 LETTER-CLUE WORDS 1. bend 2. bone 3. bore 4. cape 5. dear 6. down 7. draw 8. drip 9. gate 10. glad 11. gray 12. helm 13. howl 14. land 15. mark 16. mash 17. mask 18. mode 19. nail 20. neat 21. nice 22. open 23. pace 24. pant 25. part 26. raid 27. rink 28. shop 29. snap 30. soft 31. sold 32. sour 33. span 34. spar 35. tall 36. turn

61 TRIVIAVISION 1. Agnes 2. Arthur 3. Arvid 4. Astro 5. Belker 6. Bilko 7. Boris 8. Caine 9. Cathy 10. Cosmo 11. Cullen 12. DeVito 13. Florence 14. Hamilton 15. Hayes 16. Kitt 17. Ledger 18. Lily 19. Lobo 20. Lovey 21. Lynde 22. Mearth 23. Micky 24. Milton 25. Nicole 26. nurse 27. Opie 28. Oscar 29. Paladin 30. Pappy 31. Paulsen 32. Redigo 33. Ricardo 34. robot 35. Stavros 36. Tabitha 37. tennis 38. Trixie 39. Velda 40. Wilma 41. Wishbone 42. writers.

109 THREE OF A KIND Acacia, addled, attest, azalea, babble, bazaar, bikini, bobbin, budded, cannon, casaba, cheese, deepen, eleven, entree, esteem, feeble, fluffy, freeze, gaggle, giggle, giggly, hubbub, inning, kidded, lulled, mammal, padded, papaya, recede, seemed, tattle, veneer, wheeze.

120 MOVIE FILL-INS 1. Adventure 2. Alibi, 3. Baker 4. Barred 5. Belle 6. Buck 7. Cash 8. Crumb 9. Crusade 10. Daisy 11. Field 12. Fire 13. Foot 14. Future 15. Heaven 16. Hooch 17. July 18. Kill 19. Magnolias 20. Major 21. Mermaid 22. October 23. Opera 24. Poets 25. Sally 26. Shrunk 27. Talking 28. Turtles 29. Under 30. Volcano 31. Voyage 32. Weapon 33. Weekend 34. Wire 35. Woman

151 BY DESIGN bank, blue, blur, boot, brig, brim, city, clap, coat, coda, damp, deed, disc, dumb, else, exit, gift, glue, grim, iota, mole, pair, plod, rank, rift, ripe, root, tent, true, twin, wade, wire, again, armor, fairy, frost, glide, goose, idiom, mercy, music, onion, plain, plant, castle, hamper, mister, tumble, amnesty, compact, deflate, generic, mermaid, precept, probity, thought

156 TAIL TAG Mind, disc, crow, wool, lung, glib, brawl, limit, tang, grass, shed, debris, sewing, ghost, tinge, equal, livid, dabble, expels, sauna, avows, scald, dean, noodle, exile, envy, yonder, real, love, ember, ringlet, team, meager, raid, dream, mere, elopes, speaker, reader.

159 FATHER KNOWS BEST 1. Once Around 2. The King And I 3. Hide In Plain Sight 4. Summer Rental 5. Indiana Jones And The Last Crusade 6. Friendly Persuasion 7. Ghost Dad 8. There's No Business Like Show Business 9. Arachnophobia 10. The Great Santini 11. Cookie 12. Yours, Mine And Ours 13. Lethal Weapon 14. Houseboat 15. Home Alone 16. Kramer Vs. Kramer 17. Cat On A Hot Tin Roof 18. The Addams Family 19. Mr. Mom 20. Bye Bye Birdie 21. Parenthood 22. Honey, I Shrunk The Kids 23. Poltergeist 24. Please Don't Eat The Daisies 25. Cape Fear 26. Author! Author! 27. Old Yeller 28. To Kill A Mockingbird 29. The Sound of Music 30. Life With Father 31. God's Little Acre 32. Jaws 33. Islands In The Stream 34. Wall Street 35. Andy Hardy's Blonde Trouble 36. Father Of The Bride 37. Cheaper By The Dozen 38. Sounder

160 MATH FUN 1. Ninety-five 2. Sixteen 3. Three 4. Sixty-six 5. Five 6. Sixty-five 7. Twelve 8. Six 9. Forty 10. Twenty-nine 11. Fifteen 12. Three 13. Nine 14. Four 15. Nine 16. Sixty 17. Eighty-four 18. Seven 19. Five 20. Sixty-seven 21. Twenty 22. Two 23. Six 24. Fourteen 25. Ninety 26. Nineteen 27. Eighty 28. Four 29. Seventeen 30. Ninety-one 31. Fourteen 32. Seven 33. Sixty-nine 34. Two

166 EQUATIONS

1 + 3 = 4	3 + 3 = 6	4 − 4 = 0	7 + 1 = 8	8 − 5 = 3
1 + 4 = 5	3 + 6 = 9	5 + 3 = 8	7 − 2 = 5	8 − 7 = 1
1 + 6 = 7	3 − 0 = 3	5 + 4 = 9	7 − 3 = 4	9 + 0 = 9
2 + 6 = 8	3 − 1 = 2	5 − 1 = 4	7 − 7 = 0	9 − 3 = 6
2 + 7 = 9	4 + 2 = 6	6 + 0 = 6	8 + 1 = 9	9 − 7 = 2
2 − 2 = 0	4 − 3 = 1	6 − 5 = 1	8 − 4 = 4	9 − 9 = 0

169 TAIL TAG

Quinine, error, radio, order, roan, noble, exact, tried, dull, louder, robot, tang, glum, manner, relief, frown, nails, squeal, last, tend, debuts, salad, darns, surprise, equation, narrow, wool, lamb, beware, exodus, sooner, rather, ruse, eggs, shrub, bowl, limb, brow, water.

173 JACKPOT

5-letters words Chase, choir, cider, cinch, citer, cuter, flesh, fully, hoard, inane, lodge, motto, pasta, steel, super, token, treed. **6-letters words** Azalea, become, bureau, chaise, decade, dilute, domain, export, finder, hemmed, iceman, icicle, impart, marina, parody, person, poncho, rhumba, rugged, sarong, sizzle, thresh, thrush, urchin, winder.

175 QUOTE ENDINGS

1. Again 2. Best 3. Boils 4. Broth 5. Bush 6. Clean 7. Crown 8. Cure 9. Divine 10. Done 11. Fall 12. Fire 13. Forget 14. Gold 15. Grow 16. Hatched 17. Hire 18. Home 19. Leap 20. Lining 21. Man 22. Mended 23. Milk 24. Never 25. Nine 26. Noise 27. Once 28. Play 29. Pours 30. Receive 31. Star 32. Stream 33. Teacher 34. Thoughts 35. Today 36. Together 37. Waste 38. Well 39. Worm 40. Wrath

176 + AND x SEARCH

Adept x alert, awake x learn, azure + daunt, basic + rusty, braid + leafy, carat + mercy, chair x dealt, cider + medal, cobra + sable, crisp + spite, eagle x eight, easel + pasta, enjoy x major, genie + penny, hobby x rebel, jaded + muddy, joint + raise, lurch + pored, misty x upset, model x today, moist + spied, music x paste, opera x skein, pleat + sheep, queue x teeth, quiet x taint, racer x yacht, sense x tango, siren x strut, taboo + zebra.

181 HIDDEN MEANINGS

1-N, 2-r, 3-I, 4-S, 5-D, 6-u, 7-t, 8-n, 9-h, 10-v, 11-p, 12-f, 13-m, 14-O, 15-w, 16-Z, 17-o, 18-V, 19-x, 20-a, 21-c, 22-J, 23-U, 24-e, 25-E, 26-s, 27-G, 28-Y, 29-d, 30-P, 31-H, 32-I, 33-b, 34-C, 35-K, 36-L, 37-B, 38-i, 39-T, 40-X, 41-q, 42-R, 43-Q, 44-F, 45-k, 46-W, 47-j, 48-M, 49-A, 50-y, 51-g.

189 SCAVENGER HUNT

	C	M	T	B	P	D
Homes	Chateau	Mansion	Trailer	Bungalow	Palace	Duplex
Magazines	Child	Mad	Time	Brides	People	Discover
Computers	Chip	Memory	Terminal	Byte	Program	Data
Detectives	Chan (Charlie)	Mason (Perry)	Tracy (Dick)	Brown (Father)	Poirot (Hercule)	Drew (Nancy)
Instruments	Cornet	Mandolin	Tuba	Banjo	Piccolo	Drum

WORD LISTS

191 JACKPOT   Axiom, beset, blank, bulky, caper, chasm, cheep, chief, chime, crier, crimp, crust, edger, frisk, grain, idler, latex, musky, niche, ninth, nurse, octet, paced, phone, plane, rally, relax, renew, rhino, roped, scare, shake, shale, skate, skier, spire spout, spree, stair, steel, swank, swine, table, taper, tarry, taxed, theft, thick, twine, vista.

192 TAIL TAG   Hatch, hosed, drag, gained, divulge, erased, damp, plum, maze, equals, sprig, gels, swapped, doubt, taped, divider, rescued, deaf, flan, neck, kings, stormy, yell, labor, rings, shaved, dries, skip, prizes, stag, grain, near, roar, repent, thug, goes, skied, dumb, back.

193 PHRASE PLAY   A chip on the shoulder, A diamond in the rough, A pretty kettle of fish, As luck would have it, Bring home the bacon, Cannot hold a candle to, Food for thought, Hit the nail on the head, In one ear and out the other, In the final analysis, Jump on the bandwagon, Let the cat out of the bag, Never a dull moment, Once in a blue moon, Rub the wrong way, Sow your wild oats, Take a dim view of, The milk of human kindness, Turn over a new leaf, Up the creek without a paddle

195 ROMAN NUMERALS   Adlib, alien, alive, axiom, axis, axle, clinic, clips, deliver, delved, differ, dig, dissolves, dive, elite, elixir, elver, excise, exist, feline, flivver, folio, gaslit, helix, lie, lien, lily, livelihood, liver, livery, mix, olive, polite, prolix, recliner, revolver, saline, saliva, salver, salvo, slid, slight, sling, slits, sliver, solve, valve, wolves.

196 MATH FUN   1. Seven 2. Fifty 3. Two 4. Seventy-six 5. Nineteen 6. Fifty 7. Two 8. Sixteen 9. Ninety 10. Five 11. Eighty 12. Four 13. Thirty-seven 14. Sixteen 15. Twenty-four 16. Six 17. Nineteen 18. Twenty-six 19. Nine 20. Ninety-nine 21. Six 22. Thirty-one 23. Five 24. Fifteen 25. Sixty 26. Three 27. Twelve 28. Twenty 29. Sixty 30. Twenty 31. Five 32. Ninety-five 33. Two 34. Nine 35. Sixty-one

203 ANOTHER + AND x SEARCH 5-letters adieu + noise, aired + nerve, alarm x spank, along + irony, cadet x elder, entry + later, false + talon, field x geese, gleam + steel, great x sieve, inane + orate, inset + onset, lathe x ratio, mince + tenor, pedal x sedan. **7-letters** anatomy x epitaph, beeping + respond, detente x mileage, dragnet x wriggle, eclipse x lenient, freezer + general, neatest + vestige, parasol + vitamin.

204 TAIL TAG CHALLENGER Elks, schism, meek, knack, kiss, sting, grime, eave, educate, exult, tier, rain, news, shirt, tremble, elastic, club, blimp, proof, fern, nice, ether, rind, dentist, them, mouth, help, pill, lurk, kneel, loft, tuxedo, opened, doodle, each, hill, least, thin, none.

206 MOVIE FILL-INS 1. Adventure 2. Bamba 3. Beverly 4. Beyond 5. Color 6. Day Off 7. Fire 8. Friday 9. Heart 10. Hendersons 11. Hill 12. Home 13. Jacket 14. Life 15. Living 16. Masters 17. Millions 18. Nile 19. Peace 20. Pink 21. Rose 22. Sisters 23. Stone 24. Success 25. Susan

219 TAIL TAG Credit, task, knee, evict, trio, overt, triple, exists, strains, sash, host, thrilled, dated, dire, error, really, yanks, sink, kinds, solve, elves, soul, lull, lucid, dress, skips, sneers, solid, dart, tenor, rare, earn, news, sports, straw, wrap, pelt, talc, cards.

222 CHRISTMAS AROUND THE WORLD 1. caroling in neighbors' yards late at night 2. kindly old witch who gives gifts 4. Santa's servant who dresses in 16th-century Spanish clothes 6. plaited white Christmas bread 10. breakfast buns eaten on Saint Lucia Day 11. Christmas Eve meal 12. demon who carries a whip and chains as punishment for naughty children 14. Christmas crib lined with moss in the crèche 18. person entering a house to ''let in Christmas'' carrying evergreen twig 20. hot punch made of spices, sweet liquors, raisin and nuts 21. Greek Christmas carols 23. Father Christmas 24. German manger scene 25. pudding of barley, milk, butter and mushrooms 27. elf playing practical jokes who eats Christmas Eve rice pudding 30. star-shaped lantern 31. Father Christmas 33. processions of people reenacting Mary and Joseph's search for lodging 34. Pennsylvania Dutch version of the manger scene 36. Spanish children put their shoes near a window and wake to find them filled with small gifts 38. Christmas decoration hung on the wall with cards stuffed inside 39. man wearing a mask carrying greenery and kissing whomever he can catch under it 42. candy loaf of roasted almonds in caramel syrup 43. goat made of straw representing the steed who brings Santa Claus 44. Christmas carolers

223 LOOSE LETTERS Boats, paper, boned, ruder, fasts, tinier, right, lager, baled, state, sacks, waded, purer, caste, hazer, rattle, hovel, pored, stings, crams, tucks, final, griped, scant, moths, triple, cries, cider, enter, steps. **PROVERB:** Sudden friendship, sure repentance.

229 MATH FUN 1. ninety-one 2. forty 3. eleven 4. four 5. two 6. seventy-nine 7. fifty 8. fifteen 9. sixty 10. eighty 11. thirty-three 12. zero 13. seventy-two 14. three 15. forty-nine 16. seven 17. six 18. fifteen 19. one hundred one 20. fifteen 21. twenty 22. nine 23. twenty-six 24. ninety-nine 25. thirty 26. nine 27. thirty-two 28. six 29. sixty-three 30. two 31. fifteen 32. ninety 33. twelve 34. eighty-nine 35. nine

232 TRIVIA TOURNEY 1. Akron (Ohio) 2. Apple 3. Benoit (Joan) 4. Berwanger (Jay) 5. boot 6. China 7. Clio 8. corona 9. Flounder 10. googol 11. Helsinki 12. Holly (Buddy) 13. hope 14. Jerry (''Anchors Aweigh'') 15. Kennedy (John F.) 16. knot 17. Landers (Ann) 18. Leo 19. Monroe (James) 20. Orion 21. Oscar 22. palindrome 23. Paris 24. Rodin 25. ruby 26. shalom 27. Thailand 28. Tigers 29. tutu 30. Yeager (Brigadier General Charles E.)

WORD LISTS

234 TAIL TAG Land, dream, mainly, yelp, peasant, tiara, army, yodel, lies, schism, monk, kilter, rebus, shark, knows, simmer, rich, hovel, leader, ramp, pries, smog, gentle, eight, trump, poke, exert, timidly, yolk, king, genie, esteem, movie, excuses, sight, take, egos, swarm, mark.

239 HOLIDAY WORDS Akin, ankh, avid or (diva), dais, dank, dash, data, ding, dint, dish, disk, gain, gait, gang, gash, gist, gnat or (tang), hand, hang, hank, hind, hint, inky, kind, king, knit, navy, saga, said, sand, shad, shag, shin, sigh, sing, sink, skid, skin, skit, snag, snit, stag, stay, tank, task, than, thin, this, tidy, tiny, vain, vast, yank.

244 + AND x SEARCH Adieu x faint, adobe x gloat, alien x twill, ample + gypsy, armor + tempt, banjo + dense, blink + suite, blond x epoch, borne x early, burro + sorry, bylaw + melee, chard x slate, error + hardy, flair x stain, force x north, grasp x yeast, heard + piano, hilly + paler, homey x tamed, hover x saver, jewel x lower, joint + slice, kitty + satin, mania + tenth, namer (or reman)+ nomad, peach x tease, peony x slope, prose x proud, react x roast, rival + waved, sedan x under.

251 "MIXED" FRUITS AND VEGGIES 1. apple 2. apricot 3. artichoke 4. asparagus 5. avocado 6. banana 7. beet 8. broccoli 9. brussels sprouts 10. carrot 11. celery 12. cherry 13. corn 14. cucumber 15. Date 16. eggplant 17. grape 18. lettuce 19. lima bean 20. onion 21. orange 22. peach 23. peas 24. radish 25. spinach 26. strawberry 27. tomato 28. turnip 29. watermelon 30. zucchini

254 TAIL TAG High, hostel, legal, loosen, nowhere, exits, scour, raze, examine, elect, taper, rind, drew, whisk, kelp, prince, echo, ordain, nugget, tagged, dozed, divert, tint, thus, spurn, next, token, nears, story, yard, dine, east, tinkers, snip, plates, stash, halt, tamer, rise.

256 APPETIZERS Antipasto, bouillon, canapés, carrots, caviar, celery, cheese, cider, clams, consommé, crackers, dip, egg rolls, fried zucchini, fruit, ham, herring, juice, mushrooms, nuts, olives, oysters, pâté, pickles, radishes, sardines, sausage, scallions, shrimp, soup.

257 SANTA'S SEARCH Bags, beard, bells, Blitzen, boots, bows, candy, cheerful, children, chimney, Christmas, Comet, Cupid, Dancer, Dasher, dolls, Donner, elves, fireplace, gifts, happy, holiday, hope, jolly, list, mail, merry, Mrs. Claus, North Pole, Prancer, red suit, reindeer, roof, Rudolph, sleigh, snow, stockings, toys, tree, Vixen, winter, wonder.

262 TAIL TAG CHALLENGER Yell, limp, prod, dimples, sand, diva, arch, hall, lunch, hold, dazed, drama, able, eggs, shop, prom, moss, stern, newer, rocket, till, lisp, proud, deal, lord, depth, heist, teak, knack, kilt, taut, torn, numb, bower, rough, hiss, stupor, rush, hourly.

263 LOOSE LETTERS Hosing, meter, coping, archer, grander, wined, ailed, exert, facet, breath, inner, deter, price, finer, holly, brads, grave, simper, rowed, cords, pints, sewer, carer, filed, rawer, noses, olden. **PROVERB:** Too much pudding will choke a dog.

266 MATH FUN 1. ninety-seven 2. eighty 3. forty 4. four 5. seventeen 6. fifty-one 7. seven 8. sixty 9. three 10. fifteen 11. five 12. sixty 13. fifty-eight 14. four 15. sixteen 16. eight 17. seventy 18. five 19. thirty-two 20. eight 21. forty-five 22. five 23. ninety 24. nine 25. thirty-eight 26. thirteen 27. fifty 28. five 29. sixty-six 30. eleven 31. two 32. six 33. fifty-nine 34. nine 35. three

275 NAME ANAGRAMS Andre, Annie, Betsy, Bruce, Caleb, Carol, Clare, Claud, Craig, Cyril, Daryl, Debra, Della, Diana, Edgar, Edwin, Eliot, Elvis, Ethan, Freda, Grace, Greta, Lance, Laura, Leona, Lewis, Lloyd, Lydia, Lyman, Mabel, Madge, Marge, Marla, Miles, Nancy, Nelda, Norma, Olive, Pearl, Rosie, Selma, Shari, Susie, Zelda.

277 TAIL TAG Quick, keen, nursery, yens, shave, exit, tough, hexed, dazed, drag, glib, barked, diesel, lives, seldom, many, yell, lucky, yard, deft, toaster, rings, stag, grass, songs, solo, omelets, stupefy, yolks, sued, dream, mink, ketch, hails, sits, slob, beards, sizes, silver.

278 JACKPOT Aired, avert, billy, bound, bower, budge, caulk, chafe, cheat, chose, coder, comet, covet, doter, dusky, epoch, erupt, ferry flail, flame, flood, flown, freed, frisk, homer, large, lathe, limed, patio, plier, prove, refer (refer), revel (lever), ricer, roper, sedan, shave, shyly, slate, sleep, spill, stark, terse, totem, toter, under, upset, video, vigil, vowed, women.

284 SIX-LETTER WORD SEARCH Absent, accuse, answer, assort, assure, astray, basket, cashew, catsup, closer, crease, desert, disarm, escort, hushed, insert, master, pester, phrase, reside, resist, resort, rosary, saddle, satire, senate, simmer, staple, weasel.

402

WORD LISTS

285 HALF & HALF 1. habit, place 2. great, hotel 3. apart, piece 4. irate, ounce 5. badge, their 6. braid, hedge 7. attic, paved 8. scoot, train 9. hello, pecan 10. chain, elder 11. crimp, moose 12. minor, shady 13. divan, glaze 14. cynic, ideal 15. snowy, threw 16. avert, voice 17. empty, roper 18. dress, waste 19. ensue, scant 20. leery, moist 21. acted, haunt.

286 + AND x SEARCH Adapt + stage, adopt + groom, album + cobra, argue + beget, armed x comet, arose + goose, attic x eater, bland x trait, brood x photo, bugle x eight, cared + mirth, crest x elegy, domed x timed (or demit), dried + maize, earth + sired, enact + tease, evade + grace, gland x train, hunch + panic, inert x scene, maxim + taxed, orbit x robed, prior x stint, prose x trout, range x tangy, spend x steed, steam + tread, twice + unite.

288 THE YOUNG GIRL'S ROOM 1-U, 2-D, 3-A, 4-R, 5-O, 6-G, 7-F, 8-I, 9-M, 10-X, 11-E, 12-W, 13-L, 14-S, 15-J, 16-Q, 17-P, 18-H, 19-B, 20-K, 21-V, 22-N, 23-T, 24-C.

290 SCAVENGER HUNT

	B	C	P	R	S	M
Capitals	Brussels	Cairo	Prague	Rome	Seoul	Moscow
Card games	bridge	canasta	poker	rummy	solitaire	monte
Dogs	beagle	collie	poodle	retriever	spaniel	mastiff
Movies	Bambi	Casablanca	Psycho	Rocky	Superman	Marnie
Composers	Bach	Chopin	Puccini	Ravel	Sousa	Mozart

296 SPOONERISMS 1. bank loan 2. bear hug 3. coast guard 4. date line 5. fair ball 6. fan mail 7. far cry 8. fire drill 9. funny bone 10. gas main 11. glad hand 12. gold rush 13. high tide 14. John Doe 15. junk mail 16. lame duck 17. laughing gas 18. name tag 19. party hat 20. red light